He's determined to claim

The Right Bride?

Three absolute classic, contemporary romances
from three favourite Mills & Boon authors!

In June 2010 Mills & Boon bring you
two classic collections, each
featuring three favourite romances
by our bestselling authors

THE ITALIAN'S BABY OF PASSION

The Italian's Secret Baby by Kim Lawrence
One-Night Baby by Susan Stephens
The Italian's Secret Child
by Catherine Spencer

THE RIGHT BRIDE?

Bride of Desire by Sara Craven
The English Aristocrat's Bride
by Sandra Field
Vacancy: Wife of Convenience
by Jessica Steele

The Right Bride?

SARA CRAVEN

SANDRA FIELD

JESSICA STEELE

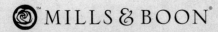

MILLS & BOON

First published in Great Britain 2010
Harlequin Mills & Boon Limited,
Eton House, 18-24 Paradise Road, Richmond, Surrey TW9 1SR

THE RIGHT BRIDE? © by Harlequin Enterprises II B.V./S.à.r.l 2010

Bride of Desire, The English Aristocrat's Bride and *Vacancy: Wife of Convenience* were first published in Great Britain by Harlequin Mills & Boon Limited in separate, single volumes.

Bride of Desire © Sara Craven 2006
The English Aristocrat's Bride © Sandra Field 2005
Vacancy: Wife of Convenience © Jessica Steele 2005

ISBN: 978 0 263 88105 9

05-0610

Printed and bound in Spain
by Litografia Rosés S.A., Barcelona

BRIDE OF DESIRE

BY
SARA CRAVEN

Sara Craven was born in South Devon and grew up in a house full of books. She worked as a local journalist, covering everything from flower shows to murders, and started writing for Mills & Boon in 1975. When not writing, she enjoys films, music, theatre, cooking and eating in good restaurants. She now lives near her family in Warwickshire. Sara has appeared as a contestant on the former Channel Four game show *Fifteen to One* and in 1997 was the UK television *Mastermind* champion. In 2005 she was a member of the Romantic Novelists' team on *University Challenge – the Professionals*.

Don't miss Sara Craven's exciting new novel, *His Untamed Innocent,* available in July 2010 from Mills & Boon® Modern™.

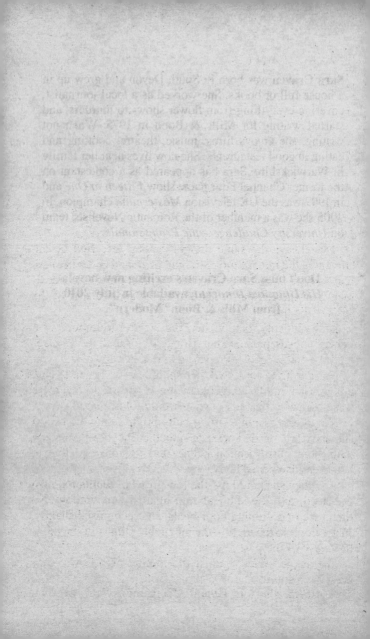

PROLOGUE

IT WAS always the same dream. A long, deserted beach, stretching out into infinity. Straight, firm sand under her bare feet. No twists, no turns. No rocks or other place of concealment anywhere. Near at hand, the hiss and whisper of the sea's rising tide.

And suddenly, behind her, the steady drumming of a horse's hooves, pursuing her. Drawing closer all the time, relentless—inescapable. Preparing to ride her down…

Not daring to look over her shoulder, she began to run, going faster and faster, yet knowing as she did so that there was no escape. That her pursuer would follow her always.

She awoke gasping, sitting bolt upright in the big bed as she stared into the darkness, dry-mouthed, her heart pounding to the point of suffocation and her thin nightdress sticking to her sweat-dampened body.

And then she heard it—the low growl of thunder almost overhead, and the slam of rain against her window. No tidal race or galloping hoof-beats, she recognised shakily. Just a storm in the night—the inevitable climax of the mini-heatwave of the past few days.

She sagged back against the mound of pillows, suppressing a sob.

A dream, she told herself. Triggered by the weather.

Nothing more. Only a dream. And one day—one night soon—it would let her go. *He* would let her go. And she would know some peace at last. Surely…

CHAPTER ONE

As ALLIE came down the broad curving staircase, she paused for a moment to look at the view from the big casement window on the half-landing.

There was nothing new to see. Just the grounds of Marchington Hall in all their formal splendour, unfolding over immaculately kept lawns down to the gleam of the lake in the distance. To her right, she could just glimpse the mellow brick walls of the Fountain Court, while to the left dark green cypresses sheltered the Italian Garden.

But on a day like this, when the air seemed to sparkle after the rain in the night, the vista made her heart lift. It even made her feel that being forced to deal with all the petty restrictions and irritations of life at the Hall might be worth it, after all.

Worth it for Tom's sake anyway, she thought. I have to believe that. I must. Because there is nothing else…

Her throat tightened suddenly, uncontrollably, and she made to turn away. As she did so, she caught sight of her own reflection, and paused again. She looked like a ghost, she thought soberly. A pale, hollow-eyed, fair-haired phantom, without life or substance. And as tense as if she was stretched on wire.

Part of that, of course, was down to last night's storm. Part, but not all.

Because it also had to do with the ongoing battle over the upbringing of her fourteen-month-old son, which, in spite of her best efforts, seemed to be turning into a war of attrition.

She'd just been to visit him in his nursery, to make sure that he hadn't been woken by the thunder, but had been faced by the usual confrontation with Nanny, looking disapproving over this disruption to Tom's routine.

'He's having his breakfast, Lady Marchington.'

'I'm aware of that,' Allie had returned, counting to ten under her breath. 'In fact, I'd like to help feed him. I've said so many times.'

'We prefer to have as few distractions at mealtimes as possible,' Nanny returned with regal finality.

And if I had the guts of a worm, Allie thought grimly, I'd stand up to the boot-faced old bag.

But behind Nanny's portly and commanding frame, she knew, stood the outwardly frail figure of Grace, the Dowager Lady Marchington, her mother-in-law, known irreverently in the village as the Tungsten Tartar.

Any overt clash with Nanny led straight to 'an atmosphere' in the nursery, and also resulted in Allie becoming the target of the elder Lady Marchington's icy displeasure. An experience to be avoided.

Anything for a quiet life, she'd told herself as she'd left the nursery, closing the door behind her. And, my God, was this ever a quiet life.

She supposed that for Tom's sake she wouldn't have it any other way. He was Hugo's heir, she reminded herself stonily, so she should have known what to expect.

Besides, on the surface at least, the Hall had all the necessary elements to supply him with an idyllic childhood.

But I'd just like to be able to enjoy it with him, she thought rebelliously. Without Nanny standing guard as if I was a potential kidnapper instead of his mother.

He said his first word to her, not me. And it wasn't Mama either, which hurt. And I missed the moment he took his first step, too. It's as if I don't feature in the scheme of things at all. I gave him birth, and now I'm being sidelined. It's a ludicrous situation to be in.

Most of her friends were young marrieds, struggling to

cope with child-rearing alongside the demands of their careers. They must think that, apart from the tragedy of being widowed at twenty-one, she'd pretty much fallen on her feet.

After all, she had a large house to live in, a staff to run it, and no money or childcare problems.

Besides, some of them clearly thought that the premature end of her marriage was a blessing in disguise too, although they never said so openly.

And if they did, Allie thought, sighing, could I really deny it?

She walked slowly across the hall and, drawing a deep breath, entered the dining room. Grace Marchington was seated at the head of the table—although 'enthroned' might be a better description, Allie thought as she fielded the disparaging glance aimed at her denim skirt and white cheesecloth blouse, closely followed, as usual, by the glance at the watch—just pointed enough to be noticeable.

'Good morning, Alice. Did you sleep well?' She didn't wait for an answer, but picked up the small brass bell beside her place and rang it sharply. 'I'll ask Mrs Windom to bring some fresh toast.'

Allie took her seat and poured herself some coffee. 'I'm sorry if I'm late. I popped in to see Tom on my way down.'

'Not a terribly convenient time, my dear, as I think Nanny has mentioned to you.'

'Oh, yes,' Allie said. 'She has.' She fortified herself with some coffee. 'So, perhaps she could suggest when it would be more appropriate for me to visit my own son. Because somehow I always seem to get it wrong.'

Lady Marchington replaced her cup in its saucer in a measured way. 'I'm not sure I understand you, Alice.'

Allie took a breath. 'I'd like to see Tom first thing in the morning without it being regarded as an unreasonable request. In fact, I'd love to be there when he wakes up, so that I can sort out his clothes and bath him, and then give him his breakfast. That's surely not too much to ask.'

'Are you implying that Nanny is incapable in some way

of supplying Tom's needs? May I remind you that she was entrusted with the care of Hugo as soon as he was born.'

'I do realise that, yes,' Allie said wearily. *I've never been allowed to forget it.*

'And I'm sure you also recall that there was a time, after Tom's birth, when Nanny's presence became indispensable?'

The dagger between the ribs...

'Yes, I had postnatal depression for a while.' Allie kept her tone even. 'But I got over it.'

'Did you, my dear? Sometimes I wonder.' Her mother-in-law gave her a sad smile. 'Of course, you are still grieving for our beloved boy, which may account for the mood swings I sometimes detect. But I'm sure Dr Lennard would be happy to recommend someone—a specialist who could help you over this difficult period in your life.'

Allie's lips tightened. 'You think that wanting to look after my small child means I need a psychiatrist?'

Lady Marchington looked almost shocked. 'There are many different levels of therapy, Alice. And it was only a suggestion, after all.'

As if signifying that the matter was closed, she turned her attention to the pile of post which had been placed beside her, as it was every morning. And, as she did so, Allie suddenly spotted the pale blue envelope with the French stamp, halfway down, and stifled a small gasp.

A letter from Tante Madelon, she thought, and felt the hair stand up on the back of her neck. Was that the real reason for last night's dream, and not the storm at all? Why she'd heard all over again the sibilant rush of the incoming tide and the thunder of the pursuing hoofbeats? Because somehow she'd sensed that all the memories of Brittany she'd tried so hard to bury were about to be revived?

Her heart was thumping against her ribs, but she knew there was no point in claiming the letter. That wasn't the way the system worked. All the mail delivered to the Hall came to Grace first, to be scrutinised before it was handed out to staff and family alike.

And if she thought you were taking an undue interest in any item, she was quite capable of taking the day's post to her private sitting room and letting you seethe quietly for half a day, or even twenty-four hours, before handing it over with the mellifluous words, 'I think this must be for you.'

'It's madness,' Allie had once told Hugo heatedly. 'Your mother is the ultimate control freak. Why don't you say something?'

But he'd only looked at her, brows raised in haughty surprise. 'Mother's always dealt with the mail. My father preferred it, and I don't see it as a problem.'

But then Hugo had seen very little as a problem, apart from the utter necessity of providing a son and heir for his beloved estate. That, in the end, had been the driving force—the obsession in his ruined life. Two ruined lives, if she counted her own, and she tried hard not to do that. Bitterness, after all, was futile, and damaged no one but herself. Regret, too, altered nothing.

But was she still mourning her late husband, as her mother-in-law had suggested? In her innermost heart, she doubted that. The suddenness of his death had certainly been an acute shock, but she suspected her reaction was largely triggered by guilt because she'd never really loved him.

For a long time she'd felt numb—too emotionally paralysed even to feel relief that the nightmare of their marriage had ended—but that had been over and done with long ago.

Slowly and carefully, she'd begun to find herself again, and somehow she had to move on from that—to regain the here and now, and stop allowing Grace to treat her as some kind of cipher—even if it did end with blood on the carpet.

How to go about it, of course, was not so clear, she told herself ironically. Because her mother-in-law seemed to hold all the winning cards.

In those tragic crowded weeks after Hugo had died with such shocking suddenness and Tom had been born, Allie herself had temporarily descended into some bleak, dark limbo.

It was then that Grace Marchington had effortlessly reassumed the role of mistress of the house. In fact, Allie could see, looking back, that she'd never really been away.

I was just the temporary usurper who gave Hugo the son he'd craved, she thought. *And after that I was supposed to retire into well-deserved obscurity, while Grace and Nanny pursued the task of turning Tom into a tintype of Marchington Man.*

But that's not going to happen, because I won't let it.

She realised, however, that she needed to conserve her energies for the battles she had to win—and Grace being anally retentive over a bunch of letters was not the most important. A minor irritation at best.

So, for the time being, she sat and ate the toast that Mrs Windom had brought, and never gave a second glance at the mail that Grace was examining with such torturous slowness. It might only be a small victory, but it counted.

She looked instead at the picture on the wall in front of her. It was a portrait of Hugo that his mother had commissioned for his twenty-fifth birthday, two years before the accident. Lady Marchington had not been altogether satisfied with the result, saying it was a poor likeness. But Allie wasn't so sure about that. The artist had given Hugo credit for his undoubted good looks, but also hinted at a slight fleshiness about the jaw, and a peevish line to the mouth. Nor had he made any attempt to conceal that the crisply cut dark hair was already beginning to recede.

It was Hugo, she thought, as he would have become if his life had taken a different path. If there'd been more time…

And suddenly superimposed on it, she realised, her heart bumping, was another face—thinner, swarthier, with a beak of a nose and heavy-lidded eyes, as blue and cold as the sea. And a voice in her head whispered a name that she'd tried hard to forget—*Remy*…

'This seems to be yours, Alice.'

She started violently as she realised that Lady Marchington, lips faintly pursed, was holding out the blue envelope.

'I presume it's from your French great-aunt,' the older woman added. 'I hope it isn't bad news.'

'I hope so too,' Allie said lightly, ignoring the hint that she should open it instantly and divulge the contents. 'But at least she's alive.'

She heard the hiss of indrawn breath, and braced herself for a chilling rebuke over inappropriate levity, but instead the dining room door opened to admit the housekeeper.

'Excuse me, your ladyship, but Mrs Farlow is asking to speak to you on the telephone. A problem with the Garden Club accounts.'

'I'll come.' Lady Marchington rose with an expression on her face that boded ill for the unfortunate Club treasurer. And for Allie, too, if she was still around when her mother-in-law returned.

As soon as she was alone, Allie went quickly across to the French windows and let herself out on to the terrace. A few minutes later she was pushing open the wrought-iron gate into the Fountain Court. It was one of her favourite places, with its gravelled paths, the raised beds planted with roses, just coming into flower, and the tall, cascading centrepiece of ferocious tritons and swooning nymphs from which it took its name.

It was an odd thing to find at an English country house, she had to admit, but it had been designed and installed by a much earlier Sir Hugo, who'd fallen in love with Italy while on the Grand Tour, and had wanted a permanent memento of his travels.

Allie loved the fountain for its sheer exuberance, and for the cool, soothing splash of its water which made even the hottest day seem restful. She sat on one of the stone benches and opened Tante's letter. She read it through swiftly, then, frowning, went back to the beginning, absorbing its contents with greater care.

It was not, in fact, good news. The writing was wavery, and not always easy to decipher, but the gist of it was that all was far from well with her great-aunt.

It seems that this will be my last summer at Les Sables d'Ignac. However, I have had a good life here, and I

regret only that so long has passed since we were
together. You remind me so much of my beloved sister,
and it would make me truly happy to see you again, my
dearest child. I hope with all my heart that you can
spare me a little time from your busy life to visit me.
Please, my dear Alys, come to me, and bring your little
boy with you also. As he is the last of the Vaillac blood,
I so long to see him.

My God, Allie thought, appalled. What on earth could be
wrong with her? Tante Madelon had always given the impression that she was in the most robust of health. But then she hadn't
seen her for almost two years—and that was indeed a long time.

She realised, of course, that her great-aunt must be in her late
seventies, although her looks and vigour had always belied her
age. In fact, to Allie she'd always seemed immortal, only the
silvering of her hair marking the inevitable passage of time.

Soberly, she thought of Tante as she'd seen her last. The
older woman's pointed face had been drawn and anxious, but
the dark, vivid eyes had still been full of life. Full of love for
this girl, her only living relative.

'Don't go back, *ma chérie*,' she'd urged. 'There is nothing
for you there. Stay here with me…' Her voice had died away,
leaving other things unsaid.

And Allie had replied, stumbling over the words, her head
reeling, her emotions in shreds, 'I—can't.'

Now, she took a deep breath to calm herself, then slowly
re-read the postscript at the end, the words running down the
page as if the writer had been almost too weary to hold the pen.

Alys, I promise there is nothing that should keep you
away, and that you have no reason to fear such a visit.

In plain words, Tante was offering her assurance—the essential guarantee that she thought Allie would want. Telling
her, in effect, that Remy de Brizat would not be there. That
he was still working abroad with his medical charity.

Only it wasn't as simple as that. It wasn't enough. He might not be physically present, but Allie knew that her memory—her senses—would find him everywhere.

That she'd see him waiting on the shore, or find his face carved into one of the tall stone megaliths that dotted the headland. That she'd feel him in every grain of sand or blade of grass. That she'd hear his laughter on the wind, and his voice in the murmur of the sea.

And, in the fury of the storm, she would relive the anger and bitterness of their parting, she thought, as she'd done last night. And she shivered in spite of the warmth of the morning.

Besides, she had too many memories already.

Her breathing quickened suddenly to pain. Words danced off the page at her. *Please, my dear Alys, come to me…*

She closed her eyes to block them out, and heard herself repeat aloud—'I can't.'

Then she crushed the letter in her hand, and pushed it into the pocket of her skirt.

She got to her feet and began to wander restlessly down the gravelled walk, forcing herself to think about other things—other people. To build a wall against those other memories.

Turning her thoughts determinedly to the Vaillac sisters, Celine and Madelon. During the Second World War, their family had sheltered her grandfather, Guy Colville, an airman forced to bail out on his way home. He'd broken his leg during his parachute descent, but had managed to crawl to a nearby barn, where Celine Vaillac had found him.

The Vaillacs had nursed him back to health, and risked their lives to keep him hidden and fed, eventually enabling him to be smuggled north to the Channel coast and back to England in a fishing boat. It was part of family folklore, and a story she'd never tired of hearing when she was a child.

She thought how romantic it was that Guy had never forgotten the pretty, shyly smiling Celine, and how, as soon as the war ended, he'd returned to their rambling farmhouse with his younger brother Rupert, to make sure that she and her family had all survived relatively unscathed, and discover whether Celine shared similar memories of their time together.

That first visit had been followed by others, and, to Guy's surprise, Rupert had insisted on going with him each time. When eventually Guy had proposed to Celine, and been accepted, his brother had confessed that he too had fallen in love with her younger sister, Madelon, a vivacious imp of a girl, and suggested a double wedding.

It was a real fairy-tale, Allie thought wistfully, but the happy ending had been short-lived—for her grandparents at least. Celine had always been the fairer of the two, and the quieter. A girl slender as a lily and ultimately as delicate. Because what should have been the straightforward birth of her first child had developed unexpected and severe complications which, tragically, she had not survived.

Guy had been totally devastated, firstly by the loss of his adored wife, and by having to learn to cope with a newborn motherless son. He had naturally turned to Rupert and Madelon, who'd provided him with the deep, steadfast support he needed, in spite of their own grief. Ironically, they themselves had remained childless, pouring their affection and care into the upbringing of their nephew, forming unbroken ties into Paul Colville's adult life.

So, Tante had been an important part of Allie's background from the moment she was born. It had only been when both Guy and her husband had died that she'd finally decided to return to Brittany, renting a house in Quimper for a while. Allie and her father Paul had visited her there on several occasions, although her mother had never accompanied them, making the excuse that she was a poor sailor, who found the ferry crossing a nightmare.

Looking back, Allie always suspected that Fay Colville had resented her husband's deep affection for his French aunt, and that it had been jealousy rather than *mal de mer* that kept her in England. She'd also openly disliked the fact that Allie had been christened Alys, rather than the Anglicised Alice that she herself always used.

Fay had become a widow herself by the time Tante had found herself a cottage by the sea in place of the family farm, which had been sold long ago, and was now a complex of *gîtes*. Even then, she had rejected each and every offer of hospitality from Madelon Colville, but she'd objected almost hysterically when Allie had suggested she should visit her great-aunt by herself.

'Are you mad?' she'd stormed. 'What will Hugo think?'

Allie lifted her chin. 'Does that matter?'

'Oh, don't talk like a fool.' Fay glared at her. 'You don't seem to have a clue how to keep a young man interested.'

'Perhaps because I suspect it's only a passing interest,' Allie told her coolly.

'Nonsense. He's taken you down to the Hall, hasn't he? Introduced you to his mother?'

'Yes,' Allie agreed reluctantly.

'Well, the invitation must be a sign that she approves of Hugo's choice.'

'And what about my own views on Hugo's choice? Supposing I don't approve?'

'That,' her mother said sharply, 'is not funny.'

But I, thought Allie, wasn't joking.

Her attitude to Hugo Marchington had always been ambivalent. At first she'd been convinced she was falling in love, carried away by the sheer glamour of him. She'd frankly enjoyed dining in top restaurants, being whisked off to polo matches, race meetings, regattas, and all the other leading events in the social calendar.

But, as weeks had become months, she'd realised that she simply did not know her own mind. And if he was indeed planning to ask her to become engaged to him, as she'd suspected, she had no real idea of what answer to give him. Which, by then, she should have done.

Naturally, she'd been flattered. Who wouldn't have been? In previous eras Hugo would have been considered the catch of the county, because he was rich, handsome, and he could be charming.

Yes, she thought. That was the sticking point. Could be—but wasn't always. In fact he'd sometimes revealed the makings of a nasty temper, although he had invariably been contrite afterwards.

And, in spite of all the assiduous attention he'd paid her, she hadn't been altogether convinced that his heart was in it. He might, in fact, have been behaving as he was expected to do.

At the beginning of their relationship he'd made a couple of serious attempts at seduction, which Allie had fended off just as seriously. He hadn't repelled her physically—but nor had he stirred her blood to the point of surrender. His kisses had never made her long for more. But she'd been aware that could have been due to an element of emotional reserve within herself, which, in turn, gave her an aura of coolness that some men might find a challenge.

At any rate, she'd known that giving herself in the ultimate intimacy would have implied a level of commitment that she had simply not been prepared for. Or not with Hugo Marchington—not yet. Although she had supposed that might change eventually.

In view of her lukewarm attitude, she'd been genuinely surprised when, instead of writing her off as a lost cause sexually, and looking for a more willing partner, he'd continued to ask her out.

I wonder, she'd thought, if his mother's told him it's time he settled down, and I'm handy and reasonably presentable, but not so devastating that I'll ever outshine him.

Having met Lady Marchington, she had quite believed it. She had also believed that she genuinely ticked enough of the right boxes to be acceptable. And her mother's Knightsbridge address would have raised no eyebrows either.

All the same, in her lunch hours at the private library where she'd worked as an assistant, she had found herself scanning the job columns for work that would take her away from London.

Maybe I should have obeyed my instincts and moved. Even gone back to college, perhaps, and improved my qualifications. And somehow persuaded my mother that it would be a good thing.

But if I had there would have been no Tom, and, in spite of everything, the thought of him not being here—never having been born—is too awful to contemplate.

Allie brought her restless wanderings to a halt, and gazed around her, assimilating once again the full baroque splendours of the Fountain Court.

I love it, she told herself wryly. But I don't belong here. I never did. The Hall is not my home, but it has to be Tom's. Some good has to come out of all this unhappiness.

He belongs here. I made that decision, and I have to remain for his sake.

But I have to find something to do with my own life. I'm edgy all the time because I feel confined at the Hall—claustrophobic. I have no actual role to play, so I spend my days just—hanging around. It's boring, and it's not healthy either.

And I won't think of the life I might have had if I'd done as Tante Madelon begged and stayed in Brittany, because that was never an actual possibility—always just a dream. And a dangerous dream at that.

Because, once again, she realised, there was a sound echoing in her head—the sure, steady beat of a horse's hooves coming behind her, just as she'd heard them so many times over the past months, sleeping and waking. Following her—getting closer all the time.

She said aloud, 'It's just my imagination playing tricks, nothing else. Imagination—and more guilt.'

She went slowly back to her bench, her great-aunt's letter like a lead weight in her pocket, and sat down. Although all she really wanted to do was put her hands over her ears and run.

But I've already done that—twice, she thought, her throat closing. And now, God help me, I have to live with the consequences.

All of them…

And if that means facing up to my memories, and exorcising them for ever, then so be it.

CHAPTER TWO

SHE'D fainted, she remembered, sliding from her chair at the breakfast table one morning under Grace's astonished eye. That was how it had all begun. And it hadn't been the family's usual doctor who'd answered the summons to attend her ladyship, but a locum, young, brisk, and totally unimpressed by his surroundings.

He'd insisted on seeing Allie alone, questioning her with real kindness, and eventually she'd realised he was suggesting she might be pregnant. And suddenly she'd found herself crying, and unable to stop, as she told him how utterly impossible that was, or ever could be. And of the constant pressure she'd been under during her four months of soulless marriage, both from Hugo and his mother, to somehow bring about a miracle and give him the child he craved.

'He doesn't believe any of the consultants.' Her voice had choked on a sob. 'He says it's my fault. But I don't know what to do. I don't know what he *expects* me to do.'

Confronting Hugo and Grace, the doctor had announced that Lady Marchington had been under a great deal of stress since the wedding, and was in dire need of a complete break, well away from the Hall and its environs.

'A holiday,' Grace had pondered aloud. 'Somewhere in the sun, perhaps, where they have good facilities for wheelchairs.' She gave the interloper an icy smile. 'It is, after all, my son who has suffered the real trauma here.'

'I'm afraid I haven't made myself clear.' The doctor was a stocky man, with sandy hair and a pugnacious expression with a built-in ice deflector. 'Lady Marchington actually needs to get away from all that. Build up her resources. Surely she has friends or family she could go to—somewhere she could relax in undemanding company for a while?'

'I have a very dear great-aunt in Brittany,' Allie said quietly, looking back at him, aware of Grace's barely suppressed fury at the word 'undemanding'. She drew a breath. 'She would have me to stay with her, I know.'

'Ideal.' He nodded. 'Walks on the beach, congenial surroundings, platters of *fruits de mer*, and plenty of sleep. That's what I prescribe. Worth a ton of tranquillisers or sleeping pills.'

'You may as well go,' Hugo told her bitingly after the doctor's departure. 'God knows you're of little use here.'

'And perhaps while you're away,' Grace added with steely annoyance, 'you can consider what you owe to the Marchington name, and come back in a more amenable frame of mind to attend to your duties as Hugo's wife.'

But I'm not his wife. The words screamed in Allie's brain. Because he's not physically capable of being my husband. We all know this, why must we go on with this terrible pretence? Why do I have to lie beside him in bed, being punished by his anger for something that isn't anyone's fault—just a tragic reality.

She wanted to cry again, but this time with the sheer relief of knowing that she was going to escape it all—just for a little while, although eventually she would have to come back…

'Dearest girl, you look like a ghost,' was her great-aunt's concerned greeting on her arrival at Les Sables d'Ignac. 'And there are deep shadows under your eyes. Are you not sleeping?'

'Well, Hugo does tend to be a little restless. And life has been pretty hectic since the wedding.' She managed a laugh. 'I seem to be public property. People want me to join committees—open things. And Hugo's mother is so much better at that kind of stuff. It all gets—a bit much sometimes.'

There was pause, then Tante said gently, 'I see.'

But please don't see too much, Allie begged under her
breath. Or ask questions that I can't answer.

The house was just as she'd remembered, its living room
occupying the entire ground floor, where a comfortable sitting
area, with two large sofas, flanked a fireplace with a wood-
burning stove and was divided from the kitchen area at the
far end by a large dining table, covered in oilcloth and surrounded by four high-backed chairs.

She found herself chatting almost feverishly during the
evening meal, describing Marchington Hall itself, and its
history, recounting anecdotes about some of Hugo's most interesting ancestors, while Tante listened, delicate brows
slightly lifted, sometimes offering a faint smile, but more
often not. She made her own polite enquiries about Fay's
health, and Hugo's progress, accepting the halting replies
without further comment.

And when the meal was over, she announced quietly but
firmly that Allie should have an early night, and shooed her
upstairs. The window in her room was open, its shutters
folded back, so that the filmy drapes moved in the breeze from
the sea. Allie could hear the splash and hiss of the tide, the
rhythm of its ebb and flow producing a faintly soporific effect.

She undressed swiftly, and put on her cotton nightdress.
Her final act was to remove her wedding ring and place it in
the drawer of the bedside cabinet.

Alice, Lady Marchington, belonged in England, she told
herself. Here, for these few precious weeks, she was going to
be Alys again. She would live entirely in the present, closing
her mind against the recent past and forbidding herself to contemplate the future, although she was aware there were
decisions that would have to be made. But somehow— *somehow*—she would build up the strength to do what she had to
do in order to survive.

She slid under the crisp white covers of the bed, stretching luxuriously, rediscovering the pleasures of space and
privacy, guiltily grateful not to encounter Hugo's bulk beside

her. And not to be made to endure the frustration of his fruit-
less, angry demands.

She fell asleep almost at once, and woke to the pale, sunlit
sky of early morning. The wind had freshened in the night,
and beyond the cliff-edge the waves were tipped with white.
She could taste the salt in the air, and felt her heart lift.

She showered swiftly, dressing in cut-off grey linen pants
with a white shirt knotted at the waist, thrust her feet into red
canvas shoes, and made her way noiselessly out of the house.

A walk, she thought, to make sure she was properly awake,
and then she'd drive into Ignac and pick up the bread and
some breakfast croissants at the *boulangerie*.

The bay immediately below the house was a wide crescent
of pale sand, backed by a jumble of rocks and boulders and
reached by a scramble of narrow steps hewn out of the stone
of the cliff-face. It wasn't the easiest access in the world,
which helped maintain the bay's privacy—the holidaymak-
ing crowds in this part of Finistere preferring beaches that
were more readily available.

Allie had never chosen to bathe here on her visits. She was
not a strong swimmer, and was wary about getting out of her
depth because of the strong off-shore currents.

Now, she picked her way across the pebbles, then slipped
off her shoes, tucking one into each pocket when she
reached the sand.

The wind whipped at her hair, sending it streaming across
her face, and she laughed aloud and began to run. 'I feel free,'
she shouted at a surprised gull, and performed a series of im-
provised pirouettes, leaping into the air. 'Wonderfully, gor-
geously free.'

And, as she did so, she heard the drumming of hooves not
far behind her. She turned swiftly and saw a powerful chestnut
horse approaching fast along the beach. On its back was a
man, hatless, his dark hair dishevelled, wearing riding
breeches and a crimson polo shirt.

Allie stepped backwards, realising with vexation that he
must have heard her bellowing at the sky, and seen her

whirling about like some poor man's dervish. As he passed, she caught a glimpse of swarthy skin in need of a shave, and an impatient sideways glance from eyes as coldly blue as the sea itself.

He called something to her, but his words were carried away by the wind, and she nodded, lifting a hand, pretending that she'd heard. Probably making some sarcastic comment on her dancing, she thought.

He's going in that direction, she noted mentally, as horse and rider disappeared round the curve of the cliff into the next bay. So—I'll go the other way.

She turned, and began to wander in the opposite direction, picking up shells as she went, eventually reaching another cove, narrower than the one she'd left, and sheltered by the steepness of the cliff.

Allie found a flat boulder and sat down, with her back to the wind, aimlessly shifting her shells into various patterns, and wishing that her life could be so easily rearranged. The question she had to ask herself was—how long could she go on living with Hugo? Especially when being treated as some kind of scapegoat in this ludicrous pretence of a marriage.

She'd been emotionally blackmailed into becoming his wife, standing beside his hospital bed as he begged her not to leave him. Told her that he needed her—depended on her.

Manoeuvred and manipulated by his mother, and hers, too, she hadn't known which way to turn. Had been warned that she could be risking his chance of recovery if she walked away. Except there *was* no chance, and everyone knew it. Especially the medical staff.

So I let them convince me, she thought drearily. Told myself I was necessary to him, and, even if I didn't love him, I told myself I could at least have compassion for all that strength and vigour, destroyed for ever by a stupid collision on a polo field. That I couldn't—let him down.

At the time, she reflected bitterly, it had seemed—easier. But how wrong she'd been.

Shuddering violently, Allie swept the shells off the rock

into oblivion, almost wishing that she could go with them. Because there was no pattern to her life, and no solution either. Just endurance. Because, however unhappy she might be, Hugo was in a wheelchair, requiring permanent nursing, and she still couldn't abandon him. She'd have to go back.

But she would at least make the most of this all too brief release. She glanced at her watch, realising it was time she was getting back to the house. She was getting hungry, and besides, Tante would be wondering where she was.

She jumped down from her rock and turned, her hand going to her mouth, stifling a cry. While she'd been sitting there, daydreaming, the sea had been coming in—not gently, but in a strong, steady rush, as she knew it sometimes did along this coast. Tante had warned her about it in the past, insisting that anyone staying at the house must always check the tides before using the beach.

But I didn't. I didn't give it a moment's thought. I assumed it was on the ebb...

She looked at the waves, already encroaching at each end of the cove, cutting off her retreat whichever way she turned, and felt sick with fear. There was seaweed on the boulders behind her too, indicating how far the sea could reach.

Oh, God, she thought, I must do something. I can't just stand here, watching the water level rise.

She realised she might have to swim for it, although she knew she'd be struggling even if the sea was like a millpond. On the other hand, if she wasted any more time, she risked being washed against the jut of the overhanging cliff, she realised, swallowing a sob in her throat.

Then, suddenly, there was rescue.

The horse seemed to come from nowhere, eyes rolling, head tossing as it galloped through the waves, urged on by its rider. As they reached the strip of sand where Allie stood, transfixed, the man leaned down, hand extended, spitting an instruction at her in a voice molten with fury.

She set a foot in the stirrup that he had kicked free, and found herself dragged up in front of him, left hanging across the saddle, with her head dangling ignominiously, his hand holding her firmly in place by the waistband of her trousers.

She felt the horse bound forward, and then there was water all around them, the salt spray invading her eyes and mouth, soaking the drift of her hair, chilling the fingers that were gripping the girth until they were numb.

She could feel the fear in the chestnut's bunched muscles— sense the anger in the air from its rider—although he was talking constantly to his mount, his voice quiet and reassuring.

She was scared and aching, every bone in her body shaken as the horse plunged on. She closed her eyes against the diz-ziness induced by this headlong dash, praying that he would not stumble. That the drag of the sea would not defeat him.

She never knew the exact moment when the almost violent splashing of the water stopped, but when she next dared to look down, she found herself staring at sand, and the begin-nings of a rough track leading upwards.

Then the horse was being pulled up, and her rescuer's hold on her was suddenly released. She raised a dazed head, real-ising that he was dismounting, and then she herself was sum-marily pulled down from the saddle, without gentleness, and dumped on the stones.

She sank to the ground, coughing and trying to catch her breath. She felt sick and giddy from that nightmare ride, aware too that her clothes were sodden, and her hair hanging in rats' tails.

She looked up miserably, tried to speak and failed, silenced by the scorching fury in the blue eyes, and the battery of fast, enraged French that was being launched at her without mercy.

As he paused to draw breath at last, she said in her school-girl's version of the same language. 'I'm sorry. I don't under-stand.' Then she put her face in her hands and burst into tears.

He swore murderously. She could interpret that at least. Then there was a taut silence, and a clean, if damp, handker-chief was thrust between her fingers.

'You are English?' He spoke more quietly, using her language, his voice clipped, the accent good.

She nodded, still not trusting her voice.

'*Mon Dieu.*' He shook his head. 'Yet you come here to a dangerous shore—alone, and at such an hour, to stroll as if you were in a London park? Are you quite insane?'

She lifted her head. Looked up at him as he stood, soothing his horse with a paradoxically gentle hand.

He was slightly younger than she'd thought, probably in his early thirties, but no friendlier for that. She assimilated a beak of a nose, a formidable chin with a cleft, and a strong mouth with a sensual curve to its lower lip. And his eyes were truly amazing—a colour between azure and turquoise, fringed by long lashes. And brilliant now with the temper he was trying to control. But more, she thought, for the horse's sake than hers.

She said huskily, 'I should have been more careful, I know. But I was thinking about—something else.'

He gestured impatiently. 'But I warned you to go back. Why did you ignore me?'

'I—didn't hear what you said—not properly.'

He muttered something else under his breath. 'You are no doubt accustomed to people shouting at you,' he added contemptuously. 'And have learned to disregard it.'

Allie sank her teeth into her lower lip. Yes, she thought, but not in the way you imagine.

'Again, I'm sorry.' She wiped her face with the handkerchief, detecting a faint fragrance of some masculine cologne in its folds.

'I did not believe it when I looked down from the top of the cliff and saw you there in the Cauldron,' he said harshly. 'We call it that because when the tide is full the water seems to boil over the rocks.'

Allie shuddered. 'I didn't know. I—I've never gone that way before.' *And I wouldn't have done so this time if I hadn't been trying to avoid you...*

'I was almost tempted to leave you,' he went on. 'Instead of risking my life, and my even more valuable horse, to come to the aid of a stranger and a fool.'

She lifted her chin. 'Oh, don't spare me. Please say exactly what you think,' she invited, with a trace of her usual spirit.

'I shall,' he told her brusquely. He added, 'Roland, you understand, does not care for the sea.'

Then perhaps you should have left me. It would have been one answer to my problems...

The thought ran like lightning through her head, but was instantly dismissed as she contemplated the shock and grief that Tante would have suffered if the sea had indeed taken her.

Besides, when faced with it, oblivion had not seemed nearly so desirable, and she knew she would have fought to survive.

She swallowed. 'Then Roland's a true hero.' She got slowly to her feet. 'And—thank you for having second thoughts,' she added with difficulty. She smoothed her hands down her wet trousers, and stopped as a sudden realisation dawned. 'Oh, God, I've lost my shoes. They were in my pockets.'

'I hope you do not expect me to go back for them,' he said with asperity.

'Oh, no,' Allie returned, almost poisonously sweet. 'I think saving my life places me under quite enough obligation to you for one day.'

'Or perhaps not,' he said slowly. 'Where are you staying, *mademoiselle*?'

For a moment, this form of address threw her. Then she remembered her discarded wedding ring. He would naturally assume she was single, and she should put him right instantly. But...

'Why?' she asked, still edgy. 'Are you hoping to be rewarded for bringing back the stray?'

The firm mouth curled. 'You mean there are people who would pay to have you returned to them? *Incroyable.* However, I hope it is not too far,' he added smoothly. 'It could be an uncomfortable journey in bare feet.' He watched the variety of expressions that flitted across her face with an appreciation he did not bother to disguise. 'Or would you prefer to ride back to your accommodation on Roland?'

Neither, she thought. I'd much rather the past hour had

never happened. I wish I was back in my room at Les Sables, turning over to sleep again.

'Please make up your mind, *mademoiselle*.' He glanced at his watch. 'I am not a tourist. Unlike you, I have work to go to.'

One day, she promised herself. One day, I'll think of something to say that will wipe that smirk out of your voice.

Except that presupposed they would meet again, which was the last thing she wanted—to keep running into a man who regarded her as a bedraggled idiot.

She lifted her chin. 'Thank you,' she said. 'I think I'd better accept your offer. As long as Roland has forgiven me for his unexpected dip.'

'He has a nature of the most amiable.' He cupped his hands. 'Put your foot here,' he directed, and as she nervously complied he tossed her up into the saddle as if she were thistledown, then began to lead Roland up the slope. 'You had better tell him where he is to take you,' he added over his shoulder.

She said unhappily, 'I'm staying with Madame Colville at Les Sables.' She could just imagine Tante's reaction when she turned up, barefoot on the back of a strange horse, looking like a piece of sub-human flotsam. She added unwillingly, 'I'm her great-niece.'

'Ah,' he said. 'I did not know she had such a relation. But then she is my father's patient, not mine.'

She frowned. 'Patient? You mean you're a doctor?'

'You find it hard to believe? Yet I assure you it is true,' he said. He made a slight inclination of the head. 'Remy de Brizat at your service.'

As she hesitated, he added, 'Now you are supposed to tell me your name, *mademoiselle*. Or is it a secret?'

Not a secret, she thought. But not the whole truth either, which is very wrong of me. But perhaps this is my morning for behaving badly. And anyway, we're unlikely to meet again, so what harm can it really do?

She said, quietly and clearly, 'I'm called Alys, *monsieur*. Alys—Colville.'

'Alys,' he said reflectively. 'A charming name—and French too.'

She wrinkled her nose. 'In England, I'm plain Alice.'

At the top of the slope, he halted Roland and stood looking up at her, his smile faintly twisted. 'You are wrong,' he said softly. 'You could not ever be plain—anything.'

There was an odd, tingling silence, then he added briskly, 'Now, move back a little, Alys, if you please, so that Roland can take us both.'

She did as she was told, feeling awkward, and hoping the exertion would explain the sudden surge of colour in her face. Remy de Brizat mounted lithely in front of her.

'Hold on to me,' he instructed. 'The medical centre in Ignac opens in one hour, and I must be there.'

Reluctantly, she put her hands on her companion's shoulders, then, as the big horse moved off, she found herself being thrown forward, and hastily clasped her arms round his waist instead.

'*Ça va?*' he queried over his shoulder, as Roland's stride lengthened into a canter.

'I think so,' Allie gasped, clinging on for grim death, and heard him laugh softly.

It wasn't really that far, she realised, as the grey stones of Tante's house came into view. If she'd been wearing shoes she would have walked it easily, and saved herself the embarrassment of being forced to hug her unwanted rescuer, let alone be forced to travel with her face pressed against his muscular back.

When they reached the cottage, he insisted on dismounting and lifting her down.

'Thank you,' Allie said stiffly, trying not to overbalance. 'For—everything. I—I owe you a great deal.' She held out her hand. 'Goodbye, Dr de Brizat.'

His brows rose. 'Not Remy?'

'It's hardly appropriate,' she said, in a tone borrowed wholesale from Grace. 'After all, we're hardly likely to see each other after this.' She added pointedly, 'I don't intend to dice with death a second time.'

'Very wise, *ma belle*.' He took her hand and raised it swiftly to his lips, making her start at the casual intimacy. The pressure of his mouth and the graze of his unshaven chin against her fingers was an experience she could have well done without. 'Because tradition says that now I have saved your life it belongs to me, and I think you should live it to the full, and that I should help you to do so.'

He swung himself back into the saddle and grinned down at her. His teeth were very white against the darkness of his skin. 'And eventually,' he told her softly, 'you will call me Remy. I promise it. *Au revoir, ma chère* Alys.'

And, with a word to Roland, he cantered off, leaving Allie staring after him, aware of the sudden, uncomfortable flurry of her heartbeat.

As she went into the cottage Tante was just coming downstairs, trim and elegant in black tailored trousers and a white silk shirt, her silver hair confined at the nape of her neck with a black ribbon bow.

'My ears are playing tricks on me,' she complained. 'I thought I heard a horse outside…' She stopped, her eyes widening in alarm as she surveyed Allie. '*Mon Dieu, chérie*—what has happened to you?'

Allie sighed. 'I stupidly let myself get cut off by the tide,' she admitted. 'In a place called the Cauldron.'

'Alys.' Tante sat down limply on one of the kitchen chairs. 'People have drowned there. You could have been one of them.'

Allie forced a smile. 'Except that your doctor's son came riding by, and gallantly carried me off across his saddle bow.' She stretched, wincing. 'I'm now a walking bruise.'

'It is no joking matter. You could have lost your life.'

'But I didn't. I'm simply minus a pair of shoes.'

Tante shuddered. 'You must never take such a chance again.'

'Believe me,' Alice said grimly, 'I don't intend to.'

'And it was Remy who saved you?' Tante made the sign of the cross. 'I shall go to see him, thank him for giving you back to me.' She brightened. 'Or, better, I shall invite him to dinner.'

Allie shifted restively from one bare foot to another. 'Is that strictly necessary? I did thank him myself, you know.' *After I'd taken a hell of a tongue-lashing.*

Tante pursed her lips. 'Madame Lastaine, who keeps house for the doctors at Trehel, is no cook,' she stated decisively. 'Remy will be glad of a good meal, *le pauvre.*'

'He seemed perfectly fit and healthy to me,' Allie said coolly.

Tante gave her a long look. 'Dear child, you seem—put out. Is it possible that you are blaming Remy in some way, because he did not let you drown?'

Allie bit her lip. 'Naturally, I'm grateful. But that doesn't mean I have to like him. Or that I have any wish for another encounter,' she added clearly, tilting her chin. 'And I hope his patients don't expect to receive any sympathy when they go to him.'

Tante's brows rose. She said mildly, 'I have never heard of any complaints about his attitude since he returned to Ignac. *Au contraire.* He is said to be skilful, and well-liked.'

Allie paused on her way to the stairs. 'He's not always worked here, then?' she asked, before she could stop herself.

'After he qualified he worked for a medical charity, firstly in Africa, then in South America. But it was always understood that he would one day fulfil the wishes of his father and grandfather and join the practice in Ignac.' Tante's smile was bland. 'I have always found him both charming and considerate. However, I shall not invite him here against your wishes, *chérie.*'

'Thank you.' Allie hesitated, her fingers beating a tattoo on the stair-rail. 'I just feel we're—better apart, that's all.'

'*D'accord.*' Tante's gaze shifted from her great-niece's flushed face to her restless hand. 'I notice that the sea took more than just your shoes, *ma mie,*' she remarked. 'It seems that your wedding ring, too, has gone.'

Allie's colour deepened. 'Not—entirely. It's upstairs. I—I simply decided not to wear it, that's all.'

'Ah,' Madelon Colville said meditatively. 'I am interested that you found that a simple decision.'

'I didn't mean it like that.' Allie took a deep breath. 'I took it off because I wanted to find the person I used to be—before my marriage. Somewhere along the way she seems to have vanished, but I really need to have her back.' She lifted her head. 'To be—Alys Colville again. Even if it's only for a little while.' She hesitated, sighing. 'But I suppose that's impossible. Everyone round here—all your neighbours—friends—will know I'm married. You must have mentioned it.'

'I told no one, *mon enfant*,' Tante said quietly. 'It was not news I ever wished to share. I have always believed that mistakes in one's family circle should be kept private. And I had known for some time—long before his tragic accident—that you did not love this man. Your letters made it clear.'

'But I hardly mentioned him.'

Tante's smile was kind. 'Exactly, *chérie*.' She paused. 'When I received the invitation to your wedding I wrote to your mother, begging her not to allow you to ruin your life. Saying that such a marriage would have profound difficulties, even if you adored each other.'

She shrugged wryly. 'Her reply was very angry. She said that I knew nothing about it. That you were devoted to your fiancé, that my interference was not needed, and it would be better for everyone if I stayed away.'

'She said you'd decided the journey would be too much for you.' Allie bit her lip. 'Oh—I should have known…'

'Well, that is all in the past now. It matters only that you are here now, *ma chère*. And if you wish to be Alys Colville again—then that is how it shall be.'

She became brisk. 'Now, go and change, and I will try to repair the damage the sea has done to those expensive clothes.'

Allie turned obediently, then paused. She said in a low voice, 'Am I crazy—to pretend like this?'

'Not crazy,' her great-aunt said slowly. 'But perhaps—not very wise.'

Allie's smile was swift and bleak. 'Then I'll just have to be very careful, too,' she said, and made her way to her room.

CHAPTER THREE

THE sun had gone behind a cloud, and Allie got up from the bench, shivering a little.

She'd sat there long enough, she thought, tormenting herself with her memories. Now it was time to go back to the house and draft a letter to Tante, explaining why any return to Les Sables was impossible for her—now or in the future.

I can't do it, she told herself with anguish. Because, even now, the pain of that time is still too vivid and too raw.

She entered the house through a side door, and went straight upstairs. After Hugo's death, and in spite of Grace's protests, she'd moved out of the master suite she'd reluctantly shared with him into this smaller room at the back of the house. It wasn't as grand and formal as some of the others, and she liked its creamy-yellow walls, and the warm olive-green curtains and bedcover. Over the months it had become her refuge.

She sat down at the small writing table that she'd bought at an antique fair, and drew a sheet of paper towards her. She sat for a moment, tapping her pen against her teeth and staring out of the window in front of her, as she tried to come up with an excuse that her great-aunt would find even feasible, let alone acceptable.

Her room overlooked the vegetable garden, and the now-deserted stableyard. After the accident, Hugo's hunters had been sold, along with his polo ponies. Except, of course, for

poor little Gimlet, who'd broken both forelegs in that terrible
crashing fall in the final chukka, and had had to be put down
on the field there and then.

'He was the lucky one,' Hugo had said with scalding bitterness when they'd told him. At that time he'd seemed to recognise the full extent of his injuries, Allie thought unhappily.
It was later that he'd come to believe in his own self-will
rather than the prognosis from the medical experts.

Sighing, she wrote the date. Well, it was a start, she told
herself wryly, then paused as there was a swift tap on her door.
It opened instantly to admit her mother-in-law.

'So there you are,' she commented. 'Mrs Windom has
brought in the coffee. Are you coming down?'

'Later, perhaps. I'm replying to Tante Madelon's letter.'

'Ah.' Grace paused. 'Did she have anything particular to
say?'

'She's not well,' Allie told her quietly. 'She'd like me to
visit her—and take Tom with me.'

'No,' Lady Marchington said, swiftly and sharply. 'You
can't possibly go to Brittany, and even if you did consider it
you certainly couldn't take Tom. It's out of the question,
Alice, and you know it.'

Allie found herself reeling back mentally under the onslaught.

Of choice, she wouldn't have mentioned Tante's letter, or
its contents, precisely because she knew what the reaction
would be. And because she had no intention of going.

Yet now she found herself bristling furiously, as a spirit of
angry rebellion suddenly surged up inside her. This, she
thought, is the last damned straw. I've had as much of her interference in my life as I can stand. I'm *not* living under a dic-
tatorship, and it's time I made that clear.

She said coldly, 'I wouldn't be *allowed* to take my own
child on holiday to visit a close relative? Is that really what
you're saying?' She shook her head. 'I can't believe it.'

'Then you'd better suspend your disbelief.' Grace's expression was grim. 'I have no intention of permitting my

grandson to be whisked out of the country—and to France, of all places.'

'Why not? Was one of the Marchington ancestors killed at Agincourt?' Allie tried to speak lightly, in spite of the anger building inside her.

'Don't be flippant,' Grace snapped. 'What I'm saying is that our lives are not going to be turned upside down at the behest of one arrogant old woman. I simply won't permit it.'

'Please don't speak about Tante like that,' Allie said icily. 'The invitation came to me, and I'll deal with it as I see fit.' She paused, steadying her breathing. 'I'm not a child. I'm twenty-two years old, and I don't need your permission, or anyone else's for that matter, to stay in Brittany with the woman who practically brought up my father.'

She met Lady Marchington's furious gaze in open challenge. 'Anyway, why shouldn't I go? Give me one good reason.' *If you dare...*

Spots of colour burned in the older woman's face. 'Tom's far too young for a journey of that nature.'

'A night on a ferry and a couple of hours by car?' Allie's tone was derisive. 'Babies far younger make similar trips every day.'

'But Tom isn't just any child. He's the Marchington heir. You have your position to consider. And his.'

Allie's gaze remained stony. 'And is that your only objection? Because Tom isn't just a Marchington. He has Colville and Vaillac blood too. And it's entirely natural that Tante should want to see him, especially as she's in bad health. After all, he's the last of her line, too.'

Grace's mouth hardened. 'Breton peasant stock. Hardly anything to boast about.'

'They're brave, and strong, with good, loving hearts,' Allie returned icily. 'That would be enough for most people.'

'Now you're just being difficult.'

'Under the circumstances,' Allie said, 'that is almost amusing. Only I don't feel like laughing.'

'Alice—for heaven's sake. There was enough talk last time

when you simply—disappeared, for weeks on end, leaving poor Hugo to cope alone.'

'Hardly alone. He had you, his nanny, a full-time nurse, and all the staff to look after him. I was pretty much surplus to requirements—except in one respect, of course.'

She paused. 'And I came back. As I always intended. Was there more talk then? Or did I redeem myself because at last I was doing my duty by my brave, disabled husband, and giving him the child he'd been demanding with such monotonous regularity?'

There was another taut silence.

'Sometimes,' Grace said, 'you sound so hard, Alice.'

'Do I?' Allie's smile didn't reach her eyes. 'I wonder why?'

'And I'm hurt that you should be making this kind of decision without consulting me.'

You, thought Allie, wouldn't be hurt even if I hammered a stake through your heart.

'As soon as that letter arrived I knew exactly what that woman would want,' Grace added angrily.

'Oh, come on,' Allie defended. 'You talk as if Tante's always demanding attention, and that's simply not true.'

'Oh, she's more subtle than that,' her mother-in-law said derisively. 'Your mother warned me, of course, that she was a born manipulator.'

Well, the pair of you should know, Allie countered silently.

'Well, let's agree to disagree over that too, shall we?' she suggested quietly.

'And French houses don't have proper damp-proof courses.' Grace tried a new tack. 'Tom might catch a chill.'

Alice leaned back in her chair. 'He doesn't stay still for long enough. And I don't want him wrapped in cotton wool all the time. He's a little boy, for heaven's sake.'

'Yes, he is, and I'm not sure you realise just how important he is to the future of the Marchingtons.'

'On the contrary. I've had it drummed into me that he *is* the future of the Marchingtons, God help him.' Alice said shortly. 'Before, during and after he was born, God help *me*.'

There was a silence. Then Lady Marchington said, 'Alice, listen—please.' She looked older suddenly, and weary. Almost scared. 'You can't possibly go back to that place. It would be madness.'

There were two heartbeats of silence as Allie looked back at her. Her voice was even. 'In what way—madness?'

Her mother-in-law put up a hand to smooth her already immaculate hair. 'Well—perhaps madness is a slight exaggeration. All the same, you must see why you shouldn't go back there. And I'm sure your mother would agree with me.'

'I don't doubt it,' Allie returned quietly. 'But it makes no difference to my decision.'

Lady Marchington took a deep breath. 'If Madelon genuinely wishes to see Tom, perhaps—arrangements could be made for her to come to England.'

'Except that it isn't right to uproot someone of her age,' Alice said quietly. 'Particularly when she's unwell, and I'm young and healthy and can make the trip perfectly easily.'

What am I saying? Why am I making all these arguments for a case I'd already decided to lose? Because it's too late to say so. Because, by this totally unwanted and unwarranted intervention, Grace has backed me into a corner, and if I'm ever to establish any independence for myself I cannot give way over this issue. And, as a result, I now have to go back to Les Sables d'Ignac, even though it's the last thing I want in this world.

I have to. There's no choice now. It's make or break time...

Oh, God, why couldn't she have kept quiet? Given me the chance to find some kind of valid excuse for staying away. For escaping this nightmare?

'Plymouth to Roscoff overnight,' she added with a shrug, forcing herself to sound casual. 'Then a leisurely drive down to Les Sables. Tom will love it.'

'You can't take Tom,' Grace said harshly. 'If you insist on going, it must be alone.'

'You mean that after deserting my husband on the last visit, I should desert my son this time?' Allie asked ironically.

'Imagine the gossip that would cause. And I don't choose to feature as a neglectful mother. Besides,' she added squarely. 'It would give me the chance to really *be* with Tom for once. To spend some real quality time with him on my own, so that we can get to know each other properly.'

'On your own? But you'll have to take Nanny.'

When hell freezes over...

Aloud, 'Thank you,' she said politely. 'But I wouldn't dream of it. I'm perfectly capable of driving my own car, and caring for Tom like any other mother. In fact, I'll love it. Besides,' she added practically, 'Tante has no room for another guest at the cottage, and it's the holiday season over there.'

I want my life back, and I want my child back too, she thought. And if this is the only way, then I'll take it.

Grace clearly realised she had lost the advantage, and her mouth was a slit. But her voice was composed again. 'I see. So, when are you thinking of going?'

'I thought—as soon as I can get a ferry booking.' Allie looked back at her calmly, just as if her stomach wasn't tying itself into knots at the prospect. She added, 'I think I'll pass on the coffee. Tante will be waiting for my reply.'

Grace nodded. 'Then clearly there's nothing more to be said.' She gave a small wintry nod, and left the room.

The ferry was crowded, and it seemed to take an age before her deck was cleared and Allie was able to drive down the ramp into the busy port of Roscoff.

It was a clear, bright morning, but the crossing had been a choppy one. Tom had not liked the motion of the ship, and had proclaimed as much all night long. He'd not been sick, just angry and frightened—and probably missing Nanny's confident, capable handling, Allie acknowledged exhaustedly. And for the first time she wondered if Grace and her mother had been right. She was too inexperienced, and he was too young for such a trip.

But, as she'd waited restlessly to be called to her car, she'd seen umpteen other babies, much younger than hers, who seemed perfectly relaxed and cheerful about the whole experience.

It's all my own fault, she told herself, for not insisting on looking after him myself from Day One, and to hell with postnatal depression. Other women manage, and I could have done, too. Well, from now on things are going to change. Permanently.

She couldn't pretend it would be easy. Nanny had greeted the news of the trip in ominous silence, and the days leading up to departure had been cloaked in an atmosphere that could only have been cut by a chainsaw.

But, when Allie had taken no notice, she'd been forced to accept the situation.

It might not be a very worthy triumph, thought Allie, but for someone who'd been consistently ignored since Tom was born, and made to feel incompetent and ungrateful when she protested, it was eminently satisfying.

She got well free of Roscoff and its environs, then stopped at a *tabac* in a convenient village, ordering a *café au lait* and a croissant, while Tom had milk, and made himself agreeably messy with a *pain au chocolat*.

She gave him a perfunctory wipe down to remove the worst of the crumbs, then strapped him back into his safety seat with his favourite blue rabbit. Before they'd gone half a mile, the combination of the previous restless night and warm food caught up with him, and he fell peacefully and soundly asleep, leaving Allie to concentrate on her driving.

Last time she'd come this way, she'd pushed the car swiftly, almost recklessly, aware of little but her own wretchedness, but now she had precious cargo on board, and her control was absolute. She slotted some cool jazz into the CD player, and headed steadily south towards Ignac, knowing that she would easily reach Tante's house by lunchtime.

Tom slept for an hour and a half, and then woke, grizzling. Allie parked on the wide verge at the side of the road, changed him quickly, gave him a drink, then let him play on the rug she'd spread on the grass. Propped on an elbow, she watched him, smiling, as he carefully dismembered a large leaf.

He turned his head and saw her, according her the sudden vivid grin that lit up his face, before stumping energetically in her direction, grabbing her shoulder to steady himself.

'Who's my wonderful, clever boy?' she praised, hugging him. And who certainly *isn't* going to be bow-legged through walking too soon? she added silently, recalling a recent bone of contention at home.

They stayed for another sunlit half-hour before Allie decided they should be on their way again. Tom made a token protest as he was strapped into his baby seat, but she soon tickled him into good humour again, nuzzling her face into his neck so that he laughed and grabbed at her hair.

An hour and a half later, Ignac began appearing on the signposts. She saw the name with a sense of relief, because it had been a long time since she'd undertaken so long a drive. Although so far it had been an easy, even enjoyable journey, with only moderate traffic to contend with in places.

The joys of midweek travel, she thought. Most of the holidaymakers arrived at the weekend, and are now relaxing at their hotels and *gîtes*, leaving the roads open for me, bless them.

'*Courage, mon brave,*' she told Tom, who was beginning to be restive again. 'We're nearly there.'

Mentally, however, she was already bracing herself, unsure of what she might find when she reached Les Sables.

Tante disliked the telephone, regarding it as something to be used only in the direst emergencies, and the letter expressing her delight at Allie's visit, and confirming the suggested arrangements, had been in the same wavering hand as before.

Not for the first time, Allie wished there was someone she could confide in about her worries. Someone who also cared about Tante.

Once there was, she thought—and stopped right there, her lips tightening. She could not let herself remember that—even though every landmark—every direction sign in the last hour—had been battering at her memory with their own poignant reminders.

But what else could she have expected? she asked herself with a sigh. Those few brief weeks with Remy had given her the only real happiness she'd ever known. How could she even pretend she'd forgotten?

Tante had warned she would find Ignac much changed, but apart from the new villas, all white and terracotta in the sunlight, which had sprung up like mushrooms on the outskirts, the little town seemed much the same.

Its church was ordinary, and Ignac didn't possess one of the elaborately carved calvaries which were among the great sights of the region, but its busy fishing harbour bestowed a quiet charm of its own.

The narrow streets were already crammed, with parked cars on both sides, and as she negotiated them with care she realised that the town square ahead was a mass of striped awnings.

'Of course,' she said aloud. 'It's market day. I certainly forgot about that.'

The market was drawing to its close, the stalls being swiftly dismantled, rails of clothing and boxes of household goods being put back in vans, although last-minute shoppers still lingered at the food stalls, hoping for bargains.

But we, she thought, always came early to buy...

She forced her attention back to the road ahead, braking gently as an old lady stumped out on to the pedestrian crossing just ahead, waving her stick to signify her right to priority. She was accompanied, apprehensively, by a younger couple, and as she reached the middle of the crossing she stopped suddenly, and turned to upbraid them about something, using her stick for emphasis. The other woman looked at Allie, shrugging in obvious embarrassment, as all efforts to get the senior member of the party moving again ended in stalemate.

She wants to have her say, and she wants it now, Allie thought, reluctantly amused. And, until it's over, we're going nowhere.

People were pausing to watch, and smile, as if this was a familiar occurrence.

He seemed to come from nowhere, but there he was,

joining the trio on the crossing, a tall, lean figure, dark and deeply tanned, casual in cream jeans and an open-necked blue shirt. He was carrying two long loaves of bread, and a plastic bag that Allie knew would contain oysters. He transferred it to his other hand, before he bent, speaking softly to the old lady, while his fingers cupped her elbow leading her, gently but firmly, to the opposite pavement.

For a moment it looked as if she might resist, then the wrinkled face broke into an unwilling grin and he laughed too, lifting her hand to his lips with swift grace. Then, with a quick word and a shrug to her grateful companions, he was gone again, vanishing between the remaining market stalls as quickly as he'd arrived.

Allie sat and watched him go, her hands gripping the wheel as if they'd been glued there. She thought numbly, But it *can't* be him. It can't be Remy because Tante said—she promised—that I'd have nothing to fear.

Nothing to fear…

An impatient hooting from the vehicles behind brought her back to the here and now, and she realised, embarrassment flooding her face with colour, that the total shock of seeing him had made her stall the engine. She restarted carefully, and set off, waving an apologetic hand to the other drivers.

She threaded her way out of town and on to the narrow road which led to Les Sables, before yanking the wheel over and bringing the car to an abrupt halt. She sat for a moment, her whole body shaking, then flung open the car door and stumbled out, kneeling on the short, scrubby grass while she threw up.

As she straightened, her head swimming, her throat and stomach aching, she heard Tom's frightened wail from the car, and dragged herself to her feet in instant contrition.

'It's all right, darling, Mummy's here.' She found a packet of wipes in the glove compartment and hastily cleaned her face and hands, before releasing Tom from his harness and lifting him into her arms. She sat down on a flat boulder a few feet away from the car, and held him close against her, patting him and murmuring soothingly while she waited for her heartbeat to settle. And she tried desperately to make sense of what had just happened. But failed.

There is nothing that should keep you away...

The words were indelibly printed on her brain. Unforgettable.

The wording of Tante's letter had suggested—had seemed to promise—that Remy was still far off in South America. So how could he possibly be there in Ignac, charming tough old ladies into compliance, buying food from the market, clearly as much at home as if he'd never been away?

She should have told me the truth, she thought passionately. Should have warned me that he was here. Except that if she had nothing would have dragged me here, and she knew it.

Perhaps, she thought, Tante doesn't know he's come back. Maybe it's a temporary thing—some kind of furlough—and she hasn't heard.

But she discounted that almost at once. Her aunt's house might be secluded, but it wasn't in limbo. Every piece of gossip, every item of local news, found its way to her sooner or later.

Besides, Remy's father, Philippe de Brizat, was Tante's doctor—and his father before him, for all she knew.

Of course the news of Remy's return would have been shared with her.

Anguish stabbed at her. It seemed unbelievable that her beloved and trusted great-aunt should have deliberately set out to deceive her like this. Unless she knew that the first time she did so would also be the last.

She must, Allie thought sombrely, be really desperate to see me again—to see Tom—even to contemplate such a thing.

Her immediate instinct was to turn the car and drive back to Roscoff. Get the first possible return sailing. But, apart from all the other considerations, that would mean returning to the Hall with her tail between her legs, losing any advantage she'd gained in her belated bid for independence.

I could still visit Tante, she thought, but make it a brief visit—not stay for the ten days as planned. That should be safe enough.

After all, France is a big country, and Brittany's not its only region. Plus, it's still early enough in the year for there to be hotel vacancies. I could take Tom exploring the Auvergne, or the Dordogne. Even go as far as the Côte d'Azur.

Anywhere, she resolved, as long as it was far—far away from Remy de Brizat. Because Tante was so terribly wrong, and she had *everything* to fear from encountering him again.

Her arms closed more tightly around Tom, who wriggled in protest, demanding to be set down.

She held his hands, steering him back to the car as he paced unsteadily along, face set in fierce determination.

'I know the feeling,' she told him as she lifted him back into his seat for the short drive to Les Sables. 'And from now on, my love, it's you and me against the world.'

The house stood alone, grey and solid against the slender clustering pine trees behind it. Allie eased the car along the track, remembering her father's concern that Tante should have chosen such an isolated spot.

'It wouldn't do for me,' he'd said, shaking his head. 'The silence would drive me crazy.'

Tante had laughed gently. 'But there is no silence, *mon cher*. I live between the wind singing in the trees and the sound of the sea. It is more than enough.'

The front door was open, Allie saw, and a woman's small, upright figure had emerged, and was standing, shading her eyes against the sun, watching the car approach.

It's Tante Madelon, Allie realised with astonishment. But if she's been ill, surely she should be in bed, or at least resting on the sofa.

She brought the car to a halt on the gravelled area in front of the house and paused for a moment, taking a deep breath. She'd already decided on her strategy. No reproaches or recriminations. Instead, she too would practise a deception—she would pretend that she'd simply driven through Ignac and seen no one. As far as she was concerned, Remy de Brizat was still on the other side of the world.

And if Tante mentioned his being back in Ignac, she would produce a look of faint surprise, maybe even risk a polite question about his life in Brazil. Or had he, in fact, moved on from there?

She'd tried so hard not to think about that. Not to wonder where he was and what he was doing.

And now it seemed as if all her desperate efforts to blank him out of her mind had been in vain.

Ah, well, she thought bleakly, as she marshalled her defences. Just as long as it doesn't show.

And she opened the car door and got out, smiling resolutely.

Madelon Colville had never been a large woman, but now she seemed to have shrunk even more. In Allie's embrace, she felt as insubstantial as a captured bird. But her eyes were still bright, shining with love and pleasure, and her voice was husky with emotion as she murmured words of welcome.

'Dearest child, you cannot know what this means to me.' She looked towards the car with unconcealed eagerness. 'Now, where is your little son?'

Finding himself on show, Tom decided to be shy, and buried his face in his mother's neck. But Tante was unfazed by the reaction.

'It is all too new and strange for him,' she declared. 'But soon we will be friends—won't we, *chéri*?' She took Allie's hand. 'Now, come in, and meet Madame Drouac, who looks after me. She is a widow, like myself, and so good to me. However, she speaks no English, and you will not understand her *patois*, so I shall translate for you both.'

Madame Drouac, who was standing at the range, stirring a pan of something that smelt deliciously savoury, was a tall, angular woman with a calm face and kind, shrewd eyes. As she shook hands, Allie was aware of being subjected to a searching look, followed by a low-voiced exchange with her great-aunt.

But Allie did not need a translation. She remembers me from the last time I was here, she told herself without pleasure. Recalls who I was with, too.

'Amelie thinks you have become thin, *ma mie*.' Madelon spoke lightly. 'She says we must fill you with good food. Also *le petit*.'

She indicated an old-fashioned wooden highchair, polished to within an inch of its life, which was standing at the table. 'She has loaned us this for Thomas. Also the cot, where her own son slept. He has married a girl from Rennes,' she added with a shrug. 'And she does not need them for her baby. She wants everything that is new. So Amelie is pleased that her things will be used once more.'

She paused. 'I have told her that you are a widow, Alys, but also that your marriage only occurred after you left here and returned to England.' Her gaze was steady. 'You understand?'

'Yes,' Allie said woodenly. 'Yes, of course.'

Lunch was a thick vegetable soup, served with chunks of bread, and there was cheese to follow.

Tom made a spirited attack on his soup, using his spoon like a stabbing spear. He was assisted in his efforts by Madame Drouac, who talked softly to him in Breton, and occasionally clucked at him like a hen, which provoked a joyous toothy grin. Shyness, it seemed, was a thing of the past, Allie saw with relief.

'He usually has a nap in the afternoon,' she mentioned as they drank their coffee.

'Very wise,' said Tante. 'I do the same.' She gave Allie a long look. 'And perhaps you should rest also, *ma mie*. You are pale, and your eyes are tired.'

'Well, I have had more peaceful nights,' Allie admitted ruefully. She hesitated. 'Would it be all right if I took a shower first? I feel as if I've been wearing these clothes for ever.'

Tante covered her hand with her own. 'You must do exactly as you wish, *chérie*. This is your other home. You know that.'

It's probably my only real home, Allie thought, as she carried Tom upstairs. The room had been rearranged, with its wide bed pushed under the window in order to accommodate the cot—a palatial, beautifully carved affair. For a moment,

Allie felt almost sorry for the daughter-in-law from Rennes who couldn't recognise a family heirloom when she saw it. But her loss was Tom's gain, and he was asleep even before Allie had finished unpacking.

She undressed slowly, and put on her thin, white silk dressing gown before making her way to the bathroom, which boasted a separate shower cabinet as well as a large tub. 'It may be a cottage, but I insist on my comforts,' Madelon Colville had declared, when the old-fashioned fittings had been torn out and replaced.

And maybe I like mine too, Allie thought wryly, as she set out the array of exquisitely scented toiletries she'd brought with her.

She stepped into the shower and turned on the spray, letting the water cascade luxuriously over her hair and body.

The soup had been just what she needed, and, although she was still on edge, she was no longer shaking inside. Madame Drouac was clearly a good cook, and Allie found she was looking forward to the casserole of lamb that had been promised for the evening meal.

'Amelie is a jewel,' Tante had said quietly downstairs. 'I only wish she was not considered a necessity. But the doctor insisted I should have help.'

The doctor... But which one did Madelon Colville mean? After all, there were three generations of de Brizats living at the big stone house at Trehel. It could hardly be the grandfather, Georges, who had retired under protest a few years before and must now be nearing his eighties, so it had to be Philippe still—or his only son, Allie thought, biting her lip savagely. And that was something she couldn't ask.

She wished that Madame Drouac spoke even a little English, so that, among other things, she could establish exactly what was wrong with her great-aunt. Because, when she'd tried a little tactful probing, Tante had merely waved a languid hand and said that she had good days and bad ones.

'But today is nothing but good, because you are here,' she'd added.

On the other hand, Allie thought wryly, the language barrier between the housekeeper and herself meant she didn't have to answer any awkward questions about her previous stay.

She towelled herself dry, and slipped on her robe again. Back in the bedroom, she combed her damp hair into place, reluctant to use her dryer in case she disturbed Tom.

In spite of her weariness, she knew she would not sleep. She was too tense, and her brain was buzzing. She knew that for her own peace of mind she should have stayed away. That she should not have let herself be provoked into accepting such a dangerous invitation. But could she really regret what she'd done, when Tante was so clearly overjoyed to see her?

And, anyway, it was far too late for repining.

The box was unlocked at last, and all her personal demons had come swarming into the open. And somehow they had to be faced. Whatever the personal pain they might bring in their wake.

CHAPTER FOUR

SHE knelt on the bed, resting her arms on the window ledge, staring down at the bay where it had all begun.

Not very wise...

That was what Madelon had told her in warning, she thought, and it was probably the understatement of the decade. But how could I know where it would lead? After all, I only wanted some time to myself—to think, and make some decisions. And I didn't wish to be cross-examined, however kindly, over where my husband was, or why he wasn't with me.

I just—needed some peace.

I never meant there to be more to it than that. And I certainly never intended to deceive anyone, or cause any hurt.

Plus, I didn't lie. I just didn't tell the whole truth and nothing but the truth.

But then no one actually asked me to do so—or not until it was so much too late.

She stopped herself right there. She could play with words and motives for ever, but nothing could actually justify what she'd done. She'd desperately needed to be honest, and instead she'd crashed in flames. And she could blame nothing and no one but herself.

Yet here she was, two years on, knowing that she could not afford to be completely frank. That there were still things that could not be said.

A widow with a child, she thought. That was all anyone needed to know.

And although Remy might be back in Ignac, that did not necessarily imply they would meet.

On the contrary, she told herself with resolution, she would go out of her way to ensure they didn't.

I dare not risk it, she thought. For all kinds of reasons…

Sighing, she swung herself off the bed, pulling on shorts, a vest top and sandals, then went over to the cot. Tom was still fast asleep, chubby arms tossed wide, and her heart lurched as she looked down at him.

When Tante was gone, he would be all she had left to love. But he made all the agony of the past seem somehow worthwhile. She smoothed the damp, dark curls with a gentle finger, but he did not stir, so she tiptoed from the room and went slowly downstairs. The living room was empty, so presumably Madame Drouac had returned to her own abode for the afternoon, and the sun was streaming in through the open door at the rear.

Allie, drawing a deep, unsteady breath, walked out into the walled garden beyond.

The wind had dropped, and there were just a few faint streaks of high cloud, motionless against the baking blue of the sky.

She sat down on the grass, her back against the solitary ancient apple tree, and stared upwards, shading her eyes with her hand. So many days like this, she thought, breathing in the scent of earth and sun-warmed grass. So many memories jarring her mind again. Splintering her inner calm. Waiting inexorably to be dealt with.

Closing her eyes, Allie, slowly and reluctantly, allowed herself to surrender to the pull of the past.

In the days following her ruthless and spectacular rescue by Remy de Brizat, she'd made a conscious decision to keep well away from the beach, even though Tante had supplied her with a tide table and told her to learn it by heart.

But, in her heart, Allie knew that the rise and fall of the sea wasn't the principal danger to be encountered.

The weather had turned intensely hot, giving her a good excuse to remain quietly in the seclusion of the garden, sunbathing and reading, as she felt her inner tensions begin to slip gently away. Or most of them, anyway.

One morning, over breakfast, Tante had mentioned that she was driving to Quimper later, to visit her accountant. 'Some papers to do with tax, *chérie*, and so boring. But you are welcome to come with me, if you wish.'

Allie had decided she did not wish. She'd waved goodbye to Madelon, then taken her rug and cushion into the garden and stretched out face downward, unclipping her bikini top with a languid hand as she did so. But the hum of insects, the whisper of the leaves, and the distant murmur of the sea had failed for once to have their usual soporific effect. She'd felt oddly restless, and even the thriller she'd been reading had palled, its plot descending, she had decided, into sheer absurdity.

She'd tossed it aside, pillowed her head on her arms, and closed her eyes, making a deliberate effort to relax her whole body, commencing with her toes, then working slowly upward. Any moment now, she'd promised herself, she would feel completely calm.

'*Bonjour*, Alys.'

For a shocked second, she thought she'd dozed off and was actually dreaming, but one startled sideways glance revealed battered espadrilles and, rising out of them, a pair of long, tanned and totally masculine legs.

'You?' She almost sat up, remembering just in time her loosened top. 'What are you doing here?'

'I wished to make sure that the events of the other morning had left no lasting trauma.' He grinned down at her, totally at his ease, casual in shorts and a cotton shirt unbuttoned almost to the waist.

'And is this how you normally make house calls?' It was difficult, she found, to glare at someone effectively when you were forced to lie prone, and all they could see was your profile. 'Just—march in without knocking or asking permission?' *And half-dressed?*

'No,' he said. 'But this is not a professional visit, you understand. Also, I met with Madame Colville on the road, and she gave me leave to visit you.'

He looked her over with undisguised appreciation, his eyes lingering, she realised furiously, on the narrow band of jade fabric that scarcely masked the swell of her buttocks.

'The sun is fierce today,' he said softly. 'And you should not risk burning such lovely skin.' He knelt down beside her, reaching for the bottle of sun lotion. He tipped some into the palm of his hand and began to apply it to her shoulders, in smooth, delicate strokes.

For a moment she was rendered mute with shock, then hurriedly pulled herself together.

'Thank you,' she said through gritted teeth. 'But I'm quite capable of doing that for myself.'

'Vraiment?' His brows lifted in polite enquiry, but he made no attempt to bring his unwanted ministrations to an end. 'You are, perhaps, a *contorsionniste*? No? Then be still, and allow me to do this for you.'

His light, assured touch on her skin sent alarm signals quivering along her nerve-endings.

I don't want this, she thought almost frantically. I—really do not...

She would have given anything to be able to sit up and snatch the damned bottle from his hand, but she was anchored to the rug. If only—*only*—she hadn't unfastened her top. And the fact that he must have seen hundreds of women with bare breasts in his career made not an atom of difference.

Because Remy de Brizat was not her doctor, and, for all his comments about trauma, she was not his patient and never would be.

He took all the time in the world, his hands lingering, while Allie, raging with the knowledge of her own temporary helplessness, lay with her eyes shut and her bottom lip caught between her teeth as she fought a losing battle over the slow, inevitable awakening of her senses.

This can't be happening to me, she thought. It just can't.

One of the reasons I ran away was because I didn't want to be touched—because I couldn't bear it any longer.

And this man—this stranger—has no right to make me feel like this—as if my skin was made of silk, and my bones were dissolving. He has no right at all.

At last he paused, running a light finger along the rim of her bikini briefs but venturing no further, and she released her held breath, thinking that her ordeal was over.

Only to find herself stifling a startled whimper when he began to anoint the backs of her thighs, moving gently down to reach the sensitive area in the bend of her knees.

'*Alors.*' With sudden briskness, he recapped the bottle and put it down beside her. 'The rest I am sure you can manage for yourself.'

'Thank you,' she said with icy politeness. 'But I think I've had enough sun for one day.'

'Perhaps you are wise,' he said, faint amusement in his voice. 'Why take more risks with such a charming body?'

Her throat tightened. 'Thank you for your concern,' she said. 'But I can look after myself.'

She fumbled for the edges of her bra top and tried to bring them together across her slippery skin, with fingers made clumsy through haste.

'Of course—as you prove so constantly, *ma belle.*' She could hear him smiling, damn him. '*Permettez-moi.*' He took the strips of material from her, and deftly hooked them into place.

Too bloody deftly altogether...

She sat up, pushing her hair back from her flushed face with a defensive hand. 'Does that fulfil your quota of good deeds for the day?' she asked stiffly. 'Or do you have other visits to make? Because I wouldn't wish to delay you on your errands of mercy.'

He studied her for a moment. 'Why do you speak to me as if I were your enemy, Alys?'

Her colour deepened. 'I—don't,' she denied shortly.

'No?' His mouth twisted wryly. 'Then I hope we do not meet when you wish to be hostile.'

She took a swift breath. 'I would actually prefer it, *monsieur*, if we didn't meet at all after this.' She lifted her chin. 'You got me out of a nasty situation the other day, and I shall always be grateful for that. But now I would really like to be left in peace to—to enjoy my vacation without any further intervention from you. I'm sure you understand.'

'I think I begin to,' Remy de Brizat said slowly. 'Tell me, Alys, do all men make you so nervous, or is it just myself?'

She gasped. 'I'm not the slightest bit nervous—of you, or anyone.'

'Then prove it,' he said, 'together with this gratitude you say you feel, and have lunch with me tomorrow.'

'Lunch?' she echoed in disbelief. 'But why should I do any such thing?'

He shrugged. 'I have already given you two good reasons,' he said. 'Besides, everyone needs to eat, and midday is considered a convenient time by most people.' The blue eyes considered her again, more thoroughly. 'And you are a little underweight, you know.'

She lifted her chin. 'Is that in your medical opinion, or for your personal taste?' she queried coldly.

He grinned at her. 'I think—both.'

Well, she'd asked for that, but it didn't improve her temper or weaken her resolve to keep him at bay.

He had a proud face, she thought, stealing a lightning glance at him from under her lashes. There was even a hint of arrogance in the high cheekbones and the cool lines of his mouth.

This was a man who was almost certainly unused to rejection, and equally unlikely to take it well.

I don't suppose, Allie mused, he's ever been stood up in his life. And—who knows?—it might teach him a much-needed lesson. And, more importantly, it will demonstrate that I'm not available. Let's hope he takes the hint.

She shrugged a bare shoulder, half smiling, as if resigned to her fate.

'Very well, then. Lunch it is. As you say, we all need to eat.' She paused. 'What do you propose?'

There was a brief silence, then he said slowly, 'There is a good restaurant on the road towards Benodet—Chez Lucette. You think you can find it?'

'Of course.'

'*Bon.* Then, shall we say—twelve-thirty?'

'Perfect.' Allie looked down demurely. 'I—look forward to it, *monsieur.*'

His brows lifted. 'Still not Remy?'

'After lunch,' she said, and smiled. 'Perhaps.'

He said softly, 'I shall live in hope. *A bientôt.*' And went.

Left alone, Allie realised she was as breathless as if she'd been running in some marathon. It was a reaction she was not accustomed to, and it scared her.

All I had to do, she thought, swallowing, was tell him, '*I'm married.*' And he would never have troubled me again. It was that simple. So why didn't I say it? Why let him go on thinking I'm single? Available?

Oh, stop beating yourself up, she adjured herself impatiently. As long as you brush him off, why worry about the method? And after tomorrow he certainly won't be coming round again.

She would change her brand of sun oil, too, she decided broodingly. Find an alternative with a different scent—one that wouldn't remind her of the play of his hands as he massaged it into her warm skin each time she smelt it.

She said aloud, 'Whatever it takes, I *will* be left in peace. And to hell with Remy de Brizat.'

'Are you quite well, *chérie*?' Tante studied her anxiously. 'You seem tense—restless—this morning.'

'I'm fine,' Allie assured her, wandering out into the garden to sneak a look at her watch. Twenty-five past twelve, she thought. Excellent. He should be at Chez Lucette by now, and ordering his aperitif. Probably looking at his watch too, gauging my arrival.

I wonder how long he'll wait before it dawns on him that he's struck out for once? That I've not simply been delayed, but that I shan't be joining him at all?

And what will he do then? Eat alone at his table for two? Or pretend he has an urgent case to go to before the egg hardens on his face?

Whatever—it serves him right, she told herself defensively, although she was totally unable to rationalise this conviction.

And she was sure there were plenty of ladies in the locality who would be happy to help soothe his bruised ego, she added, ramming her clenched hands into the pockets of her skirt.

'Alys?' Tante was calling from the back door, surprise in her voice. 'Alys, you have a visitor.'

She swung round just in time to see Remy de Brizat walk out into the garden. He was dressed much as he had been the day before, with emphasis on the casual, his sunglasses pushed up on his forehead.

For a moment, Allie could only gape at him. When she spoke, her voice was husky with shock. 'What are you doing here? I—I don't understand...'

His smile was sardonic. 'I decided against the restaurant after all, *ma belle*. It occurred to me that you would have difficulties in getting there. So I put food and wine in the car so that we can picnic instead.' He added solicitously, 'I hope you are not too disappointed?'

'No,' she said. 'That's not the word I'd have chosen.' She swallowed. 'How did you know that I wouldn't meet you?'

He shrugged. 'One minute you were spitting at me like a little cat. The next you were—honey. It was too much of a *volte face* to be entirely credible.'

'And, of course, you wouldn't just take the hint and stay away?'

'I considered it.'

'Then why are you here?'

'Because you intrigue me, Alys. Enough, certainly, to risk another rebuff.' He added softly, 'Also, I still wish to hear you call me Remy.'

He held out his hand. 'It's only lunch, *ma mie*. Shall we go?'

Is it? she thought, feeling the rapid thud of her heart. Is that really all it is?

Tell him, counselled the warning voice in her head. Tell him the truth now. Say that you misled him the other day because you were upset and didn't know what you were saying. That it wouldn't be appropriate for you to see each other again because you have a husband in England.

Then it will be over, and you won't have to worry any more. You want peace of mind? Then take it. Because this could be your last chance.

And she found herself looking down at herself—at the thin blouse, the straight white skirt and the strappy sandals. Heard herself saying, 'I—I'd better change. I'm not really dressed for a picnic.'

'You look enchanting,' he said. 'But—just as you wish.'

Her glance was scornful. 'Now, we both know that isn't true.'

Inside the house, Tante looked at her, her forehead puckered in concern. 'My dear child, are you sure you know what you're doing?'

'Yes,' Allie said, and paused to kiss her cheek. 'It's fine, really,' she whispered. 'We're just going to have lunch—one meal together. And that's all.'

Then I'll tell him I'm married, she thought as she ran upstairs. And it will finally be finished.

Madness, Allie thought, returning bleakly to the here and now as tears burned in the back of her eyes and choked her throat. Sweet, compelling, uncontrollable madness. That was what it had been—how it had been.

One man—*the man*—was all it had taken to breach the firewall around her. Just the touch of his hand had altered all her perceptions of herself, destroying once and for all the myth of her invulnerable reserve.

How could she have known that she'd simply been waiting—waiting for him? Remy…

His name was a scream in her heart.

She drew her knees up to her chin, bent her head, and

allowed herself to cry. The house was asleep, so thankfully there was no one to hear her agonised keening or the sobs that threatened to rip her apart.

For two years she'd had to suppress her emotions and rebuild her defences. Never allowing herself to reveal even for a moment the inner pain that was threatening to destroy her.

Now, at last, the dam had burst, and she yielded to the torrent of grief and guilt it had released, rocking backwards and forwards, her arms wrapped round her knees. Until, eventually, she could cry no more.

Then, when the shaking had stopped, she got slowly to her feet, brushing fronds of dried grass from her clothing, and went into the house.

She washed her face thoroughly, removing all traces of the recent storm, then carefully applied drops to her eyes, before returning to her room. Tom had not stirred, and she stretched herself on the bed, waiting with quiet patience for him to wake up, and for the rest of her life to begin.

She must have dozed, because she suddenly became aware, with a start, that he was standing, vigorously rattling the bars of his cot. As she swung herself off the bed and went to him, he gave his swift, entrancing grin, and held out his arms.

She picked him up, rubbing noses with him. 'And hi there to you too. Want to play outside?'

Tante was there ahead of them this time, sitting placidly under a green and white striped parasol, her hands busy with her favourite embroidery, a jug of home-made lemonade on the wooden table at her elbow.

She looked up, smiling. 'Did you rest well, *chérie*?'

'It was good not to be moving,' Allie evaded. She put Tom down on the blanket that had already been spread on the grass in anticipation, rolling his coloured ball across the grass for him to chase before sitting down and accepting the glass of lemonade that Tante poured for her.

And now it was high time to face a few issues. And with honesty, this time around, if that was possible.

'I came across a little drama in Ignac today,' she remarked, trying to sound casual. 'A fierce old lady having some family battle in the middle of the road, and refusing to give way.'

Tante chose another length of silk from the box beside her. 'That would be Madame Teglas,' she said composedly. '*Pauvre femme*, she hates her unfortunate daughter-in-law, and is convinced that her son wishes to put her in a home. Therefore she makes these scenes in public.' She shook her head. 'One day, she will be run over.'

'She nearly was—by me.' Allie was proud of the faint amusement in her voice. 'Luckily, Remy de Brizat came along and calmed her down.'

She waited tensely for Tante's response, but the older woman merely nodded, unfazed. 'He is her doctor, and one of the few people who can deal with her tantrums.'

'I see.' Allie hesitated. 'That—sounds as if he's back for good?' she ventured.

Madelon Colville threaded her needle with care. 'His father hopes so, certainly. The other partner at the medical centre was diagnosed with Parkinson's disease a year ago, and wished to retire, so Remy returned to take his place.' She looked at Allie over the top of her glasses. 'You were surprised to see him, *peut-être*?'

'A little, maybe.' Allie hand-picked her words. 'I guess I—assumed he would still be in Brazil, or wherever the charity had sent him next.'

Tante nodded. 'And you feel, I think, that I should have told you he had come back?'

'No,' Allie said, then, 'Well, maybe. I—I don't know…' She paused. 'Does he know that—I've come back, too?'

'I saw no reason to tell him.' Tante shrugged, her face and voice calm. 'Two years have passed since you parted, *ma chère,* and the world has moved on—as Remy himself has done. He has dismissed the past and come back to resume his life here, just as he should.

'And you also made a decision—to lead your own life in England, with this beautiful child.' Her eyes dwelled thoughtfully on Tom. 'He is the important one now, and that other time, here with Remy, is over and gone, and should be forgotten.'

She paused. 'Besides, he may even be married himself when the summer ends.' She added expressionlessly, 'No doubt you will remember Solange Geran?'

No doubt...

The pain was suddenly back, slashing savagely at her, forcing Allie to stifle her involuntary gasp.

'Yes,' she returned steadily. 'Yes, of course I do.'

How could I possibly forget her—the girl who finally brought my make-believe world crashing in ruins around me?

And now—dear God—Remy has come back—to her. I did not bargain for this...

And how can I bear it?

She drank some lemonade, letting the cold tartness trickle over the burning sandpaper that had once been her throat. She made herself sound politely interested. 'Her *gîte* business— is it doing well?'

'It seems that it is. She has converted another barn, and no longer has time to deliver eggs.' Tante set a stitch with minute accuracy. 'Although I had already ceased to buy from her,' she added almost inconsequentially.

Tom was fast approaching again, clutching his ball to his chest. Allie persuaded him to relinquish it, and rolled it again for him to pursue.

She said quietly, 'And now she's going to be a doctor's wife, just as she always wanted.' She forced a smile. 'It's— good that things have worked out so well—for all of us.' She sat up, swallowing the rest of her lemonade. 'And now, maybe, we should talk about you.'

Tante shrugged again. 'I am no longer young. What else is there to say?'

'Quite a bit,' Allie said crisply. 'Are you going to tell me what's wrong? Why you've been seeing the doctor?'

'The ailments of the elderly,' Tante dismissed almost airily. 'So boring to contemplate. So wearying to discuss.'

Allie stared at her. 'It can't be that simple,' she objected.

She paused. 'You do realise that your letter implied that you were practically at death's door?'

Tante concentrated on her embroidery. 'As I told you, I have good days and bad days, *ma mie*. I must have written to you on a bad one.'

Allie drew a sharp breath. 'And when Madame Drouac came to look after you—I suppose that was just a bad day too?'

Madame Colville looked faintly mournful. 'All these details—so difficult to remember.'

'Then perhaps I should simply ask your doctor.'

'Ask Remy?' Tante mused. 'I wonder if he would tell you. Or if it would indeed be ethical for him to do so without my permission.'

In the silence that followed, Allie heard herself swallow. She said, 'I—I didn't realise. I thought you were his father's patient.'

'When Dr Varaud left, there was some reassignment.' Tante waved a hand. 'I was happy to consult Remy instead.' She gave a slight cough. 'To reassure you, *ma chère*, I have always found him most kind—most understanding.'

'I'm delighted to hear it.' Allie's tone was wooden. Oh, God, she thought, her stomach churning. If she's under some medical regime, then he may come here. What am I going to do? What can I do?

She leaned forward almost beseechingly. 'Darling, why won't you tell me what the problem is—and how serious? We could always get a second opinion.'

'Because it would change nothing.' There was a finality in Madelon Colville's voice. 'And, believe me, *mon enfant*, I am content for it to be so. In life, at my age, one can only expect the unexpected.' She smiled. 'So, *chérie*, let us simply enjoy this time we have together, *hein*?'

Allie stared at her. Her great-aunt seemed almost tranquil, she thought in unhappy bewilderment. More than that, she'd swear that Madelon even had an air of faint satisfaction. Was that how someone really prepared to relinquish their hold on a good life well lived? She could hardly believe it.

At the same time, it was clear that any expression of sorrow and regret on her own part would not be welcomed. So, in spite of everything, she would have to do her best to remain cheerful and positive.

But at least her concern over Tante might help distance the renewed anguish that hearing about Remy had inevitably evoked.

And the local grapevine worked like a charm, she reminded herself. News of Tante's visitor from England would soon spread. She could only hope that Remy, too, would want no reminder of the betrayal and bitterness of two years before, and take his own avoiding action.

'It's over,' she whispered feverishly to herself. 'And I have to accept that, just as he's done, and deal with it.'

And, at the same time, pray that it's true...

She drew a trembling breath as she reached for Tom as he scurried past and lifted him on to her lap, holding him tightly.

It's your future that matters now, my darling, she told him silently. Your future, and nothing else. And I'll fight tooth and nail to protect it.

CHAPTER FIVE

THE rest of the day passed slowly. Allie felt constantly on edge, acutely aware of how many topics were necessarily taboo. She was thankful that Tom was there to provide a welcome focus for everyone's attention. His earlier shyness all forgotten, he basked in the unbounded sunshine of approval from Tante and Madame Drouac.

Even so, there were odd pitfalls to be negotiated.

'Amelie says that Thomas has very beautiful eyes,' Tante reported smilingly as Allie came downstairs, slightly damp from an uproarious bath and bedtime session with her son. 'She thinks such an unusual shade of blue.'

'The Marchingtons are all blue-eyed,' Allie returned, rather lamely.

'She feels too that he is most advanced for so young a child,' Madelon Colville added blandly. 'She understood you to say that he has only just passed his first birthday.'

Allie's face warmed. 'I think that may have lost a little in translation,' she said lightly. 'I shall have to work on my French.'

And also watch my step from now on, she added silently. Madame Drouac is clearly nobody's fool.

They spent a quiet evening, preferring to listen to music rather than watch television. But it was not long before Tante announced that she was tired and going to bed.

'And I think you would benefit also from an early night, Alys.'

Allie nodded. 'I'll be up soon.'

But when the Chopin *nocturne* ended, she slid Debussy's *'Prelude à l'après midi d'un faune'* into the CD player, and settled back against the cushions to listen, allowing the music to recapture for her all the drowsy, languid warmth of a magical afternoon. A time when anything could happen.

Like that first afternoon with Remy, she thought, a fist clenching in her stomach. Never to be forgotten.

She'd sat tautly beside him in his Jeep, she remembered, her hands gripped together in her lap, staring through the windscreen without absorbing much. Conscious only of the man beside her.

'Relax, Alys,' he had commanded softly. 'Or you will make me nervous too.'

'Not much chance of that,' she muttered.

'No?' There was amusement in his voice. 'You would be surprised. But you will feel better, perhaps, when you have had something to eat.'

'It's not always a question of blood sugar levels, *monsieur le docteur*,' she countered. She shook her head. 'I still don't know why I'm doing this.'

'I hi-jacked you, *chérie*,' he said cheerfully. 'I like to look at something beautiful during my mealtimes.'

Her brows lifted. 'Really? I thought most Frenchmen preferred to look at what was on their plates.'

'Then you know very little about Frenchmen.'

'And,' she said, 'believe it or not, I was perfectly happy in my ignorance.'

He burst out laughing. 'One day, *ma mie*,' he said, 'I shall remind you of that.' He turned the Jeep off the narrow coast road they'd been following, and drove inland along a rough track towards a circle of standing stones silhouetted against the horizon.

'Don't tell me,' Allie commented brightly as he brought the vehicle to a halt. 'This used to be a place for human sacrifice, and I'm the main course.'

Remy grinned at her. 'Legend says that they were all bad

girls from nearby villages, lured here by a local saint in the
guise of a handsome young man, who turned them to stone
when they refused to repent their wicked ways.' He took a rug
from the back of the Jeep and tossed it to her. 'Maybe a sacrifice would have been kinder.'

'And the *men* who weren't saints?' she enquired tartly, as
he lifted out a hamper. 'Who'd contributed to the girls' down-
fall? I suppose they got off scot-free?'

'That might depend, *ma belle*, on whether or not they were
found out by their wives.'

Allie gave him a cold look and followed him, holding the
rug against her as if it provided some kind of defence.

They walked through the stones and down into a small
sheltered hollow, where Remy spread the rug on the short
grass and began to unpack the basket. Allie stationed herself
at a distance and watched. It was, she reflected, quite a sophisticated performance, with covered pottery dishes, gleaming silverware, a white linen cloth, and crystal glasses
wrapped in matching napkins. Not a plastic spoon or limp
sandwich in sight. And a means to an end if ever she'd seen
one.

Seduction-by-Sea, she told herself wryly. And I wonder
how many other girls he's brought to this same secluded spot?

On the other hand, what could it possibly matter? He was
here with her for the first time and the last, and whatever plans
he might have for post-prandial entertainment were doomed
to disappointment.

Unless, of course, he decided to use force...

For a brief moment something cold and dead lodged like
a stone within her, and was immediately dismissed.

No, she thought, he would never do that. Because he would
never have to. There would be no lack of willing women in
his life. Enough, probably, to embellish the whole of Finistere
with stone circles if truth be told.

'You look very fierce, Alys,' he commented. 'Calm yourself with some pâté. It has come from the Intermarche, so it
is quite safe.'

Allie, remembering what Tante had said about the cooking at Trehel, was betrayed into a giggle.

'Ah,' he said. 'I see poor Liliane's fame has reached Les Sables. And yet as a housekeeper she is—*formidable*. No speck of grime is allowed to exist. *Mais, malheureusement*, the food is also massacred.' He shook his head. 'We try—my grandfather, my father and I—to keep her from the stove, but at the same time we do not wish to hurt her feelings. She is a kind soul.'

The pâté *was* good, she discovered, as were the thick slices of ham, the chunks of smoked sausage, and the sliced duck breast that followed. To accompany the crusty *baguette* there was a slab of butter in a refrigerated dish, and a creamy local cheese, wrapped in a checked cloth.

The wine Remy poured for them both was pale and crisp, but she was told there was also mineral water, if she preferred.

She decided to risk the wine, sipping circumspectly, and if he noticed her restraint he made no comment.

To complete the meal there were strawberries, in a bowl lined with green leaves.

Allie pushed her plate away with a little sigh of repletion. 'That was—delicious.'

'And I am forgiven for having kidnapped you?'

'I'll overlook it,' she said. 'This once.'

He smiled at her lazily. 'I hope it will never again be necessary.' He paused. 'I regret there is no coffee, but I think it should be made and drunk while it is fresh. Although, being English, you drink only tea, perhaps?'

'Not at all,' she said. 'Besides, my grandmother was French, don't forget.'

'The Vaillac sisters.' He began to put the used things back in the hamper. 'My grandfather knew them as young girls, and says they were both beauties.' He paused. 'He was surprised, I think, when Madame Colville decided to return. And pleased, too. He says it is good to come back to the place where you were born. So many—just leave.'

He put the hamper to one side and refilled their glasses.

'He says also that this is not your first visit. That you came here with your father while I was working abroad.'

'Yes, I did,' she said. 'More than once.' She paused. 'Which makes my idiotic behaviour on the beach the other morning even more unforgivable. I—should have known better.'

'And I,' he said, 'could have been kinder.'

He had moved closer, she realised suddenly, and his hand was only a couple of inches from hers. She looked down at the long fingers with their short, well-kept nails, and remembered how they'd felt, touching her skin. A tiny flame of forbidden excitement sprang into life deep within her, and had to be suppressed.

She hurried to fill the silence. 'You speak marvellous English.' *Oh, God, I sound all eager and—girly.*

He shrugged. 'When I qualified, I worked in Britain for a while. Also America. And when I was employed by the charity English was the common language too. So now, of course, I am given the tourists to deal with at the medical centre.'

'Yes,' she said. 'Of course. Well, I'll—try to lessen your workload and not get sick.'

His mouth quirked. 'You are all consideration, *ma mie*, but you seem to be in good health. You are still pale, of course.' His hand closed round her wrist. 'And your pulse is too rapid,' he added softly. 'But I do not think the symptoms are dangerous.'

Oh, but you're wrong—so wrong, she thought wildly. Because I've never been in such danger before. Never…

She glanced down, realising that his fingers were entwined with hers now, and that somehow his other arm was encircling her shoulders. She felt his cheek against her hair. Became aware that he was lifting her hand, brushing her knuckles gently with his lips, then turning it to press a kiss into the centre of her palm. It was the briefest of caresses. Yet she felt it jolt through her entire body like an electric charge.

And heard herself whisper desperately, 'No—please. No.'

He released her instantly, but he did not move away from her. She could feel the warmth of him through her thin shirt. He said quietly, 'No to a kiss, *ma belle*? Or—no, I may not undress you, as I so much wish to do, and make love to you here in the sunlight?'

'No to any of it. All of it.' She stumbled over the words. 'You mustn't... I can't...' She added desperately, 'Please take me home.'

There was a silence, thoughtful rather than laced with the anger she'd expected.

He stroked her cheek, then smoothed her hair back behind her ear, his thumb gently brushing the lobe. He said softly, 'Are you a virgin, Alys?'

She stared wildly in front of her, not daring to turn her head and meet his gaze. She said huskily, 'You have no right to ask me that.'

'You think not? But between lovers it is a matter of some importance.'

'We are—not lovers.' Her tone had become a croak.

'Not yet, perhaps. But one day—one night soon—it will happen.' He added levelly, 'As you know well, Alys. So do not let us pretend any longer, or play games with words. It follows that I need to know if you are truly as inexperienced as you seem.'

She still could not look at him. She spoke reluctantly, stumbling a little. 'Then—no. I've had sex—before.'

'Ah,' he said meditatively. 'You do not appear to recall it with pleasure.'

She bit her lip. 'It was at a college party,' she said at last. 'In an empty bedroom with someone who'd never paid me much attention before. And nothing really changed, because it was awkward, uncomfortable, and thankfully over very quickly.' She tried to smile. 'Afterwards, I wanted to die of embarrassment. My only excuse, and I'm not proud of it, is that I'd had too much to drink.'

And I've never told anyone before—so why now? Oh, God, why you...?

'What a terrible confession,' Remy said, after a pause. He reached for the bottle and held it out to her. 'Have some more wine.'

She gasped indignantly, turning on him, then halted. How could she have ever thought his eyes were cold? she asked herself dazedly. They were so alive and brilliant with laughter, mingled with something that might almost have been tenderness.

She mumbled, 'It's not funny.'

'No,' he said. 'It is not.' He poured the rest of the wine on to the grass, and returned the empty bottle to the basket.

He said softly, 'Let me tell you something, *chérie*. A man who chooses to make love to a girl when her senses are dulled with alcohol is a fool. When you come to me, Alys, I promise you will know exactly what you are doing at every moment.'

Her heart was battering her ribcage. She said thickly, 'It will never happen.'

His brows lifted. 'You doubt my resolve, Alys? *Eh, bien…*'

He reached for her almost casually, pulling her against him so that she was lying across his body. Then he bent his head, and his mouth took hers—slowly, but very surely.

She knew she should resist. The need to do so was imperative. Absolute. But she had no defence against the warm, mesmerising power of his kiss. And the complete absence of any kind of pressure was her undoing. His lips moved on hers with a tantalising gentleness wholly outside her experience. The tip of his tongue probed softly, coaxing her to open to him. To allow the caressing mouth to take her to a new and more sensuous level.

Almost imperceptibly Allie found her body relaxing against his, her breathing quickening unevenly as she yielded to the intimate exploration of the inner contours of her mouth, the delicate, provocative play of his tongue against hers.

And when at last he raised his head and looked down at her, the blue eyes grave and questioning, she breathed, 'Remy,' on a little sigh, and her arms went round his neck to draw him back to her again.

At once his kiss deepened, hardening into a new dimension of heated possession, and Allie responded passionately to his demands, her own mouth as eager—as seeking.

The blood seared her veins as she clung to him, her fingers

gripping the strength of bone and muscles in his shoulders through the thin shirt as she tasted—breathed with desire—the erotic male scent of him.

His hand lifted to cup her breast, his thumb stroking its tender peak slowly and rhythmically, teasing it to quivering arousal until she moaned softly into his mouth, her body arching towards him.

Hunger was burning her now—melting her with the first real discovery of her own female physicality. Making her aware of the scalding rush between her thighs. Rendering her defenceless against whatever he might ask of her.

Slowly, almost lingeringly Remy took his mouth from hers, his hand from her body. Even moved back a little, pushing his hair from his face.

She looked up at him, her eyes half closed, drowsy with need as she began one by one to unfasten the buttons on her shirt. To offer herself.

Only to find his hand closing round hers, halting her.

He said huskily, his breathing ragged, 'You taste of strawberries and wine, Alys.' He paused, shaking his head almost dazedly. 'But now I think—I know—that I should take you home.'

'But I thought…' The stumbling words were out before she could prevent them, their bewildered message unmistakable.

Oh, God, she thought, shamed to the bone. I'm pleading with him for sex when he's already turned me down. Please—this can't be happening to me.

Words slunk from the past to haunt her. *Useless—stupid—frigid…* All the taunts, the accusations, coming home to roost. Branding her for ever with their terrible truth.

Shocked blood rushed to her face as she realised, too, what she must look like, dazed with desire, her hardened nipples thrusting against the cling of her dishevelled blouse. Stunned, she scrambled away from him, clumsy in her haste. 'Yes—yes, of course. I—I'm sorry. We should go. Tante will wonder…'

And then the words ran out on a little gasp, and she could only put her hands over her face, unable to bear the renewed humiliation of seeing the pity in his eyes when he looked at her.

Remy said something half under his breath, and his hands clamped firmly round her wrists, tugging them away.

'You think, maybe, that I do not want you?' The question was almost harsh. 'But you are so wrong, Alys. I hesitate only because I do not wish you to think I am like that other man. That I ask only for the pleasure of the moment. For us, that can never be the choice, and we both know it. There must be more between us than just a meeting of bodies.'

'Then—what?' Somehow, Allie forced the question from trembling lips.

He sighed. 'I think that I need you to trust me, *mon ange*.'

'I do.' Her protest was swift.

'But not enough. Believe me.' His tone was quiet but forceful. He cupped her face between his hands, the blue eyes intense. 'How can you, when you hardly know me? When we hardly know each other?' He shrugged, his smile crooked. 'So—that must change. And I—I will have to learn patience.'

'So will I.' Her admission was shy. She turned her head, pressing a kiss into the warmth of his palm.

'Ah, *mon coeur*.' He took her back into his arms, holding her close for a few heart-stopping moments, releasing her with open reluctance. 'We had better go now,' he muttered roughly. 'Before I am tempted beyond endurance.'

Allie's glance through her lashes was mischievous as he helped her to her feet. 'Isn't that why you brought me here in the first place?'

'Of course.' His mouth twisted ruefully. 'But I am only human, Alys, and therefore allowed to hope—being no saint.'

'I'm glad.' She glanced round at the standing stones. 'The local variety took a tough line with straying girls. Maybe he could have used a little humanity too.'

'Perhaps we were right not to risk his anger?' Remy suggested. Then, as she turned away, he halted her. 'Wait, *ma mie*, I need to tidy you a little.' She obeyed, standing demurely while Remy carefully rebuttoned her gaping shirt and brushed tell-tale fronds of dried grass from her clothes and hair.

'But I can do nothing about your eyes, *chérie*, or your beautiful mouth,' he added huskily. 'You look entirely like a girl who has been in the arms of her lover. I only hope your great-aunt does not bar me from her house.'

She won't do that. The words remained on her lips, unsaid, as she suddenly realised, with a kind of shock, that she could guarantee no such thing. Tante Madelon was a woman of another generation entirely, with strict views on marriage and its obligations, even when it was clearly as ill-advised and wretched as Allie's was.

And as it would remain.

Because, all too soon, this brief respite would be over, and she would have to go back. Back to the misery of emptiness and blame.

She glanced sideways at him as they drove away, thinking of the strength of the arms that had held her, the grace of his mouth. Feeling her starving body clench in a swift, primitive craving that screamed out for the ultimate fulfilment.

She'd denied herself a normal life, she thought desperately, trying to appease her conscience. Surely she was entitled to some happiness—just for a while—wasn't she? A little sweetness to comfort her in the barren time ahead? Was it really so much to ask?

She saw, in the wing mirror, the image of the stone circle, pointing grimly, like so many warning fingers, towards the sky. And realised, as her heart skipped a beat, that her question had been answered.

To hell with it, she told the unseen forces of retribution. I won't give him up. Not yet. Because I can't. And if there's a price to pay, then I'll just have to face that when it happens.

They said little on the way back to Les Sables. The road ahead was empty, and Remy took one hand from the wheel, clasping her fingers lightly as they drove.

So this is first love, she thought, turning to feast her eyes on him. Come to me at last.

And she saw his mouth slant in a swift smile, as if he'd read her thoughts.

As they drove up to the house, Tante emerged, and stood waiting for them. Her face was tranquil as she watched Remy go round to the passenger door and help her great-niece, very circumspectly, to alight, but Allie was not deceived.

She's probably been pacing the rug since we left, she thought with a sigh.

Remy must have sensed the same thing, because he said, with a touch of dryness, 'As you see, I have returned her safely, *madame*.'

She picked up his tone. '*Mon cher* Remy, I never doubted you for an instant.' She paused. 'May I offer you some coffee before you depart?'

'*Merci, madame*, but I think I must get back to Trehel. I have some matters to discuss with the builders.' He made her a small polite bow, then turned to Allie, his face smooth, but little devils glinting in his eyes. '*Au revoir*, Alys. I hope you will permit me to call on you again?'

She looked down at her feet. 'Why, yes. Thank you. If you wish. That would be—very nice,' she added wildly.

'Then I too shall look forward to it.' There was only the slightest tremor in his voice, but the wickedly prim face he pulled at her as he walked towards the Jeep was almost her undoing.

As he reached it, another vehicle—a blue pick-up—suddenly pulled in behind him with a crackling swirl of gravel. The driver's door was flung wide, and a girl jumped down.

She was small, with silver-blonde hair and a pretty heart-shaped face, all huge brown eyes, and a sexy mouth painted bright pink, with her finger and toenails enamelled to match.

She possessed a shapely figure bordering on the frankly voluptuous, set off by tight white trousers and a scoop-necked top in a stinging shade of violet. And she was smiling widely as she ran across to Remy and kissed him on both cheeks, standing charmingly on tiptoe in order to do so.

'*Chéri.*' She had a soft, throaty voice. 'I thought I recognised your Jeep. But why are you here?' She turned to Madelon. 'Please tell me you are not ill, *ma chère madame*.'

'Not in the least,' said Tante briskly. 'Dr de Brizat has been kind enough to show my great-niece from England something of the surrounding area. That is all.'

'You, Remy? Turned tour guide?' The newcomer gurgled with laughter. '*Mon Dieu*, the world will end tomorrow. And I thought your every moment outside work was spent either with Roland or on the renovations at Trehel.'

'Not every moment,' Remy returned coolly. 'I allow myself some leisure—from time to time.'

Her eyes widened extravagantly in a way that Allie decided must have taken hours of practice. 'Then your friends can hope to see more of you, maybe? What a pleasure that will be.'

She turned to Allie, her gaze flickering over her. A glance that assessed and dismissed. 'So—an English visitor.' She made it sound as if the other girl had escaped from a zoo. 'Then we must all do what we can to ensure that you enjoy your vacation—*Mademoiselle*…?' She paused questioningly.

'Alys,' Remy supplied quietly. 'Alys Colville.'

'*Enchantée*. And I am Solange Geran.' The smile flashed again, but the brown eyes were watchful. 'I am sure we shall become friends. You intend to remain for a long time with *madame*, I hope.'

Under the gush, the message reached Allie loud and clear.

She considers me no contest, she thought. But, all the same, she'd be delighted to hear that I'm leaving tomorrow.

She shrugged gracefully. 'My plans are—fluid at the moment.'

'But mine, unfortunately, are not,' Remy said briskly. 'So, forgive me, but I must go.' As he swung himself into the Jeep he looked briefly across at Allie, his lips miming a swift kiss before driving away.

'*Alors*, I must find my purse,' Madelon Colville said as the noise of the engine faded. 'I presume you have brought the eggs, Solange?'

Solange was looking at the road, her lower lip held in her teeth, but when she turned back she was dimpling. 'But of course. *Une douzaine, madame, comme d'habitude.*'

'Then bring them inside, if you will,' Tante directed. 'Come, Alys, and help me with the coffee.

'Solange's parents bought the farm from me,' she added in an undertone as she led the way into the house. 'But when her late father's health began to fail she took a government grant and began converting the barns and outbuildings into *gîtes*, which have been a great success. The egg business is now merely a sideline, but at least it enables her to get away from Ravac.'

She pursed her lips. 'Since she was widowed, Madame Geran has become something of a trial, I understand.'

Allie understood too. We could almost start a company, she thought. Difficult Widows R Us.

She said shortly, 'Solange has my sympathy.'

Tante gave her an ironic look. 'I doubt, *mon enfant*, that she would welcome it. Do you?'

It was an awkward little interlude. Solange arrived with the eggs, and accepted her cup of coffee with pretty thanks. Sitting at the table, listening to her chat away to Tante, Allie was aware that she was being covertly studied, and with no friendly eye.

And until a short while ago, *mademoiselle*, I didn't know you existed either, she told the other girl silently.

Solange was amusing about the problems of running *gîtes*, especially Allie noted, where English guests were concerned. Their eccentricities, messy habits, and petty meannesses were dwelt on with particular relish. But her other main topic was Trehel, and the barn there that Remy was converting into a house for his own occupation.

'It has taken so long, he is almost in despair,' she confided. She sighed portentously. 'But he would employ Gaston Levecq, in spite of all our warnings.'

'The Levecqs lost their youngest child to meningitis,' said Tante. 'And *madame* suffered terribly with depression afterwards. Remy may have felt Gaston needed the distraction of a new project. And he is a good workman.'

'Oh, I agree that it is going to be beautiful. All the top floor is finished now, and the view from the main bedroom is *formi-*

dable.' Solange played coyly with the handle of her coffee cup. 'Remy has asked me to help with the décor, you understand?'

She drank the remains of her coffee and rose. 'And now I must deliver the rest of the eggs,' she announced brightly. 'People will be wondering where I am.'

After she left, there was silence. Then Allie said, her smile forced, 'I think I've just been warned off her territory.'

Tante's voice was troubled. *'Mon enfant*—when you have gone back to your own life, she will still be here, and Remy too. Are you being quite fair?'

Allie bent her head. 'Tante—please don't ask me not to see him again, because I don't think that's possible.'

Madelon Colville gave a heavy sigh. *'Mon Dieu,'* she said, half to herself. 'Has it already gone so far and so fast?'

Colour rose in Allie's face. 'No,' she protested. 'Nothing's—happened.'

Her great-aunt's brows lifted. 'Nothing? You mean, *en effet*, that you have not yet given yourself to him?' Her little shrug was a masterpiece of Gallic cynicism. 'Well, it is only a matter of time. Every word that was spoken—every look—proclaimed that.'

'But we didn't…'

'Precisely.' Madame Colville nodded grimly. 'Alys—I say this only from love. It might be better for you to go now. Leave Brittany before real damage is done.'

Allie looked at her across the table, sudden tears hanging from her lashes. She said, 'I don't think I can.' And her voice broke.

CHAPTER SIX

ALLIE got up early the next morning. She pulled on shorts and a tee-shirt, and let herself quietly out of the house. She didn't go down to the beach, but walked along the top of the cliff until she reached a patch of grass, where she sat. She turned her face to the sun while the fresh sea breeze lifted the strands of her light brown hair, letting the cloud of Tante's anxiety which had hung over her since the previous day dissipate, while her heart thudded in eager anticipation.

She did not have to wait long before she was aware of Roland's hoofbeats, quiet on the short turf, and horse and rider dark against the pale morning sky.

He said softly, 'I knew you would be here.' He reached down a hand, pulling her up on to the saddle in front of him. Settling her carefully.

'Won't Roland mind?' She ran a hand over the glossy mane.

'He will have to accustom himself.' As they moved off, he said, 'Is there anything you wish to ask me, *ma belle*? Anything you need to know?'

'No.' His arms around her conveyed all the lovely certainty she needed. She found herself thinking Poor Solange, then added aloud, 'Unless you have something you want to say to me?'

'Many things.' He pushed up the sleeve of her tee-shirt and kissed her bare shoulder, his lips warm and lingering against her cool skin. 'But they will have to wait.'

'Where are we going?'

'To have breakfast,' he said. 'At Trehel.'

'Oh,' she said, a touch doubtfully. 'Your family won't mind?'

His lips touched her hair. 'They will have to accustom themselves also.'

'But how will I get back?'

'Naturally I shall drive you home, before I go into Ignac. Or did you think I would send you back on Roland?'

'It crossed my mind,' she admitted, and heard him laugh softly.

They were quiet for a while, then she said, 'Do you know this is only my second time on the back of a horse?'

'*Vraiment?* I hope you are a little more comfortable this time. And that you do not find it as frightening.'

'Oh, I'm still a little scared,' she said. 'But for very different reasons.'

'Ah, *mon ange.*' His voice was gentle. 'Alys, you must know that I would never willingly do anything to hurt you.'

Or I you. Never willingly. But I know in my heart that I shall—because I can't help myself...

Perhaps their need for each other would be like a summer storm, she thought with sudden sadness. Raging for a while, then blowing itself out, with no lasting harm in its wake. Maybe even enabling them to say goodbye as friends.

'*Qu'as-tu,* Alys?' He must have sensed her disquiet. 'Is something the matter?'

'No, nothing. Except—I was thinking how strange life is. How unexpected.'

'You think so?' She heard the smile in his voice. 'Yet I know I have been waiting for you since the day I was born. Is it not the same for you?'

'Yes,' she told him quietly. 'Oh, yes.'

And knew, with sadness, that she spoke only the truth. But that it was all, tragically, too late...

Trehel was an old grey stone house, massive among its surrounding grasslands and trees, with three storeys of shuttered windows that seemed to be watching like half-closed eyes as they rode up. Allie could only hope the scrutiny was friendly.

Remy walked Roland round the side of the house to a large courtyard holding stables and outbuildings.

There was a big barn set well back from the yard, and Allie could hear the noise of sawing and hammering emanating from it.

'Is that where you're planning to live?' she asked as Remy dismounted and lifted her down.

'Yes,' he said, then looked at her, his mouth twisting ruefully. 'Ah, Solange must have told you. What else did she say?'

Allie shrugged. 'That it hadn't gone entirely to plan.' *Also, she happened to mention the view from the bedroom.*

'The building work has been more slow than I had hoped,' he admitted. 'However, it should be finished soon.'

'May I see round it?'

'Of course, but not now,' he said, tossing Roland's reins to the elderly man emerging from the stables. He added softly, 'One day, *ma belle*, when we have more time.' And the promise in his voice warmed her skin.

Then he took her hand, and led her into the house.

She found herself in a huge kitchen, with a long table at its centre. A tall white-haired man was busying himself at the range with a kettle as they came in, and the two dogs of indeterminate breed who were lying beside him looked up, thumped feathery tails on the rug, then relapsed into doing very little again.

The man turned, and Allie found herself being studied by shrewd blue eyes under bushy eyebrows.

He said, 'So, Remy, who is this lovely girl you have brought to brighten our morning?'

'I wish you to meet Alys, Grandpère. She is Celine Vaillac's granddaughter. *Ma mie*, this is my grandfather, Georges de Brizat.'

'But of course.' The rather stern mouth softened into a warm smile. 'I was foolish not to have known at once. You are very like her, *mademoiselle*.'

And you, she thought. One look at you, and I know exactly what Remy will be like as he grows old.

And she felt pain slash at her as she realised she would not be there to see him…

Oh, God, she thought, this is all so wrong. I shouldn't even be here now. The whole situation's getting out of hand.

But she recovered herself instantly, shook hands, murmuring a polite greeting, and sat at the table to be served with warm rolls, cherry jam, and large bowls of hot chocolate.

'Where is Papa?' Remy asked.

'The Richaud baby. They telephoned at dawn after the first contraction, I think.'

'Well, it is understandable,' Remy said tolerantly. 'After four girls, Richaud is desperate for a boy.' He grinned. 'It has become a matter of public concern, Alys. They have been laying odds in the Café des Sports.'

Her mouth was suddenly bone-dry. 'Poor woman—to have so much expected of her,' she managed, and gulped some of her chocolate.

Georges de Brizat came and sat at the head of the table, followed hopefully by the dogs. He gave Allie another thoughtful look. 'You are staying with Madame Colville, *mademoiselle*? She is well, I hope.'

'Absolutely fine.' She forced a smile.

'Good.' His nod was faintly abstracted. 'Good. You will tell her I was asking about her? Also, give her my best wishes?'

'Yes—yes, of course.'

'We knew each other many years ago, during the bad years of the Occupation. She and her sister were brave girls. Brave and very beautiful.' He paused. 'They had happy lives—with their Englishmen?'

'Yes,' Allie returned, faintly surprised. 'Very happy.'

He nodded again, then applied himself to his breakfast.

One of the dogs came and laid a chin on her leg, and she stroked his silky head and fondled his ears, before slipping him a morsel of bread and jam, while Remy watched her with such tender amusement that she wanted to get up from her chair, and go round the table into his arms, to remain there for ever.

But he was getting briskly to his feet. 'I must go and shower. Get ready for work.' As he passed his grandfather's chair, he dropped a hand on the old man's shoulder. 'Be gentle with Alys, Grandpère. No Resistance-style interrogation, *s'il te plaît.*'

When they were alone, Dr de Brizat cleared his throat. 'Remy likes his joke, Mademoiselle Alys. But a beautiful girl at the breakfast table is a rarity in this house, so I am bound to be intrigued. How did you meet my grandson?'

Allie carefully added butter and jam to her remaining fragment of roll. 'I was on the beach below Les Sables. Remy warned me about the tide, but I stupidly took no notice, so he—came back for me.'

'He behaved with great wisdom,' said his grandfather. 'You are planning a lengthy visit to Madame Colville?'

She flushed. 'I'm not altogether sure of my plans—at the moment.'

She was bracing herself for more questions, when the rear door opened, and a voice called, 'Remy? *Tu es là?*' Solange Geran walked into the kitchen. She presented a more muted appearance this morning, in denim jeans and a matching shirt, her hair pulled back from her face.

She checked when she saw Allie, looking thunderstruck. 'You?' Her tone was less than friendly. 'What are you doing here?'

Georges de Brizat got politely to his feet. '*Bonjour*, Solange. As you see, we have a guest for breakfast.' He added mildly, 'I hope you have no objection?'

'Why, no. I mean—how could I?' The girl gave a swift trill of laughter. 'How absurd. It was just—a surprise to see Mademoiselle Colville again—so soon.' She glanced around. 'But where is Remy?'

'Taking a shower,' his grandfather returned. 'May I pass on some message?'

'No, thank you.'

'You are quite sure? It must have been a matter of some urgency to bring you here at such an hour.'

The pretty mouth was sulky. 'It is my mother,' she said. 'The trouble with her knee. She complains that she hardly slept last night. I hoped that Remy would call at the farm on his way to Ignac.'

'I regret that will not be possible, as he will be driving Mademoiselle Alys to Les Sables before going to work.' He added tranquilly, 'But if you bring your mother to the medical centre later in the morning, he can examine her there.'

'Since my father's death, my mother rarely leaves the house.'

Monsieur de Brizat shrugged. 'Then, instead, I will request my son to pay her a visit once he returns from the Richauds'.' His tone was dry. 'He used to attend *madame*, so he is well acquainted with the case.'

In spite of her embarrassment, Allie had to stifle a giggle. Game, set and match to Dr Georges, she thought.

Solange's face was like a mask. She said stiffly, 'That is—kind. I shall tell Maman to expect him.'

'D'accord.' He waited for a moment as she stood irresolute. 'There was something else, perhaps?'

'No, no.' It was Solange's turn to shrug. 'At least—just a matter of some curtain fabric. But that can wait for another time. When Remy is not quite so—occupied.' She looked at Allie, a faintly metallic note creeping into her voice. *'Au revoir, mademoiselle.* I am sure we shall meet again—soon.'

'I look forward to it,' Allie responded, without an atom of sincerity.

A thoughtful silence followed Solange's departure.

Allie drew a breath. 'I seem to be in the middle of some kind of situation here. Please believe I—I didn't know.'

'You are sure there is anything to know?' Dr de Brizat sighed a little. 'Like all the Gerans, Solange is industrious, ambitious, and single-minded. She has a mother who is a trial, and she does not intend to spend her entire life cleaning cottages for tourists.' He paused. 'But any plans she is making for the future are hers alone.'

His sudden smile was mischievous. 'Let me assure you also, *ma petite*, that she has never been asked to breakfast.'

But that, thought Allie, reluctantly returning his smile, does not make me feel any better about all this.

Remy came striding in, tucking a grey and white striped shirt into charcoal pants, his dark hair still damp from the shower.

Allie was sharply aware of the scent of soap he brought with him, mixed with the faint fragrance of some musky aftershave, and was ashamed to feel her body clench in sheer longing.

He snatched car keys from a bowl on the huge built-in dresser that filled one wall, then reached for Allie's hand, pulling her to her feet. '*Viens, chérie.*'

She managed to throw a hasty *au revoir* over her shoulder to his grandfather, and heard him reply, '*A bientôt*, Mademoiselle Alys.' Which meant that he expected to see her again, she thought, as Remy whisked her into the Jeep and started the engine.

She said breathlessly, 'Do you live your entire life at this speed?'

'No.' The smile he slanted at her was wicked. 'There are times, *mon ange*, when I like to take things very slowly indeed. You would like me to demonstrate?'

'Not,' she said, struggling not to laugh, 'in a moving Jeep, *monsieur, je t'en prie.*'

He gave an exaggerated sigh. '*Eh, bien, chérie, tu as raison, peut-être.*'

There was a brief silence, and when he spoke again his voice was quiet and infinitely serious, 'But I am beginning to question, Alys, how long I can exist without you, and that is the truth.'

She felt a tide of heat sweep through her body, leaving behind it an ache beyond remedy. 'Remy—this isn't easy for me.'

'And you think it is for me?' His laugh was almost bitter. 'That I expected to feel like this—to know how completely my life has changed in so short a time? That I even wished it, when a few days ago I was not even aware of your existence? No, *mon amour,* and no.'

The passion in his tone almost scared her, and Allie bent her head. She said half to herself, 'Oh, God, I shouldn't have come here…'

'Do not say so.' His voice hardened. 'Do not ever say that, *mon coeur*, because without you I would be only half alive.'

He reached out a hand, resting it on her bare leg, just above the knee, and she covered it with both her own, feeling the reassurance of its warmth as they drove in silence back to Les Sables.

When they reached the house, Remy switched off the engine, then turned to her, drawing her into his arms. He looked down at her for a long moment, before taking her mouth with his, kissing her with a thoroughness and frank expertise that left her dizzied and gasping for breath, her hands clutching the front of his shirt as if it was her last hold on sanity.

'Remy…' His name was a croak.

'I need the taste of you, *mon ange*.' His own breathing was ragged. 'To carry with me through the day.' He detached one of the clinging hands and carried it to his lips. 'I will see you tonight? You will have dinner with me?'

She nodded almost numbly, then got out of the Jeep, shading her eyes from the morning sun as she watched him drive away.

Tante was sitting at the kitchen table, reading her letters, as Allie came into the house. Her calm gaze assimilated the dishevelled hair, the wild rose flush and the faintly swollen mouth, but she made no comment.

'The coffee is fresh, dear child, if you would like some.'

'I—I had breakfast at Trehel.'

The older woman nodded drily. 'So Georges de Brizat told me on the telephone.' She paused. 'Your little web of untruth is spreading dangerously wide, *ma mie*. How long before it breaks, I ask myself?'

Allie sat down at the table, staring down at the oilcloth, tracing its pattern with a finger. She said in a low voice, 'I know I have to tell him, Tante Madelon, and I will—soon. I promise. But…'

'But you are so happy you cannot bear anything that might spoil your idyll.' Tante studied her. 'You do not trust Remy to understand?'

'I—I'm learning to trust.'

'Then learn quickly, *ma chère*.' Tante got briskly to her feet and fetched the coffee from the stove. 'Before he guesses you are hiding something—and begins to wonder if he can trust *you*.'

I should have listened to her, Allie thought wretchedly, sitting up and easing her back, stiff from sitting so long in one position on the sofa. I should have taken the risk and told Remy everything. But I was too scared of losing him. And in the end, because I was stupid and a coward, I lost him anyway...

The music had ended long ago, and she replaced the CD in its case and switched off the player.

The house was totally silent, the blackness of the night pressing against the windows, making her feel suddenly isolated—alienated.

She thought with a shiver, It's very late. I should go to bed, instead of tormenting myself with the desperation of the past.

Because Remy won't be listening to the silence, or staring into the darkness a few miles away at Trehel. He's not torturing himself with bad memories. He's put the past where it belongs and set his life back in order, the way it should always have been.

So, he'll be asleep in that enormous bed, with Solange in his arms, her bright sunflower hair across his pillow and that little victorious smile on her lips.

Solange...

Jerkily, she brought her clenched fist to her mouth. Bit savagely at the knuckle as pain ravaged her.

Solange, she thought, wincing. The girl she'd seen as an irritant, perhaps, but never a danger. Someone she'd underestimated from Day One—that she'd even allowed herself to pity a little. But perhaps her happiness with Remy had made her blind—even arrogant.

She opened the back door and stood leaning against the

frame, drawing in deep lungfuls of cool air as she fought for calm.

Because she had been happy in a way that was totally outside her experience, measuring her life only in the hours they spent together. Beginning with the dinner he'd promised her that evening…

'Richaud has a son at last,' he'd told her with amusement, as they'd sat eating lobster in a candlelit restaurant overlooking the sea. 'Papa says he will be drunk for a week in celebration.'

Allie dealt carefully with a claw. 'Is it really so important to men—this need for a male heir?'

He shrugged. 'The inheritance laws are different here, but a son at least carries on the family name, and for Richaud it also means a strong arm to help him on his land.' He looked at her, brows lifted. 'You think that is a chauvinist point of view, *ma belle*?'

'I suppose not,' she said. 'As long as it doesn't become an obsession.'

'Your father would have preferred a son?' He smiled at her. 'That I do not believe.' He paused. 'For myself, a healthy child born safely to the woman I love is all I would ever want.'

Now, whispered the voice in her head. *Be honest with him. Tell him about Hugo—the nightmare of your marriage. Tell him everything—now—and ask for his understanding—his help…*

But as she nerved herself the waiter appeared beside them, pouring more wine, whisking away the discarded pieces of shell, and the moment was lost.

And when they arrived back at Les Sables, Tante was waiting up, hiding her private concerns behind polite welcome, but clearly determined not to leave them alone together.

Remy's goodnight kiss was frankly rueful. 'Tomorrow,' he whispered. 'I am free in the afternoon. Will you come swimming with me?'

'Yes.' Allie's eyes shone as she detached herself reluctantly from his arms. 'Yes, of course.'

'We have a pool at Trehel, but I think *madame* would feel

that is too secluded.' He paused. 'So, to assure her of my good intentions, I shall take you to St Calot, where there will be many other people.'

She bit her lip. 'Remy—she really likes you...'

His tone was wry. 'Yet she still looks at me, *mon ange*, as if I were a wolf, threatening her only lamb.' He sighed. 'However, she is right to care about you. And I have only to persuade her that I care too.' He kissed her again. '*A demain.*'

Except it's not you, but me that she doesn't trust, Allie thought with sudden bleakness as she turned back into the house. And I can't blame her for that.

The weather continued to be glorious, with each sunlit tomorrow blending seamlessly into the next, and Remy making time to be with her on each of them, in spite of his workload.

But as the days passed Allie found the idea of sharing the truth with him was becoming ever more difficult. She felt totally detached from her previous life, as if Marchington Hall existed on some other planet, and the sole reality was here and now, with the man she loved and wanted so passionately.

'I am going to Vannes tomorrow, to visit some old friends,' Tante announced one evening. She added drily, 'I take it that you will not wish to go with me?'

Allie flushed. 'I'd rather stay here—if you don't mind.'

'*Au contraire, chérie.* I suspect you would not have an enlivening day with Emil and Annette. And I am also sure you will not be lonely.' She paused. 'I do not condone, but I understand, *ma chère*,' she added quietly, 'and I simply—bow to the inevitable.'

There was a silence, then Allie said huskily, 'Tante, I—I didn't mean to fall in love with him. And I can't go on deceiving him. I know that.' She lifted her chin. 'Tomorrow. I'll try and tell him then.'

'After, one presumes, you have at last rewarded his admirable restraint?' *Madame's* tone of voice conveyed a hint of true Gallic cynicism. 'You are wise, Alys. A well-satisfied man is likely to be more—indulgent.'

Allie's face burned. 'You make me sound so calculating.'

'I think you should be,' her great-aunt said frankly. 'It is time, *ma chère*, that you began to consider, very carefully, your future, and what part in it, if any, is destined for your young doctor. Because,' she added, 'he will undoubtedly wish to know.'

The weather began to change not long after Tante's departure the following morning. Clouds were massing in the west, and the wind had freshened sharply. When Allie, suddenly restless in the confines of Les Sables, went out for a walk, she could hear the roar of the waves, thrashing at the cliffs, and found she was struggling to keep her balance against some of the gusts.

By the time Remy arrived it had begun to rain, and Allie was outside struggling to deal with a recalcitrant shutter.

'Let me do it.' He pushed the stiff bolt into place. '*Madame* is not here?'

'She's spending the day with some people in Vannes.' Allie stood back, dusting her hands. She looked up at the sullen sky, with its scudding dark clouds, and sighed. 'It's hardly a day for the beach.'

'But good, perhaps, for sightseeing.' He kissed her, his mouth warm and lingering on hers, and she felt the pleasure of it lance like wildfire through her body.

She said breathlessly, 'Under cover, I hope?'

'*Naturellement.*'

She collected her bag, and threw a cotton jacket over her black vest top and cream denim skirt.

They had been travelling for several minutes before she realised they were heading towards Trehel.

'But I don't understand,' she began. 'You said—'

'That I had somewhere you would want to see.' He sent her a swift smile. 'And so I have. I hope you will not be disappointed.'

She gasped. 'Your house!' she exclaimed. 'You mean it's actually—finished?'

'All except the work I plan to do myself.' Remy nodded. He added softly, 'And you, *ma belle*, will be my first visitor.'

'Oh.' She felt her face warm. 'Well, I'm—honoured.'

'No.' His voice was gentle. 'The honour, *mon amour*, will be all mine, believe me.'

He was telling her that the waiting was over, and her throat tightened at the promise in his words—just as her body began to tingle in excitement, mingled, at the same time, with a kind of trepidation.

Because Remy might be the one to be disappointed, she thought with a pang of unease. After all, what did she know about pleasing a man? Less than nothing, as she'd been told so many times in the past. And, however much she might love Remy, she was still the same person at heart, and even his patience could not last for ever.

Frigid—fumbling—useless. The words were like scars on her psyche.

I don't have to do this, she told herself, swallowing. I can find some excuse. Tell him it's the wrong time of the month. Anything.

Maybe that I've—simply—changed my mind.

Except, of course, he would only have to touch me, she thought, feeling her entire being shiver in anticipation—and yearning...

And then they were at Trehel, and somehow it was too late to turn back, even if she'd wanted to.

It was raining heavily, so Remy parked the Jeep close to the barn, then took her hand and ran with her, pushing open the big double doors.

The room she found herself in was enormous, with a flagged floor, a large stone fireplace at one end, and a state-of-the-art kitchen at the other. Apart from that, it was still completely unfurnished, but Allie could imagine how it would look, with sofas grouped round the fire, and maybe a huge dining table where friends would eat and talk late into the evening.

But the really breathtaking feature was the long range of arched full-length windows opposite the entrance, with panoramic views over the paddock and the wooded hills beyond it.

Even with rain sweeping across in great swathes, the outlook was spectacular.

She said, with a catch in her voice, 'It's—amazing.' She wandered into the kitchen, running her hand along the marble work surfaces, admiring the gleaming oven and hob with lifted brows. 'Does it all work?'

'But of course.' Remy mimed mock pique. 'Shall I prove it by making you some coffee?' He paused. 'Or would you prefer to see the rest of the house?'

'The rest—I think.' She felt suddenly shy, her heart pounding as they walked towards the wooden staircase that led to the upper floor.

Say something, she adjured herself. Try to sound casual. Normal.

'Do you know yet how you're going to furnish it?'

Oh, God, she sounded as if she was presenting a makeover programme on television.

'I have already begun.' At the top of the stairs, Remy opened a door, and stood back to let her precede him into what was clearly the master bedroom. It was another big room, soaring up into the barn's original vaulted roof, with windows on two sides capturing every atom of light, and its expanse of wooden floor softened with sheepskin rugs.

But, above all, there was the wide bed, made even more massive by its high, ornately carved headboard. Dominating the entire space as it was clearly intended to do.

And, she realised, freshly made up, too, with crisp white linen and a glamorous satin coverlet the colour of sapphires. Mounded with snowy pillows. Waiting…

She halted, eyes widening, as she began to tremble, and felt his arms go round her, drawing her back against him. Holding her strongly.

He said quietly, 'Lie with me, Alys. Lie with me here, in my house. In my bed.'

And she turned, lifting her face for his kiss and whispering, 'Yes,' against the warm urgency of his mouth.

CHAPTER SEVEN

His kiss was deep and yearning, as if he was seeking her soul
through her lips, and Allie sank against him as a strange
weakness invaded her body, her eyes closing and her hands
clinging to his shoulders.

He raised his head at last, framing her face in his hands,
looking down at her, gravely and searchingly.

'You are shaking, *mon amour*,' he told her quietly. 'In
truth, am I so terrifying?'

'No—oh, no.' The denial tumbled from her. 'Oh, Remy,
I'm such a fool, but I couldn't bear it if you were—disappointed in me.'

He put a silencing finger on her lips. 'I love you, Alys. And
that is all that matters.' His voice was very gentle. 'Pleasing
each other with our bodies is a joy we shall learn together.'

He slipped her damp jacket from her shoulders and let it
drop, then lifted her into his arms and carried her across the
room to the bed, throwing back the sapphire quilt before
placing her with great care against the heaped pillows. Then,
kicking off his shoes, he came to lie beside her.

She turned on her side to face him, her hand going shyly to
brush a strand of thick dark hair back from his forehead, and
he captured her fingers, brushing them softly with his mouth.

'You are the dream of my life, Alys,' he murmured, then
began to kiss her, his lips touching her forehead, her eyes, her
cheekbones and her pliant mouth in a series of brief, delicate

caresses that seemed to give but then withdraw. Which tantalised but offered no immediate satisfaction.

Yet that was what she wanted, she realised, startled. What she'd craved ever since that first afternoon at Les Sables, when she'd first felt the touch of his hands on her bare skin.

She longed to be taken—to feel him inside her and know the heated steel of his arousal as he possessed her.

She moved closer, pressing herself against him, her lips finding the opening of his shirt, pushing the crisp cotton aside to caress the base of his throat before moving down to the warm hair-roughened skin of his chest.

Remy groaned softly. *'Doucement, mon ange,'* he ordered, his voice faintly breathless. 'I want to make this good for you, and for that I shall need every atom of control I possess.'

She looked up at him, running the tip of her tongue slowly round her lips. 'Are you—really so sure of that, *monsieur*?'

'Ask me again, *chérie*—later,' he told her huskily, and recaptured her mouth with his.

His hand moved to her breast and stroked it gently, moulding its softness and cupping it in his palm, before allowing his fingers to trace her nipple with a delicate precision that made her gasp as he brought it to sharply delineated arousal against the clinging material of her top.

For a moment he looked down at her, surveying the exquisite havoc he had created, the vivid eyes darkening.

'You are wearing too many clothes, *mon amour*.' His voice was a whisper.

He slipped down the straps of her top, freeing her arms, then deftly tugged the little garment over her head and tossed it aside, baring her to the waist. For a brief, searing moment she was acutely aware of her body—almost ashamed of how slender it was—how slight the curves he'd just uncovered. And her hands went up to conceal them.

But he guessed her intention and blocked her, his fingers closing firmly round her wrists.

'Don't hide, Alys,' he murmured. 'Not when I have waited

so long to see you like this. Show me, *ma belle*, how truly
lovely you are.'

He bent his head, his mouth slowly adoring each swollen
rosy peak in turn, the erotic brush of his tongue creating a
new, aching excitement that was echoed deep inside. She
sighed, her hips moving restlessly, as the sweet, languorous
torment continued, her nipples throbbing with a pleasure that
was almost akin to pain.

When he raised his head at last, she lay looking up at him,
her eyes dazed, her ragged breath sobbing in her throat.

His hands stroked their way down her body to the waistband of her skirt. He undid the small metal button at the front,
then the short zip, easing the fabric gently over her hips until
she was completely free of it and it could also be discarded.

Leaving her with just the minimal modesty of a pair of tiny
lace briefs.

Remy made a small sound in his throat, then gathered her
to him so closely that his clothing grazed her skin, his mouth
closing on hers in a new and fierce demand.

She responded almost wildly, her lips parting eagerly to
receive the thrust of his tongue, her hands tangling in the thick
dark hair to hold him to her.

And then his mouth began to move slowly downwards, caressing her throat, her shoulders, and the little valley between
her breasts, while all the time his hands were stroking her with
sensuous delight, lingering in the hollow of her hip, drifting
across the faint concavity of her belly, seeking out the silken
length of her thighs.

Touching, at last, the lace that was her only covering. Pushing
it aside so that his fingers could reach the slick core of her.
Moving on her gently, but with such exquisite precision that
when he paused she moaned aloud, her body rearing against him.

'*Oui, mon amour.*' His voice was raw with hunger.
'Yes—and yes.'

And then, at last, the lace too was gone, peeled deftly
away, and she was naked in his arms, with no barrier left to
his skilfully questing hands.

Or—dear God—his mouth…

For a moment, shock held her frozen. Then, 'No—please—you can't…' Her voice was a small, shaken whimper of distress. She tried to push his head away from her slackened thighs, but Remy's hands were closing round her wrists, anchoring them effortlessly to the bed so that this new invasion of her most intimate self could continue entirely unhampered.

And her desperate attempts to evade his caress were only making matters a thousand times worse.

With devastating purpose, his lips sought the hot moist petals of her womanhood, parting them so that his tongue could search out the tiny hidden bud within and tease it into delicious tumescent arousal.

And at each sensuous stroke she felt her writhing body succumbing to a languorous weakness, her physical consciousness shifting—spiralling helplessly to a plane whose existence she'd never guessed at before.

Until, at last, there came a moment when she no longer wanted to escape what he was doing to her, even if it had ever been possible.

She heard her breathing change, and the spiral of feeling became an irresistible force, carrying her upwards to some unknown peak of desire. A moan of agonised pleasure burst from her throat, and her body arched rapturously in sheer surrender to wave after wave of utterly voluptuous delight.

And as the storm subsided she lay panting, her sated body damp with sweat, aware that there were tears on her face. She tried to wipe them away with trembling hands, and Remy gathered her in his arms, whispering softly to her in his own language, words of reassurance, words of love, telling her how sweet she was, how clever and how beautiful, while she clung to him, her mouth quivering into a smile.

And when he eventually released her it was only so that he could more easily strip off his own clothing. Allie lay watching him through half-closed eyes as he swiftly undressed, her body shivering in renewed and unforeseen hunger when he turned back to her, naked and magnificently aroused.

It seemed impossible that her body could be capable of such desire so soon again, she thought as she opened her arms to him eagerly, taking him into her embrace and running her hands over his shoulders and back, glorying in the strength of bone and muscle—the texture of his skin. And yet she was burning up for him—melting with need.

'Do I please you, *ma belle*?' There was a smile in the huskiness of his voice as he lifted himself over her—above her. For answer, she clasped her fingers round his jutting hardness, letting her hand slowly travel its length in an appreciation that was as teasing as it was overt.

'*Sorcière,*' he whispered hoarsely. 'Witch.' And he took her with one deep, lingering thrust. She cried out in bewildered joy at the potency—the completeness of their union as he filled her. Knowing that here, at last, was the ultimate in consummation.

For a moment, he paused. 'There is no problem?'

'None.' He was so anxious for her, but it wasn't necessary. Surely he could tell how much she wanted him? she thought, half-dizzy with this new sensation, her inner muscles clenching round him—holding him.

Remy began to move without haste, his lean hips driving powerfully as he carried her with him into the surging ebb and flow of passion, and she responded avidly, instinctively, matching the rhythmic motion he was creating, her hands digging into his shoulders as her legs lifted to enclose him. To lock round him.

At once she sensed a new urgency in him that he was clearly struggling to restrain, and she knew that he was still trying to be patient, to wait until she was ready to accompany him to their mutual release.

But I, she thought, want it now...

She smiled into his eyes, her lashes sweeping down onto desire-flushed cheeks, letting her hands follow a leisurely path down his back to the flat male buttocks and stroking them with her palms, while one finger traced a delicate, enticing pattern on the sensitive nerve-endings at the base of his spine.

She heard his involuntary gasp, felt the pace of his possession quicken suddenly—fiercely. Recognised with candid female triumph the almost remorseless increase in its intensity that she had coaxed from him.

Was aware of a stirring deep inside her in reply, as warm tendrils of sensation began to spread, to intensify in their turn, splintering what little was left of her control.

Then, a voice she hardly recognised as hers cried out in wild disbelief, as the frenzy of her senses sent her pulsating body into soaring and ecstatic climax.

And Remy followed her, her name wrenched with a groan from his straining throat as he reached the frantic culmination of his own pleasure, and she felt his exhausted weight slump across her, his head heavy on her breasts as he tried to calm the tortured rasp of his breathing.

And she was content to lie like that, holding him tightly, her lips caressing the strands of sweat-dampened hair on his forehead.

Because instinct seemed to be telling her that if ever there was a moment for confession, this was it. When he was in her arms, his sated, emptied body still joined to hers like this, surely he would forgive her anything—wouldn't he?

'Remy.' His name was a breath from her lips. She put her cheek on his hair. 'Darling—there's something I have to say. Something I should have told you long ago—when we first met. Only I never knew—never guessed—we would love each other. That you would mean everything in the world to me.'

She swallowed. 'Sweetheart—*mon amour*… I—I'm married. I have a husband in England. But I don't love him, and I never did. So I'm going back to finish it, get a divorce.'

She ended on a little rush of words, and waited tautly for his response. Only there was none.

She was prepared for shock—certainly for anger and recriminations—but not—silence.

Or was he simply too stunned to speak?

She said questioningly, 'Remy—darling…?'

He mumbled something drowsy in reply, burying his face

more closely against her, his body totally relaxed, his breathing deep and steady.

My God, she thought with an inward groan, he's asleep. Which means he hasn't heard a single word I've said, even though it took every atom of courage I possess to say it.

She was tempted to wake him there and then—to repeat her stumbling confession. But he looked altogether too peaceful, all tension gone from the dark face. He was even smiling a little as he slept.

Well, Allie thought, sighing. I suppose it will keep a little longer at that. But I must tell him soon—very soon. And, on that resolve, she closed her own eyes and allowed herself to drift slowly away.

She awoke with a start, and lay for a moment totally disorientated, her heart thudding. Hugo, she thought. Oh, God, I was dreaming about Hugo.

Then she heard the rain still lashing the window and realised where she was, and why, and relief and joy flooded through her.

She turned her head slowly and looked at Remy, still fast asleep beside her. At some point he must have moved a little, lifted himself away from her, although his arm was still thrown possessively across her waist.

Did he know? she wondered with passionate tenderness. Did he have the least idea how she was feeling? Did he understand her starved body's reaction to the miracle of physical delight he'd created for her?

For the first time in years she felt totally relaxed and at peace. Also happier than she had ever believed possible.

And when he woke she would tell him so, along with, she decided, a suitable reviver.

She slid carefully from under the protection of his arm and swung her feet to the floor. From the tangle of clothing beside the bed she retrieved Remy's shirt and slipped it on, fastening a few discreet buttons on the way. She could detect the faint fragrance of the cologne he used, and she put the sleeve to her nose, sniffing luxuriously.

She pulled the coverlet over him, then padded quietly out of the room and downstairs to the kitchen, where she stood looking around her, getting her bearings.

He'd offered her coffee some lifetime ago, she told herself, so the makings had to be available.

She looked first in the refrigerator, finding milk, and mineral water too, and she uncapped one of the small bottles, drinking thirstily as she leant back against the work surface.

This would be an amazing kitchen to work in, she thought, imagining herself here with Remy, preparing a meal together.

She sighed, smiling. Well—perhaps—one of these days. But coffee would do to be going on with.

Inspection of the pale wood cupboards eventually yielded a pack of ground beans and a *cafetière*, so she filled the elegant stainless steel kettle and set it to boil, humming quietly to herself as she did so. She'd just located a set of earthenware beakers when she heard a sound behind her and turned quickly.

Solange was standing in the middle of the living room, staring at her, lips parted, eyes burning with anger and disbelief in her white face.

And Allie knew, of course, what the other girl must be seeing. The dishevelled hair, the half-buttoned shirt reaching only to mid-thigh, the shining eyes and swollen mouth. Everything about her, she realised with dismay, must be screaming Sex.

Oh, God, she thought. Why didn't I get dressed properly? '*Chienne.*' Solange's voice shook. '*Sale vache.*'

For a moment, all Allie wanted to do was run. To get away from the fury and the ugly words. And from the French girl's bitter disappointment, too—which, perhaps, was the worst thing of all. But she stood her ground, lifting her chin defiantly.

'Please don't call me names, *mademoiselle*,' she said quietly. 'I am neither a bitch nor a dirty cow. I have been making love with the man I love, and I have nothing to be ashamed of.'

Solange took a step closer, her hands balled into fists at her sides. 'You don't think so? But I tell you different. Because you do not belong here, you—*espèce de raclure.*' Her tone was a hiss. 'You are an outsider—not one of us—and Remy needs a woman beside him who can support him in his work. Someone who knows this community—who has its respect. Not a slut of an English girl who will soon be gone, back to her own filthy country.'

Allie was almost reeling under this onslaught, but she made herself stay ice-calm. And her voice reflected this. 'I think Remy is free to make his own choices, Mademoiselle Geran.'

'And what is this great choice? To degrade himself with a *putaine* like you? Well, he will soon regret that.' The other woman drew a deep, shuddering breath. 'Always—always I knew what you were. Knew that you could not wait to throw yourself into his bed.'

'What exactly are you complaining about?' Allie asked coldly. 'That I have taken your place—or that you never received an invitation?'

Solange gasped, and her head went back as if Allie had struck her, the once pretty face twisted with rage and crimson with mottled blood. She lifted her hands, bunched into a semblance of claws, and her voice was thick. 'Would he still want you, I wonder, if I scratched out your eyes?'

From the stairs, Remy said grimly, 'An interesting point, Solange, but we will not put it to the test. And now I think you should go, before you make matters any worse.'

His feet were bare, concealing his approach, and he'd clearly dragged on his jeans simply for the sake of marginal decency, because they hung, only half-fastened, low on his hips.

Solange's small red-tipped hands were suddenly uncurled. Extended in appeal.

'Remy, *chéri*, I do not blame you for this. A man has—temptations.' She tried, horribly, to laugh. 'I—I understand this, and I can forgive—'

But he cut coldly across the stumbling words. 'There is no need for forgiveness, Solange. Let me speak plainly. Local gossip may have paired us together, yet I have asked nothing from you, and promised nothing in return. This—understanding between us does not exist.'

She swallowed harshly. 'Remy—*mon coeur*—how can you say that?'

'Because it is true, and you know it.' He paused. 'And I would prefer you did not visit here again without an invitation.'

She stared at him wild-eyed, her mouth working soundlessly, then she whirled round and was gone, the big doors slamming behind her.

Remy leapt the last few stairs and came to Allie's side, sliding his arms round her and drawing her protectively against him. She buried her face in his bare brown shoulder, her voice muffled. 'That was—vile.'

'I woke up and you were gone, which troubled me.' His voice was uneven. 'And then I heard talking, and thought that my father might have arrived, or Grandpapa, and that this could cause you embarrassment.'

'I came down to make coffee,' she said. 'And she was suddenly—here. But why?'

'It is entirely my fault,' Remy said harshly. 'She used to visit often, while the work was being done, in order to find fault with Gaston Levecq, and, I think, to persuade me to employ her cousin instead. Also to offer advice that I did not need. I should have realised—and stopped it when it first began.'

The kettle came cheerfully to the boil and switched itself off. Remy released her and went to fill the *cafetière*.

He said quietly, not looking at her, 'Alys, tell me, *je t'en prie*, that she has not made you hate this house—or regret what has happened between us here.'

'No.' She shook her head vehemently. 'No one—not even Solange—could ever do that.'

She saw the tension relax from his shoulders. He said softly, '*Soit.*' And continued making the coffee.

He said, over his shoulder, 'I am relieved that it was not Grandpapa who found you just now. Seeing you like that might have provoked *une petite crise cardiaque.*'

'At least I'm wearing something,' Allie returned with mock defensiveness. 'And your shirt was the first thing I found on the floor,' she added, not altogether truthfully.

'*Vraiment?*' The brilliant eyes were dancing with amusement. 'Perhaps I should make you a present of it, *chérie*. I know it never looked so good on me.'

She said huskily, 'Everything looks good on you, Remy.' Adding silently, *And off, too…*

'*Ma bien-aimée.*' His voice was gentle. He was silent for a moment. 'It was a bad moment for me, when I found you gone from our bed. I thought perhaps you were angry with me.'

'Angry?' She was startled. 'How could I be?'

His mouth twisted ruefully. 'Then—disappointed. Because I wished to make it perfect for you—our first time together— to take away all the bad memories. But it was over far too soon.' He added with a faint groan, 'And then I fell asleep.' He shook his head. 'My only excuse, *mon ange*, is that I wanted you so very much.'

She went to him, sliding her arms round his waist and smiling up into his eyes. 'That sounds more like a very good reason than an excuse,' she told him softly, and stood on tiptoe to kiss his mouth. She added teasingly, 'And may I remind you that we both went to sleep?'

She wanted to assure him, too, that the bad memories were all gone. But how could she when there was still the appalling problem of her marriage to be dealt with? she thought, conscious of a nervous tightening in the pit of her stomach. She pressed herself more closely against him, letting the warmth of his body dispel the sudden chill inside her.

He put a finger under her chin, tilting her face up towards him. 'Yet there is something, I think, that troubles you.'

She forced a smile. 'The aftermath of Solange, I expect. She did call me some pretty foul names.'

There was a pause, then he said laconically, '*D'accord.* That must be it.'

I can fix everything, Allie told herself fiercely, as she drank the coffee he'd poured for her. Somehow, I'll make Hugo see that it was all a terrible mistake, which needs to be put right. After all, he's had time to think too. He must know that it can't go on. All it needs is a little goodwill on both sides.

She was sharply aware that Remy was watching her thoughtfully, and lowered her lashes with deliberate demureness. 'Has no one told you, *monsieur*, that it's rude to stare?'

'It would be a greater insult to ignore you, *ma belle*.' His tone was dry. 'And I stare for a purpose, you understand.'

'Which is?' She replaced the empty beaker on the counter top.

'I am making a picture of you in my head, Alys, to carry with me always.'

'Dressed like this?' Laughing, she posed, hand on hip.

'*Pourquoi pas?* But with a little adjustment, perhaps.' He leaned across and undid two more buttons on the shirt, then gently pushed it from her shoulder, exposing one pink-tipped breast. 'Mmm,' he murmured in soft appreciation. '*Perfection.* If we have to be apart, I have only to remember how you look at this moment.'

Ludicrous to feel shy after the intimacies they'd shared, but her skin warmed just the same.

'And what about me?' she challenged with a touch of breathlessness. 'May I have a picture to remember too?'

She reached for the zip on his jeans, but he captured her hands, laughing. 'You may have any image you desire, *mon amour*—but in the bedroom, perhaps, in case more unwanted visitors arrive.'

He kissed her, his mouth hot and fierce on hers, and she laughed back and ran with him, aglow and willing, towards the stairs, and the waiting bed.

A long time later, she said drowsily, 'I must go. Tante Madelon will be back by now, and wondering where I am.'

Remy trailed a lazy hand the length of her body. 'I think she will know, *chérie*, don't you?'

She moved pleasurably against the ingenious questing of his fingers. 'Almost certainly, darling. But we don't need to underline the fact.'

He rolled over suddenly, imprisoning her under his body. 'I don't want to let you go,' he told her huskily. 'I need you to stay here with me, *mon coeur*. To sleep in my arms tonight.'

'How can I?' Allie appealed ruefully. 'Tante is obviously trying to be understanding, but she has her limits, especially as I'm her guest.' She paused. 'Besides, she'll certainly expect us to be discreet.'

Remy sighed. '*Tu as raison, ma mie.* I am not thinking as I should—perhaps because I feel I am almost scared to let you out of my sight.'

She put up a hand, her fingers tender against the roughness of his chin, her voice teasing. 'Haven't you had enough of me, *monsieur*?'

He said quietly, 'I have been waiting for you my whole life, Alys. I shall never have enough.' He slid his hands under her flanks, raising her a little, so that, slowly and sweetly, he could enter once more her rapturously acceptant body.

Unlike the fierce, searing passion they'd shared earlier, when he'd taken her to some blind, mindless sphere where she'd thought she might die, this time it was a gentle almost meditative union, composed of sighs and murmurs, and subtle, exquisite pressures, so that the moment of climax rippled through her like a soft breeze across a lake. And her voice broke as she whispered his name.

Afterwards, Allie lay supine, her eyes closed, her body languid with fulfillment. But as she felt him leaving the bed, she lifted herself on to an elbow. 'Where are you going?'

'To take you back to Les Sables—after I have taken a shower.'

She smiled mischievously up at him. 'You don't want company?'

He gave her a wry look. '*Oui, naturellement.* But I am trying to learn to do without you, *ma mie.*'

She tutted reprovingly as she swung her legs to the floor and followed him into the bathroom. 'That sounds like a very dull lesson. Now, I think, my darling, that you should make the most of me when I'm around,' she added serenely as she joined him in the glass cubicle under the power spray. She poured some shower gel into her hands and began to lather his body, beginning with his shoulders, then moving downwards across his chest to his abdomen, and lower, her fingers working in small, enticing circles. 'Don't you agree?'

'*Dieu,*' he said hoarsely. 'You are insatiable. You will kill me.'

She glanced down, and laughed softly. 'Even though the evidence suggests otherwise, my love?'

'But will the evidence be strong enough to prove your case, *mon ange*?' He turned the shower full on, then reached for her, lifting her off the tiled floor, and locking her legs round his hips. '*Eh bien,* there is only one way to find out.'

She said tremulously, 'Remy—oh, God—Remy…'

It was twilight when they eventually arrived at Les Sables, but there was no light in the house, and Tante's car was missing from its usual parking place.

'I seem to have beaten her to it,' Allie said, as she opened the door. 'Perhaps I can convince her that I spent the day here quietly on my own.'

'I doubt it.' Remy followed her in. '*Madame* is a woman who has loved. She will recognise the signs.'

'And you,' she said, 'are altogether too pleased with yourself.'

He slid a hand under the fall of still-damp hair, and kissed the nape of her neck. 'But I am pleased with you, also, *chérie*. Does that excuse me?'

The sound of the telephone made them both jump.

'Is that Madame de Marchington—the great-niece of Madame Colville?' an elderly-sounding male voice enquired when Allie picked up the receiver. 'Ah, *bon*. I am Emil Blanchard. I regret to tell you that Madelon slipped on the wet pavement outside our house as she was leaving her car, and fell.'

'She fell?' Allie echoed, dismayed. 'Oh, God, is she badly hurt?'

'No, no. Our doctor made a thorough examination. But she is shocked, and bruised, of course, and it would not be wise for her to drive. So we have persuaded her to remain with us for a few days until she has recovered.' He added with faint peevishness, 'I have attempted to telephone you several times before, *madame*, but could get no answer.'

'No, I've also been out—visiting friends. I'm sorry.' Allie hesitated. 'Thank you for telling me, and please give Tante Madelon my love. I hope she's fine—very soon—and tell her that I'll take good care of the house.'

'*Pauvre madame,*' Remy said soberly, when Allie outlined exactly what had happened. 'Such accidents can be serious at her age, but fortunately she seems to have escaped lasting damage.' He paused, his expression quizzical. 'But this means, *ma belle,* that you will be alone in this isolated place. Will you feel safe?'

'Oh, I'm sure I'll be fine during the day,' Allie assured him. She also paused. 'But I might be nervous at night,' she added pensively.

'If you have problems with your nerves, *ma belle,*' Remy said solemnly, 'then you should always call a doctor.'

She said softly, 'I think I just did.' And walked happily into his arms.

CHAPTER EIGHT

ALLIE came back to the present with a start, to the realisation that she was shivering violently. The night air had gone from cool to cold now, and the last thing she needed was pneumonia, she thought, her mouth twisting wryly as she closed the back door and locked it.

Or maybe the last thing she really wanted was to go upstairs and try to sleep in that room—in the bed she'd once shared with Remy.

She'd known from the first that that was, inevitably, where she'd be expected to spend her nights, but up to now she hadn't allowed herself to think about that too closely, or examine how she would feel when she had to lie there alone.

When she would not feel the warmth of Remy's arms, the murmur of his voice, or the beloved weight of him as, stunned and breathless, they lay wrapped together after climax. Or even the steady rhythm of his heartbeat under her cheek as she drifted blissfully to sleep.

For a moment she leaned forward, leaning her forehead against the stout panels of the door as the pain of it lanced through her.

Oh, God, she thought. Knowing the truth as I did, how could I have allowed myself to be so happy? To keep silent, even though I was virtually living with him? When I was breathing and dreaming him through every passing hour?

She drew a deep breath, composing herself, then switched off the lights and made her way slowly upstairs.

Tom was sleeping peacefully, and did not stir as she trod over to the cot to check on him. She sank down on the rug beside him, her back to the wall, her arms clasping her knees in the darkness.

Moonlight had filled the room each time she'd slept there with Remy, she thought wistfully. The majority of their nights, however, had been spent at Trehel, because Remy had been concerned that Tante might regard his presence at Les Sables as an intrusion, and hadn't wanted to risk the older woman's disapproval.

The new house had occupied their time, too, when his work was done, as she'd helped him begin to turn its empty spaces into a home. Two massive sofas in pale leather had been delivered, and a hunt round the local antiques outlets had produced a substantial table and six elegant chairs.

He'd taken her shopping at the morning markets, and she had revelled in the fresh vegetables and the endless varieties of seafood on offer. Oysters were one of Remy's passions, and he'd taught her to open them with a special knife, then eat them with a squeeze of lemon juice and a sprinkle of pepper.

Mealtimes had become a delicious adventure, from the preparation stage and the cooking, down to the last crumb of cheese.

Allie had bloomed under his tutelage, and she'd known it, as her life opened up in all kinds of ways. She had even learned to ride, with the surprisingly patient Roland enduring endless circuits of the paddock on a leading rein.

And she'd soon found that Remy's work could affect him profoundly—as when he'd come back to Trehel, grey-faced and numb, having lost a five-year-old whose parents had not recognised the symptoms to viral meningitis, after an all-night battle at the local hospital. She had learned, too, that at such times he would turn to her body for his own healing, letting their mutual passion assuage in some way his anger and sense of failure.

Tante had remained in Vannes with her friends. She'd explained that she had twisted her ankle in the fall, and that the swelling was taking longer than expected to go down, but Allie had wondered wryly if her absence was prompted more by tact than actual infirmity, and if her great-aunt was hoping their attraction to each other would have burned itself out by the time she returned.

She'd spoken to Tante on the phone every day, but by tacit agreement there had been no reference between them to her relationship with Remy, or the increasingly vexed question of her marital status and its resolution.

With each day that had passed, the right moment for such a confession had seemed to became more and more difficult to find. And the longer she'd left it, the worse it had become.

She'd begun to feel as if her happiness with Remy was the equivalent of holding thistledown cupped in her hand, knowing that one strong blast of reality could destroy it for ever.

On the plus side, Solange, since the afternoon when she'd slammed out of the house, had kept her distance, although once or twice in Ignac Allie had gained the impression that she was being watched, and with no friendly eye either. But she'd spotted nothing, so maybe, she'd told herself, she was just being paranoid.

Yet the vague feeling of unease had persisted, as if she'd sensed that somewhere a thunderstorm was hovering that would bring the bright golden days of sunshine to an end.

And I was right, Allie thought, wearily raking a hand through her hair and staring ahead of her with eyes that saw nothing. Ah, dear God, I was so right…

The day had begun calmly enough, she recalled. It had been a Saturday, and Remy had had no surgery, so, after visiting the market, they'd driven to Carnac and spent the morning on the beach there, quitting the sands when they'd begun to get crowded in order to enjoy a late and leisurely lunch.

'I'd better go to Les Sables,' Allie mused as they drove back. 'I haven't set foot there for two days, and it might have burned down.'

Remy raised an eyebrow. 'I think word might have reached us by now, *ma chère*,' he drawled.

She sighed. 'I know, but I'd still better check it out. Besides, I need some more clothes.'

'*D'accord.*' As he pulled up outside the house, his arm went round her shoulders, scooping her close, his lips meeting hers in a frankly sensuous caress. 'I shall see you later, then, at Trehel,' he told her, adding huskily, 'And don't keep me waiting too long, *chérie*, because tonight is going to be a very special meal.'

Her heartbeat jolted a little in sudden excitement, mixed with a touch of panic as her instinct warned her where the evening might lead.

Swallowing, she touched his cheek. 'I won't be late.'

She paused at the door to wave, and saw his hand lift in a smiling salute as he drove away.

So the moment had come, she thought, as she turned slowly and went indoors. Remy planned to talk about their future together. She knew it. Therefore she could afford no more evasion—no more prevarication.

And she would have to speak first. Lay all her cards on the table. Explain to him that she'd dreaded saying anything that could detract from their happiness in each other, and ask for his understanding.

The first real test for both of us, she thought wryly. But if he really loves me...

She shook herself out of her reverie. Her best course was to get over to Trehel as quickly as possible and tell him everything. And, as he'd made it clear this was going to be an occasion, she would dress for that too. Soften his justifiable wrath by making herself look as enticing as possible—by appealing directly to his senses. And she knew how.

There was a dress that he'd never seen, a black silky slip of a thing, with narrow straps and a neckline that dipped far more daringly than usual, making it discreetly obvious that it required only the minimum of underclothing. She'd put it into her case on sheer impulse, but she realised now there would never be a better time to wear it.

She went up to her room, stripping off shorts and tee-shirt, and the bikini she was wearing beneath them, then showered, shampooing her hair at the same time, to get rid of all traces of salt and sand.

She might wear it up for a change, she thought, smiling to herself as she imagined Remy unfastening the clip at some point, and letting the soft strands spill through his fingers.

She applied her favourite scented body lotion, then drew on a pair of tiny black lace briefs. For a long moment she looked at herself in the full-length mirror, assessing almost clinically the seductive effect of the little black triangle against the creaminess of her skin.

I'm not a beauty, she thought, but please—*please*—let him find me beautiful tonight. Let him desire me so much that nothing else matters. That, in spite of everything, he'll know that he can't live without me—and he'll forgive me what I have to say, and wait until I'm free to come to him. *Oh, please...*

She zipped herself into the dress, then picked up a comb and began experimenting with her hair. She paused, her attention arrested by the sound of a vehicle approaching fast.

It sounds like the Jeep, she thought, bewildered, and one swift glance from the window confirmed this.

He's come to fetch me, she thought ruefully, and I'm not nearly ready yet.

Still barefoot, she began to descend the stairs, halting, a smile playing round her lips, as the door was flung wide and Remy strode into the living room below.

'You're impatient, *monsieur*,' she teased. 'You've spoiled my surprise.'

Then she saw his face and gasped, her hand tightening convulsively on the stair-rail.

He was as white as a sheet, his skin drawn tautly across his cheekbones, his mouth harshly compressed. The vivid eyes stared up at her, the ice of their contempt searing her like a living flame, and she realised he was holding something like a sheaf of papers, rolled in his hand.

'A surprise, *madame*?' His voice cut like a knife. 'I think I have been surprised enough for one day.'

He tossed the papers he was holding towards the foot of the stairs, and she realised they were, in fact, the pages of a glossy magazine.

She said hoarsely, 'I—I don't understand.'

'Then you have a short memory, *madame*,' Remy returned with paralysing scorn. 'Also a selective one, if you have managed to so conveniently forget your own wedding.'

And then, at last, Allie remembered. Oh, God, she thought with a kind of sick despair, that dreadful interview with *County* magazine that Grace had insisted on—the ghastly pictures they took of me in my dress and veil, posing me beside Hugo so it wouldn't be quite as obvious that he was in a wheelchair. The whole appalling farce. How could I ever have forgotten? Yet I did. And now—*now*—it's come back to haunt me.

She looked down at the crumpled magazine. Forced frozen lips to ask, 'Where did you find it?'

'I did not,' he denied curtly. 'Solange Geran was throwing away some old magazines her English guests had left in one of the *gîtes*, and she saw the photograph. Read the story of the bride and groom whose love triumphed over adversity.' His laugh was corrosive in its bitterness. 'A romantic story she could not wait to share with me, *naturellement*.'

Solange, she thought with a terrible weariness. Of course…

She bent her head. 'Remy—I can explain…'

'But how? By telling me that you have an identical twin who happens to share your given name? Or some other lie to add to the rest?'

The savagery in his voice made her shrink. If she hadn't been gripping the rail, she would probably have fallen.

Instead, she forced herself to stand her ground, struggling to control her voice—to hide the hideous debilitating weakness that was making her tremble all over. Because somehow she had to make him listen to her. Salvage something out of the wreckage of her hopes and dreams.

'No, it's true,' she said with quiet weariness. 'I—I am married.' She lifted her chin. 'But I was going to tell you. I—I swear it.'

'Ah, but when, *madame*?' Remy asked with cruel mockery. 'Did you plan to wait for our wedding night, perhaps? Inform me then that I had become a bigamist?'

Her throat tightened to an agony. Tears glittered on her lashes. 'Remy—don't—please.'

'Why should I spare you? he flung at her. 'When from the first you have lied to me—deceived me in this vile way?'

'I—I wanted to tell you. I—did try…'

He said slowly, 'If you had worn your ring and used your married name, then I would have known from the first. I would never have approached you.' He shook his head. 'But you did not. And Madame Colville encouraged you in this. *C'est incroyable.*'

'No,' she said. 'You mustn't blame Tante Madelon. She did her best to persuade me—to do the right thing. If I didn't, then it's my fault alone.'

'Yes.' His tone was starkly accusing. 'You—alone, as I now see.' He threw his head back, staring up at her with eyes as cold and remote as a polar ocean. '*Mon Dieu*, Alys, you knew that I loved you, and you—you let me think that you loved me in turn.'

'I did,' she said. 'I *do*. Darling, you must believe that—'

'You have a strange idea of love, *madame*. Presumably you loved your husband when you married him. Yet within only a few months of your marriage you broke your vows and gave yourself to me. The date of your wedding is given—here.' He walked across to the foot of the stairs and kicked the magazine. 'Isn't it a little early for such flagrant infidelity? What kind of a woman does such a thing?'

A desperate one…

She winced inwardly. 'I never meant you to find out—like this.'

His mouth curled. 'Now, that I do believe.'

'And I didn't marry for love,' she went on desperately. 'If you read the text with the photograph, you'll know that my—that Hugo was very badly injured in a polo accident. He's never been my husband in any real sense.'

'Then why did you marry him?' he asked scathingly. 'For money? For his title? And did you find then that it was not enough? I think maybe it was so.'

His laugh jeered at her. 'And so you came to France—to find yourself a lover and enjoy a little sexual adventure, *n'est-ce pas?* Was that my purpose in your life, *madame*? To ease for you the frustration of a disappointing marriage? I hope I gave satisfaction.'

'No,' she whispered. 'No—please—it wasn't like that. I never expected to meet you—to fall in love,' she added on a little sob.

The dark, bitter face did not soften. 'I never hid my attraction to you, Alys. You knew from the first how it was with me. Yet you never stepped back,' he said harshly. 'Never warned me that legally and morally you were beyond my reach.'

He took a deep breath. 'God knows, I am no saint, but I would never knowingly allow myself to become entangled with another man's wife, any more than I would knock him down in the street and rob him.

'But that is not everything,' he added grimly. 'That day at the standing stones I told you plainly that I needed you to trust me, but in spite of that you still kept your secret hidden—because you could not bring yourself to confide in me. And that, perhaps, is the greatest hurt—the worst betrayal of all.'

'I so wanted to.' Her voice shook. 'But I was—afraid I'd lose you.'

'No trust,' he said, flatly. 'And no faith either. *Ah, Dieu.*'

'I was going to tell you this evening,' she said huskily. 'Darling, I swear it. I had it all planned.'

'But of course,' he returned with cold mockery. 'Was it to have been before or after I committed the ultimate folly of asking you to marry me?'

'Remy, don't say that.' She spoke jerkily. 'I know I've done everything the wrong way, and I blame myself completely. But, please, can't we sit down and talk properly? I need to make you understand—'

'But I understand quite well, *madame*.' He interrupted her

stumbling words with swift impatience. 'You have made fools of us both—your husband and your lover. But he at least will never know that you have cheated him so monstrously. So he is the fortunate one.' He gave her one last scornful look. 'Although I do not envy him,' he added, and turned to go.

'Remy.' His name burst pleadingly from her throat. 'Don't do this to me—to both of us. Don't leave like this.'

He halted. Swung back, and walked up the stairs to her, his hand closing on her wrist, not gently.

'Then how, Alys?' There was a note in his voice that jarred her senses. 'Or do you hope, perhaps, for a more intimate *adieu*? For me to pay a final visit to your charmingly eager body?'

He shrugged, his mouth set in a sneer. '*Eh bien, pourquoi pas?* All else may be gone, but sex still remains. What a practical girl you are, *ma belle*.' He swung her off her feet almost negligently, carrying her up the stairs.

For a moment Allie was stunned, then she began to struggle against his bruising grip, pushing against his chest with clenched fists.

'No—Remy—no.' It was a cry of fear as well as anger. 'I didn't mean that. Put me down—now.'

But he ignored her protests, shouldering his way into her bedroom, and when he set her on her feet it was only so that he could access her zip more easily. Halfway down, it stuck, and he took the edges of her dress in strong relentless hands and dragged them apart. She heard the stitching rip irrevocably, then the silky fabric slithered down her body and pooled around her feet, leaving her, she knew, as good as naked under the inimical intensity of his gaze. Then he picked her up again, with almost insulting ease, and tossed her down on to the bed.

Dear God, she thought frantically as she twisted away, trying to cover herself with her hands. She had dressed—scented herself—for this moment. But not like this. Never like this…

She felt a sudden onrush of tears scald her face, and her voice cracked on a sob of sheer desolation as she echoed her own words aloud. 'Not like this—oh, please—not like this.'

118   BRIDE OF DESIRE

And waited in agony to feel herself touched—taken.

But there was nothing. And when, at last, she dared look at him, he was standing over her, his arms folded across his chest, his mouth a hard, angry line in the bleak mask of his face.

'Stop crying,' he directed brusquely. 'You need not be concerned. I already despise myself for having wanted you at all.' He added with contempt, 'I shall not add to my own shame by taking you.'

She watched him walk in silence to the door. Saw it close behind him. Heard the heaviness of his footsteps descending the stairs and, a moment or two later, the Jeep's engine coming to life. Listened as the sound of it faded. Leaving—nothing.

Then Allie turned on to her stomach and began to weep in real earnest, her whole body shaking with her sobs.

As she began to mourn the love that had begun to fill her life, but which was now lost to her for ever.

It was several hours later that she heard the sound of another approaching vehicle. She'd come downstairs, principally to throw away her torn dress, and had remained. She was now occupying the corner of a sofa, in her dressing gown, hugging one of the cushions for comfort as she stared sightlessly into space. But at the noise she tensed, looking apprehensively towards the door.

It wasn't the Jeep coming back, she told herself, torn between relief and disappointment. But, even worse, it might be Solange, coming to gloat.

Then the door opened and Madelon Colville came in, walking slowly, leaning on a cane.

She saw Allie and checked instantly, her brows lifting in alarm as she registered the girl's pale, stricken face. *'Qu'as tu, mon enfant?'* she demanded urgently. 'What in heaven is the matter?'

'Remy.' Allie could only manage a choked whisper. She picked up the magazine and held it out, open at the appropriate page. 'Solange found—this. And showed him.'

'*Ah, ma petite.*' Tante took it from her, giving the offending photograph a cursory glance, then tossed it aside and sat beside her, taking the cold hands in hers. 'I always feared something like this.' She paused. 'Is he very angry?'

Allie looked at her with drowned eyes. 'Furious—and so bitter, because I didn't trust him enough to tell him the truth myself. I think he cared more about that than he did about Hugo,' she added wretchedly.

Tante nodded. 'And did you tell him how you had been trapped into this marriage, and how miserable it has made you?'

'I tried, but he didn't want to know.'

'*Eh bien.*' Tante patted her hand. 'In a day or two he will be calmer, and perhaps more ready to listen.' She paused thoughtfully. 'It is difficult for him in a community like this. He is a young, good-looking doctor. He falls in love with a single girl, and the whole town will come to the wedding and wish them well. But if he is known to be having an *affaire* with a married woman, that is a different matter.' She pursed her lips. 'Foolish as it seems, some husbands might not wish their wives to be treated by such a man.

'Besides,' she added candidly. 'His own sense of honour would balk at a liaison like that, I think.'

'Yes,' Allie agreed wanly. 'I—did get that impression.' She shook her head despairingly. 'Oh, God, I've been such a stupid, *criminal* fool. Why didn't I listen to you when you warned me?' She bit her lip. 'More importantly, why didn't I listen to Remy—and trust him?' Her voice broke. 'What am I going to do?'

'Tomorrow—nothing,' Tante said briskly. 'Except rest, and recover your looks and your spirits. Then go to see him, and tell him everything about your life in England. Make him aware of the whole truth about this ill-judged marriage, and explain why, for a little while, you wished to forget your unhappiness, however unwise it may have been. If he loves you, he will listen.'

Will he? Allie wondered. She found herself remembering his eyes, burning with angry contempt, mixed with pain. His words, 'I despise myself for having wanted you,' and had to control a shiver.

There had been moments when he'd reminded her of a wounded animal, she thought with anguish, and he might be equally dangerous to approach. Nevertheless, somehow, she had to try.

She leaned forward and kissed the older woman's scented cheek. 'It's wonderful to have you back,' she said gently. 'But you're still limping. Do you think you should have driven back from Vannes?'

Tante gave her a tranquil smile. 'They are the dearest friends,' she said. 'But sometimes—enough is enough.' She paused. 'Besides, *ma chère*, I woke this morning with a premonition that you would need me before the day was over.' She sighed. 'But I hoped very much I would be wrong.'

Allie slept badly that night, and spent the following day on tenterhooks, hoping against hope that Remy might relent in some way and contact her.

If he was just prepared to hear me out it would be something, she told herself silently, as she paced restlessly round the garden.

All the same, she knew that her failure to confide in him would still be a major stumbling block to any real *rapprochement* between them.

It was all he'd ever really asked of her, and she'd failed him totally. Which was something he might find impossible to forgive. And somehow she had to prepare herself for that. Even learn to accept it.

He may not want me any more, she thought desolately. Not after what I've done. But maybe—if I talk to him—explain how it was—we could at least part as friends.

Perhaps that's the most I can ask for. And the most I can offer.

When breakfast was over the next day, she came downstairs and said, 'I'm going to Trehel.'

Tante looked her over, assessing the elegant cut of the tailored cream linen trousers and the indigo silk of the short sleeved shirt Allie was wearing with them.

'With all flags flying, *petite*?' There was a touch of wry-ness in her voice.

Allie held up her left hand, with the gold band on its third finger. 'And total honesty at last.'

Tante nodded. 'The de Brizats are an old and a proud family, my child. Remember that, and do not expect this to be easy for you.' She paused. '*Bonne chance*, Alys.'

I'll need it, Allie thought as she started the car. Every scrap of luck that's going, and every prayer answered too.

Today, the house looked quiet and brooding in the sunlight, its shuttered windows like barriers, warning her not to come too close. Or was that her guilty conscience, working on her imagination?

Stomach churning, she drove round to the back and stopped in the courtyard. Remy's Jeep, she saw, was parked in its usual place, and she breathed a faint sigh of relief. At least she didn't have to go into Ignac and confront him at the medical centre.

As she got out, she heard the dogs begin to bark in the main house, but she ignored them. Squaring her shoulders, she marched up to the barn door and turned the handle, as she'd done so many times before. But the door didn't swing open to admit her, and she realised it must be locked.

He's never done that before, she thought with a silent sigh. Yet he must know that I'd be coming come to see him. He's obviously planning to make me beg.

She lifted the brass knocker shaped like a horse's head. They'd bought it together at the market only a few days ago, because she'd said the horse looked like Roland. She beat a vigorous tattoo.

But there was no response, nor sound of movement within. Allie stepped back, shading her eyes as she looked at the upper windows, and then with a rush and a whimper the dogs were there, circling round her, tails wagging, as they pushed de-lighted muzzles at her, waiting for her to stroke and pet them.

She turned and saw Georges de Brizat, standing looking at her across the courtyard, his face like a stone. He whistled abruptly, and the dogs, reluctant but obedient, moved back to his side. He hooked his hands into their collars and kept them there.

As if, she thought with real shock, she might contaminate them.

He said, 'Why are you here, *madame*? You must know you are not welcome.'

Allie lifted her chin. 'I need to see Remy. I have to talk to him—to explain.'

'It seems that your husband is the one who requires an explanation,' he said with grim emphasis. 'Go back to him, *madame*, if he will have you. There is nothing for you here.'

Her throat tightened. 'I won't go until I've seen Remy.'

'Then you will wait a very long time,' he said. 'He has gone.' And turned away.

'Gone?' Allie repeated the word almost numbly, then ran across the courtyard to him, catching at his sleeve, her voice pleading. 'Gone where? Please, Monsieur Georges, you must tell me…'

'Must?' the old man repeated, outrage in his voice. 'You dare to use that word to me, or any member of my family? And what obligation do I have to you, *madame*—the young woman who has ruined my grandson's life and, as a consequence, broken the heart of my son, too?'

She bent her head, hiding from the accusation in his eyes. 'I—I love Remy.'

'You mean that you desired him,' he corrected harshly. 'A very different thing.'

'No.' She forced her voice to remain level. 'I love him, and I want to spend my life with him.'

He was silent for a moment. 'But his wishes are entirely different, *madame*,' he said at last, his voice gruff. 'Yesterday he contacted the Paris headquarters of the medical charity he used to work for, and volunteered his services yet again. His father drove him to the train last night, having failed to persuade him to stay. By now he may be on his way to the other side of the world.

'And why?' His voice rose. 'Because he does not ever

want to see you again, or hear your name mentioned. And for that he is prepared to sacrifice his home, his career, and all the dearest hopes of his family. He has gone, Alys, from all of us. From his whole life here. And even if I knew where I would not tell you. You have done enough damage.

'Now, leave, and do not come back. Because the answer here will always be the same.'

He moved to the back door, then halted, giving her one last, sombre look. 'It was a bad hour for my grandson when he saw you on the beach at Les Sables.'

'A very bad hour,' Allie said quietly. 'He would have done better to have left me to drown. Just as I'm dying now.'

And, stumbling a little, she went back to her car and drove away without a backward glance.

CHAPTER NINE

SHE'D returned to England two days later, even though Madelon Colville, with sorrow in her eyes, had tried everything to dissuade her.

'You cannot go back, my child. To that house—that family,' she'd insisted. 'They will destroy you.'

'But I can't stay here either,' Allie had responded wearily. 'Not when I'm constantly surrounded by reminders of him. You must see that. And, anyway, nothing matters now. Not Hugo—or Grace. Any of them.' She tried to smile and failed. 'From now on they're the least of my troubles.'

It had been a different person who'd arrived back at Marchington—someone cool and remote, who had announced quietly but inflexibly that in future she would be occupying a bedroom of her own and did not expect to be disturbed there. Someone who had refused to be deflected from her purpose, no matter how many icy silences, shouting matches, or more subtle forms of persuasion she was subjected to.

She had faltered only once, when she'd been back just over a month and had begun to realise that the unexpected interruption to her body's normal rhythms was not caused by stress. That, in fact, she was going to have a baby.

A child, she'd thought, caught between shock and sudden exhilaration, a hand straying to her abdomen. Remy's child.

She had closed her eyes in a kind of thanksgiving. I have

to tell him, she'd thought. He has to know straight away. Because when he does it will change everything. It has to...

She had shut herself away to telephone Trehel, and this time had spoken to Remy's father, Philippe de Brizat, only to encounter the same icy wall of hostility.

'How dare you force yourself on our attention again, *madame*? Have you not caused us all sufficient anguish?'

'Please, Dr de Brizat, I have to know where Remy is.' Her words tumbled over themselves. 'There's something I have to tell him urgently—something important. You must have a contact number or an address by now. Somewhere I can reach him.'

'For more messages of love?' His tone bit. 'He doesn't want to hear them. How many times must you be told? Anyway, he is in a remote part of South America, and communications are difficult. So let that be an end to it. Do not ask for him again.'

She heard him disconnect, and replaced her own receiver, pressing a clenched fist to her quivering lips. She sat like that for a long time, thinking. At last she got to her feet and went to Hugo. Expressionlessly, she told him she was pregnant, and waited for him to explode in rage.

But he didn't. For a moment his hands gripped the arms of his wheelchair so convulsively that the knuckles turned white, and then she saw him deliberately relax again. Lean back against his cushions. Even—dear God—smile at her.

'Darling,' he said warmly. 'That's wonderful news. The best ever. It's got to be a boy, of course—for Marchington. How soon can we find out definitely?'

She stared at him, astonished. Chilled. 'Hugo—don't you realize exactly what I've told you?'

'Naturally I do. I'm going to have a son and heir.' His tone was suddenly exultant. 'All my dreams have come true at last.' He shook his head. 'My mother's going to be so thrilled when I tell her.'

Your mother? Allie thought in total bewilderment. She's more likely to have me tarred, feathered and thrown out of the house to live in a cardboard box.

But once again she was proved completely wrong. Because Grace, when she broke the news to her, reacted with delight.

'It's what I've been praying for,' she said. 'Darling Hugo,' she added. 'How marvellous for him to be a father. This calls for champagne—although you won't be able to have any, Alice dear. The doctors these days say no alcohol during pregnancy, and we mustn't take any risks with your precious cargo.'

Allie stared at her, rigid with disbelief. 'Lady Marchington,' she said. 'What are you talking about? You know quite well that Hugo—that he can't—'

'Don't be absurd, dear.' Grace Marchington's mouth was still smiling, but her eyes were slate-hard as they met Allie's, in a warning as explicit as it was uncompromising. 'Of course he can. He's your husband, and you've finally done your duty as his wife. It only took time and patience, as I always told him.' She became brisk. 'Now, let's have no more foolishness, and start to make plans. I know an excellent gynaecologist.'

Allie began to feel like that other Alice, who'd fallen down a rabbit hole and found herself in a parallel universe where nothing made any sense.

But, she told herself, that was only because, in spite of everything, she'd totally and frighteningly underestimated the Marchington obsession with having an heir.

What will they do if it's a girl? she wondered wryly. Have her exposed on a hillside?

But there seemed little point in fighting them—especially when her own mother also joined in the ludicrous pretence.

Besides, Allie soon realised she'd been wrong when she'd told Tante that nothing mattered any more. Because the baby—this little child, growing so rapidly inside her—suddenly became all that mattered, as did the need to provide him with food, warmth and shelter before and after his birth.

And if that meant becoming part of this weird conspiracy of silence, then she would do it. Because his own family didn't want to know.

'Whatever it takes, little one,' she whispered, her mouth twisting. 'Whatever it takes.'

As soon as the baby's sex was definitely established, the atmosphere at Marchington Hall grew almost feverish.

Deliberately, Allie created her own inner world, concentrating her energies on her baby's well-being, and acquiescing quietly with all the arrangements being made on his behalf.

She produced an all-purpose phrase—'Whatever you think best.'—which seemed to cover everything from the colour of the nursery walls to the re-emergence of Nanny who, up to then, had been pensioned off in a cottage in the grounds.

Allie wrote to Tante, giving her a guarded version of the truth—that she'd achieved a kind of reconciliation with Hugo.

Later, she wrote again, with the news of her pregnancy, and received a formal letter of congratulation, asking none of the questions she'd secretly dreaded. Allie could only guess whether or not her great-aunt had accepted her story.

At the same time it occurred to her that Hugo, at some point, would be bound to take his head unwillingly out of the sand and start to wonder about the baby's provenance.

We're behaving like people at a masquerade, she thought, but eventually the masks will have to come off—and what then? We have to introduce some reality here, and sooner rather than later.

For instance, she thought, almost clinically suppressing her own pang of anguish, Hugo needs to know that my child's real father was good and honourable, and came from a distinguished family.

And that, whatever may have happened afterwards, this child was made in love.

Although maybe that was too much information, she decided, wincing.

But, with the baby due to be born in a matter of weeks, it was certainly high time that she and her husband stopped pretending and had a serious talk about what had happened—preferably with no one else involved.

But when she finally nerved herself to approach Hugo she found him disinclined for conversation, complaining pee-

vishly of a splitting headache. And she backed off, admitting
to herself that he didn't look well.

The following day he was dead, and the subsequent post
mortem revealed a massive brain haemorrhage.

The days that followed were largely a blur in her mind,
until she stood in the churchyard, in a black tent-like coat that
Grace had produced for her to wear, and thought that if one
more person pressed her hand and told her in quavering tones
how tragic it was that poor Hugo had not lived to see his child
born she would probably go mad. Or else scream the truth at
the top of her voice.

And then she looked across his grave, and met her mother-
in-law's icy, threatening gaze, and knew that, for the baby's
sake, she would continue to remain silent.

And I've learned to live with my secret, Allie thought, her
mouth twisting in self-loathing. To keep it well hidden and—
pretend. To live a lie—just as I did so fatally with Remy.
And—for Tom's sake—to compromise.

But no one can say I'm not being punished for my silence—past, present, and to come.

She got slowly up from the floor and went with lagging
footsteps over to the bed, lying down on top of the covers, still
fully dressed.

'And one day, if I live long enough,' she whispered,
closing her eyes, 'I may be able to forgive myself. Even if
no one else can.'

The room was brilliant with sunlight when she woke. She
sat up, pushing her hair out of her eyes as she studied her
watch, then yelped as she registered the time and realised that
the morning was gone.

Tom's cot was empty, and neatly remade, she saw, as she
grabbed a handful of fresh clothing and dashed to the
bathroom. And she'd slept through it all.

She arrived downstairs in a flurry of embarrassed apology,
but neither Tante nor Madame Drouac, busy at the sink,
seemed to share her concern.

'You needed your sleep, *ma chère*,' Tante told her. 'And *le petit* has had his breakfast, also lunch, and is now perfectly contented.' She indicated the sofa, where Tom was slumbering among a nest of cushions.

'But you're the one who needs rest,' Allie protested anxiously. 'I'm supposed to be looking after you. That's why I came. Yet I'm just making more work.'

She was aware that Madame Drouac had turned, directing an openly curious look at Allie. She broke into a torrent of words, none of which Allie understood, apparently asking Tante a question, but Madelon Colville's brief reply accompanied by a shrug indicated that it wasn't too important.

'And now I have a plan,' her great-aunt announced, when Allie had obediently demolished a large bowl of chicken soup, thick with vegetables. 'For the remainder of the day, *chérie*, you must continue to relax. Take some time alone. Drive to Pont Aven, or perhaps Concarneau. Walk and breathe fresh air, to put colour back in your face and banish the shadows from your eyes. Look at shops and visit galleries, if you will. Do whatever seems good to you. And, above all, do not worry about anything. The little one will be quite safe here with us until you return.'

Allie saw that Madame Drouac was nodding vigorously and smiling, seemingly entranced at the idea of being in charge of an energetic toddler. All the same, she tried to protest, but was firmly overruled and almost bundled out to her car.

She began to see where Tom had acquired some of his self-will.

She thought of finding some quiet place and spreading the car rug in the sunshine, but realised suddenly she'd had enough of solitude. And that she didn't need more thinking time either.

Forcing herself to remember what had happened between Remy and herself had been a series of harsh, scarcely bearable agonies, but now that her unwilling journey into the past was over and done with she was conscious of an almost imperceptible lightening of the spirit.

It was, she thought, as if she'd performed some ritual of exorcism, so that her healing process could start. And maybe she had.

So there would be no more introspection, she warned herself. No more peeling away the layers to reveal her own guilt and unhappiness. That had to stop.

Now, she needed other people around—and plenty of them. So, in the end, she went to Concarneau, walking over the bridge to the old town and mingling with the hordes of tourists. Enjoying the holiday atmosphere.

There was a group of artists painting harbour scenes, and she stood for a while, watching them at work. She was seriously tempted by one of the paintings displayed for sale—as vivid and engaging as a cartoon. She was thinking of it for Tom's nursery wall, but common sense told her it would probably never survive Grace's inevitable disapproval.

Instead, she stopped at a stall selling beautifully made wooden toys—farm animals and birds mounted on little wheels and painted in radiantly cheerful colours. She chose a duck like a rainbow, a pink pig with black spots and, after a brief hesitation, a horse with piebald markings in brilliant red and white. She paid with a smile, imagining Tom trotting about dragging them behind him.

She sat outside a bar and drank lemon *pressé* in the sunshine, politely refusing an offer from a tall, blond Dane at the next table to share his bottle of wine.

Some children were watching a puppet show nearby, whooping with glee at what was clearly a familiar story, and Allie watched them, thinking of the time when Tom would be old enough to enjoy similar entertainments.

Not long now, she thought with a swift pang. How quickly time passes.

Which reminded her…

She'd enjoyed her afternoon, but now she needed to get back to Les Sables, because she'd left Tante to cope with Tom for quite long enough, even with Madame Drouac to assist her.

She found herself frowning a little as she walked back to the car. That was something else she had to deal with—the question of Tante's health. For a woman whose letter had implied she was sinking fast, Madelon Colville seemed remarkably robust, and certainly not someone just living out her last days.

I think a little plain talking on both sides is called for here, she decided, with a touch of grimness.

And even more of it would be needed when she eventually returned to Marchington Hall. Because her next task was to remove the upper hand over Tom's upbringing from its present custodians, and establish herself as the real authority.

She was her baby's mother, and there was nothing that Lady Marchington could say or do to prevent her. Not without risking the kind of challenge that Allie knew she would fight tooth and nail to avoid.

My first act, she told herself, will be to replace Nanny with someone young, sensible, and also *fun*, who'll work with me and not against me. And I really wish now that I'd bought that damned picture.

She was so busy planning her future campaign that she took the wrong road entirely and, cursing her own stupidity, had to draw in at the side of the road and consult her map. She'd need to retrace her route to get back to the coast, she realised crossly, unless she used what seemed a winding minor road to take her across country.

Well, it would be quicker, she reasoned, restarting the car. And she'd have to concentrate on her driving, rather than scoring imaginary points from Grace, which would be no bad thing.

It was only when she'd gone more than halfway that she realised her road wandered past the other side of the stone circle where Remy had taken her on that first afternoon, and they were there, only a few hundred yards to her right, their dark shapes crowning the faint rise of the ground.

Shocked, Allie found herself braking for no fathomable reason, then fumbled her gears, stalled the engine and swore.

She sat for a moment, gripping the wheel and steadying

her breathing. It went without saying that the rational course was to drive on and not look back.

But was that because, in spite of her brave resolution, she still dared not face all of her memories? Would she always wonder, in fact, if she'd simply taken the coward's way out?

Well, there's only one way to discover the truth, she thought, undoing her seat belt. And if I can bear this, I'll know that I can stand anything.

She walked across the short scrubby grass without hurrying, telling herself with every step that she could always turn back, but knowing that she wouldn't.

She entered the ring of tall stones and stood in the middle of them, lifting her face to the sun. Wine, she thought, and strawberries. Kisses that drew the soul out of her body. The warm, calculated arousal of his hands. The day when her self-created myth of cool reserve had crumbled, awakening her body to the bewildering force of its own desires—the sweet vulnerability of passion.

Oh, no, she thought, drawing a swift, painful breath. She'd forgotten nothing. How could you ignore the time when your life had changed for ever? Pretend it had never happened?

Or even, she realised, as her heart suddenly missed a beat, make believe that she was still alone here. That every instinct she possessed was wrong, and no tall figure had emerged from the shelter of the stones behind her.

She turned slowly and looked at him across the pool of sunlit grass.

He seemed, she thought, to have been carved from granite himself, the lines of cheekbone and jaw sharply delineated, the mouth set bleakly. He was wearing khaki pants and a black shirt, open at the throat, the sleeves turned back over brown forearms.

He was also, she realised, thinner, and a century older. She hadn't realised that when she'd seen him in Ignac, because he'd been smiling as he dealt with old Madame Teglas. But he was not smiling now.

The blue eyes glittered like chips of ice as he watched her, letting the silence stretch endlessly between them. Rigidly maintaining his distance.

Allie tried to speak—to say his name—to say something— but her voice wouldn't obey her. All she could do was wait helplessly for him to take the initiative.

Which, at long last, he did.

'I was told you had returned.' His voice was expressionless. 'But I did not think it could be true.'

She squared her shoulders defensively. 'Bad news clearly travels fast. But I didn't know you were back in Brittany either. I thought—I understood that you were still in South America.'

His mouth twisted. 'Or you would not have come back?' he countered harshly.

'No,' she said. 'I would not.'

There was another silence. 'I also hear that you are a widow now.' The words seemed wrenched from him. 'A rich widow—with a baby. So you managed to achieve some kind of *rapport* with the husband you professed not to love, *hein*? Tell me something. Did he know—about us?'

'Yes,' she said, dry-mouthed. 'He knew.' *Knew, but never acknowledged—never admitted the truth.*

'And, of course, he accepted your betrayal of him. Took you back again into your rich and comfortable life as if nothing had happened.'

She shrugged, trying to erase the scorn in his voice. 'Why not? All life is a series of compromises. As I'm sure you've discovered for yourself,' she added, her mind wincing away from the thought of Solange Geran.

And she saw him move for the first time, suddenly, restlessly, taking a step forward. He said quietly, 'What are you doing here, Alys?'

'I had a letter from my great-aunt. It made me—concerned for her.' She lifted her chin. 'As you of all people should realise.' *After all, you're her doctor now, so you must know...*

'And Tante Madelon is very dear to me,' she added curtly. 'I don't want to lose her.'

Remy raised his brows. 'You feel that is a possibility?' He sounded almost curious.

'I don't know.' She shook her head. 'Although she sent for me, she seems—reluctant to discuss the situation.'

'Well, that is hardly strange,' he said. 'Under the circumstances.'

'I suppose so.' Allie bit her lip. 'So, will you explain it all to me—please?'

'I regret that is impossible.' The hardness was back in his voice. 'But give *madame* time, and she will tell you what you need to know.'

She stared at him. 'And that's all you have to say?'

'On that subject, yes.' He nodded. '*Madame* does not wish me, or anyone, to speak for her.' He paused. 'But if you are so anxious about her, why are you not with her, at Les Sables, instead of here—in this place—at this time?'

He took another step, narrowing the distance between them. 'Did you come to count the stones, perhaps? To see if one more had been added—for you?'

Allie threw back her head. 'I hardly think your saint would interest himself in our little *affaire*.' She paused. 'If it comes to that, what are *you* doing here?'

'I had to call at the Teglas farm, to attempt to resolve a problem.'

'You mean you're now expected to be a mediator as well as a doctor?' She raised her eyebrows. 'How bizarre.'

'On occasion. But I am not always successful.' For a moment his face was rueful. 'How can one reconcile two women who hate each other?'

Her throat tightened. 'You can't—especially if they are fighting over a man. Eventually one will win. The other will lose. That's—life.'

'So,' he said slowly. 'Where is the compromise there?'

'I didn't say it worked in every case.' She shrugged. 'I was just—fortunate.'

'And now fortune has brought you back here,' he said. 'Why?'

She bit her lip. 'Tante Madelon sent me out for an hour or two. I was on the way home, but I took the wrong road, and found myself passing this place. That's all.'

'*Vraiment?*' The blue eyes met hers—held them mockingly. 'Now, I have another theory. I think that, like myself, you have been drawn back here because you are unable to keep away.'

'That's absurd.'

'Is it? Then why have I always been so sure that one day, if I waited long enough, I would find you here?' His smile was like a scar. 'It is—almost amusing, *n'est-ce pas?*'

She made herself look away, aware that her heartbeat had quickened. 'My sense of humour seems to have deserted me. And, whatever your own motivation, I'm here solely because I made a silly mistake.'

'You were passing,' he said. 'You could have driven on. But you did not.'

'An impulse,' Allie said shortly. 'Which I now seriously regret.'

'At last the truth,' Remy said softly. 'Or as close to it as I can expect from you, my cheating witch. And you will have more cause for repentance when I have done with you, believe me.'

Allie felt suddenly as if the stones were closing in on her—caging her with him in this isolated place.

'Don't,' she said with difficulty. 'Please…'

'You seem nervous, *ma belle*,' he gibed. Suddenly he was within touching distance, and her pulses were quickening—threatening to run out of control—and not simply because she was scared.

'Yet what can I possibly do to you that I have not done many times before, hmm? That you have not welcomed, begged for more,' he added with hurtful insolence.

I have to get away from here. I have to get away now…

Allie moved backwards, only to find her retreat blocked by the bulk of one of the great stones, directly behind her. She leaned back against it, suddenly needing its support, because her legs were shaking. She stared up at him, her eyes pleading, her voice uneven. 'That's not how it was. You make it sound—crude. And cruel.'

'Ah, *je m'excuse, madame.*' His tone jeered at her. '*L'adultère—c'est si spirituel, n'est-ce pas? Et si gentil.*'

He rested his hands each side of her on the sun-warmed rock, so that she was in his arms, but not held there.

'So,' he said quietly. 'Give me one good reason, Alys, why I should not treat you like the whore you are.'

'Because it's all in the past, Remy,' she whispered desperately. 'It has to be. We both have—different lives now. And I—I think I've been punished enough.'

'Punishment?' His brows lifted. 'What a hypocrite you are.'

He bent his head, and his mouth took hers. Not gently. Almost brutally, in fact.

But what else did she expect? asked a dying voice inside her head. There were two years of anger and bitterness tied up in that kiss, and an infinity of loneliness and guilt in her own aching surrender to it.

He was out for revenge, and she knew it.

Yet desire, for her, was instant, unthinking. The appeasement of an emptiness that went far beyond her physical being. Her hands tangled in his dark hair, holding him to her, while her lips parted for him. He pushed up her top and she felt his hands on her bare breasts, her nipples lifting at his touch, aching with remembered sweetness.

She felt the hard, heated pressure of his erection against her thighs, and moaned her need into his open mouth, as sky, earth and grey stone swung round her in a dizzying arc.

She raised a bent knee, hooking it round his hip, pushing herself urgently against him. And if she was the beggar he'd called her, she didn't care. Because she wanted him inside her so badly that nothing else mattered. Because she longed to be entered—to be filled. To be made complete again by the only man she would ever love.

And, just before they spiralled out of control into mutual and rapturous oblivion, she wanted to hear him say that he loved her too...

Only he hadn't spoken of love. The thought rose from her reeling mind with sudden and terrible clarity. He'd spoken instead of sex, and satiation. Called her a cheat and a whore, who'd give him whatever he wanted.

I despise myself for wanting you. Those chilling words of parting that had haunted her so often during the past long months. How could she have forgotten them?

Because he'd meant them then. And all the evidence indicated that he still meant them now.

And if she let him take her like this, without tenderness or respect—use her to satisfy a physical need as if she were nothing more than a cup of water for a parched throat—then she would despise herself too.

Shame had nearly destroyed her before. She could not let it happen again, not when there was Tom who needed her. Oh, God, *Tom*...

She tore her mouth from his, pushing frantically at his chest, muttering the word 'no' over and over again, until her voice rose almost to a scream.

'*Tais toi. Sois tranquille.*' Remy captured her wrists, holding her clenched fists away from him. 'What is the matter with you?'

'It's over—that's the matter.' Her voice was thick—uneven. 'Now, let go of me, damn you.'

He made no move to release her, so she wrenched herself free, taking a few shaky steps before she sank down on the grass, wrapping her arms round her body as she tried to recover her breath.

When she could look at him, he was sitting on the grass a few feet away. He said quietly, 'What is this?'

'You can really ask that?' She pushed her hair out of her eyes, glaring at him. 'Well, it's quite simple. I'm paying for no more bloody mistakes—do you hear me? This time I'm the one that's walking away—for good.'

'You did not give that impression,' Remy said slowly. 'A moment ago.'

She shrugged. 'You caught me off guard. And you were

always terrific in bed,' she added, with deliberate insouciance. 'So for that moment I was tempted. But not any more.'

He said icily, 'Now you are the one who is crude.'

'I'm so sorry. But you won't be distressed by my coarseness for much longer.' She lifted her chin defiantly. 'Because I've finally learned my lesson. Brittany is poison to me, and I'm going back to England just as soon as it can be arranged. What's more, I'm going to persuade Tante Madelon to go too.'

He'd wrenched up a handful of grass and was studying it as if it contained a clue to the universe, but his head lifted sharply at that.

'You think she will do so?' There was an odd note in his voice.

'Why not?' Allie demanded curtly. 'She'll have a better life with me. I'll make sure she has every comfort—everything she wants.' *For whatever time she has left…*

'Of course,' he said softly. 'Your money. The great panacea, solving all problems, healing all wounds. But my family are not paupers either.'

'I'm sure,' she said. *After all, Solange is a practical girl, looking for a better life. Would she have wanted you for your eyes—your smile alone, I wonder? Or even your skill as a lover? I doubt it.*

She shook herself mentally, hurrying into speech. 'Not that it makes any difference. And from now on, until I leave, I'll do my damnedest to stay out of your way. So perhaps you'll extend the same courtesy to me.'

'You really think it is that simple?' His tone bit as he flung away the grass. 'Alys, forget what has just happened here. It was—wrong.'

She wondered if he had suddenly remembered Solange and his new obligations, and felt something freeze inside her.

'But there are things that need to be said,' he went on.

'Perhaps.' She kept her voice flat. 'But not by us. Or to each other. The time for that is long past. I have a better idea. Why don't we both just—stop? Once and for all, here and now?'

There was a silence, then he said politely, '*D'accord*—if

that is what you want. I hope you are not suggesting that we—part as friends.'

'No,' she said tautly. 'That would hardly be appropriate. I'll simply—return to my car, and let you go to yours.' As he rose lithely to his feet, she got up too, smoothing her crumpled skirt with hands that were still unsteady. She could only hope he wouldn't notice.

Keep the conversation going. Make it all sound normal. As if you aren't dying inside.

She paused. 'Or did you ride here?' she asked with ghastly brightness. She glanced about her. 'Although I don't see Roland.'

'Roland went to a new owner in the Auvergne,' he said harshly. 'I too had no plans to return, *tu comprends*.'

'Remy—no.' She was startled into open distress. 'But you loved him…' Her voice faded awkwardly as she realised what she was saying.

'Please do not disturb yourself.' His voice was cold. 'I have survived greater losses, believe me, and even their memory fades in time.' He stepped back, making her a slight ironic bow. 'I wish you well, *madame. Adieu.*'

She turned, walking out of the circle, trying not to look as if she was in a hurry, or anything but fully in control of herself and the situation.

Aware, with every step she took, that he was watching, but not daring to look back.

Telling herself, as the distance between them lengthened, that she'd done the right thing at last. Absolutely the right thing—for everyone.

And trying desperately to believe it.

CHAPTER TEN

ALLIE drove back to Les Sables, trying to use the same steely care she would have accorded to the presence of thick fog or black ice. She had to appear calm and composed, she told herself. As if that final encounter with Remy had never happened.

Because it would only distress Tante Madelon if she discovered even an atom of the truth—especially when the older woman had tried so hard to warn her that she had nothing to hope for.

What a fool I've been, Allie castigated herself bitterly. What a pathetic abysmal fool.

Did I ever—in my wildest dreams—think that Remy's attitude to me might have mellowed over the past months and several thousand miles? Did I believe in some empty corner of my heart that he would really be able to forgive me for betraying him like that?

Well, the answer to that was—yes. She'd probably done exactly that. But, then, she'd been able to indulge any sad fantasy she liked when she'd existed in the absolute certainty that she was never going to see him again.

But now she'd walked headlong into hard reality, and it had left her broken and reeling.

So much so that she took the next corner faster and wider than she'd intended, and received a bad-tempered blare on the horn from a vehicle travelling rapidly in the other direction.

However, it was only when she glanced in the mirror, berating herself for her stupid lapse in concentration, that she realised it was a blue pick-up.

Not that she should read anything into that, she thought. There must be dozens of the things around, and they couldn't all belong to Solange Geran. That glancing impression of a flash of silver-blonde hair as the truck had erupted past her was probably just a figment of her imagination. And so was the fleeting sense of something hostile and malignant aimed at her from the other vehicle, like a stone thrown through her window.

At least she hoped so. Because even the briefest glimpse of the girl who'd destroyed her life would be altogether too much to bear.

Although she was being unfair, and she knew it. She'd laid the charges for her own destruction. Solange had merely lit the fuse.

It was the thought of her wearing Remy's ring, queening it over her little domain at Trehel, that was piercing Allie's soul like an open wound.

He has to marry someone, she acknowledged wretchedly. The celibate lifestyle would have no attraction for Remy, and that enormous bed was intended for sharing. But—dear God—does it have to be Solange? Does she have to triumph quite so completely?

The road ahead of her blurred suddenly, and she pulled over on to the verge, putting her head down on the steering wheel as she fought the misery of loss that was tearing her apart.

But there's nothing I can do, she told herself, choking back a sob. Remy has gone, and it's all my own fault. I have no one to blame but myself. If I'd trusted him, been honest, Solange could have done nothing.

When she finally arrived back at Les Sables, she'd regained a measure of self-command. She sat for a long moment, arranging her face into a controlled and smiling mask. Trying to look like someone who'd enjoyed a relaxed and pleasant afternoon.

But when she walked into the living room and Tom greeted

her with a toothy grin and an exultant word that was undoubtedly *'Maman'*, while Tante and Madame Drouac beamed with pride in the background, she was rocked to her foundations.

What will he learn next? she wondered, with sudden shock. To say Papa? And she felt her throat thicken with swift tears as she hung on to her self-control like grim death.

But she managed it with the help of the new toys, which her son accepted with wide-eyed delight, and supper was a determinedly cheerful affair, as she coaxed him to repeat the 'M' word, praising his latest accomplishment with suitable extravagance.

Although she might be overdoing the hilarity, she realised, suddenly encountering a shrewdly questioning look from Tante.

When the meal was over, and she'd mopped the bathroom floor after Tom's boisterous bedtime romp in the tub, Allie came slowly downstairs.

Tante was on the sofa, knitting a Tom-sized sweater in thick blue wool, her fingers rapid, her hands held low in her lap in the Continental manner that Allie had never mastered.

'He is asleep?'

'Yes, but he went down fighting all the way.' Allie sat beside her, nerving herself for another battle. She took a deep breath. 'Darling, this afternoon gave me a real chance to think. Quite soon now, I'll have to return to England, and I'd—really like you to go with me.'

The busy hands instantly stilled. 'Go to England?'

Tante couldn't have sounded more shocked, Allie thought, if she'd suggested setting up a naturist camp in the Arctic Circle.

'Please listen,' she urged. 'It's not that outlandish a scheme. You won't tell me what's the matter with your health, but your letter clearly implied that it's something serious, and I think we should get a second opinion—before it's too late.'

Madelon Colville was staring at her almost raptly. 'Go on, *ma mie*.'

Allie swallowed. 'And while this house is gorgeous, and I can see why you love it here, and might want to stay until…' She floundered over the unthinkable, then recovered. 'What

I'm trying to say is that it's still pretty isolated, even with Madame Drouac to look after you.'

'Yes,' her great-aunt surprisingly agreed. 'That has become—a consideration.'

'Well, there's a really good cottage near the Hall. Hugo had it completely renovated for his groom, just before the accident. Everything's on the ground floor, so there are no stairs to cope with. It could be—perfect.'

'There is, however, your *belle-mère*.' Tante's tone was dry. 'Who might not welcome a Breton invasion of her property.'

'The estate belongs to Tom,' Allie said. 'Grace is only one of his trustees. I can deal with her.'

'You sound very brave, *ma chère*.'

Allie forced a smile. 'I had to wake up some time.' She paused. 'Well, what do you think of my idea?'

'It is a kind, good thought,' Tante said gently. 'But I have no wish to live in England again.'

'But you need to be looked after,' Allie pleaded. 'There must be treatment of some kind…'

Madelon Colville sighed. '*Mon enfant*, I am not ill. Just no longer young.'

'But your letter…'

Her great-aunt took her hand, patted it. 'I told you that this would be my last summer at Les Sables. And so it will. In the autumn, I plan to sell and move—elsewhere.'

'But I thought…'

'That I was dying?' The older woman shook her head. '*Au contraire, chérie.* I have every reason to live, even at my advanced age.'

'You—deceived me?' Allie felt dazed.

'*Une petite ambiguité, peut-être,*' Tante agreed calmly. 'Because, selfishly, I wished very much to see you, and also *le petit*, before more time passed. And for that I needed a very good reason. One that you would believe, and which would defeat the undoubted objections of *madame ta belle-mère*.' She paused. 'Was it not so?'

'Oh, yes.' Allie was still gasping. 'It certainly worked.'

'Then what harm has been caused?'

Oh, God, thought Allie. If you knew—if you only knew...

'And am I forgiven?' There was an anxious note in Tante's voice.

'Of course you are, darling.' Allie tried to speak lightly. 'So what shall I say when I go back? That the moment you saw me you made a lightning recovery?'

Tante's eyes were gravely questioning. 'Must you—go back, *ma petite*?'

'I have to.' Allie stared at the floor. *Where else is there for me to go? Because God knows I can't stay here.* 'After all, Marchington is Tom's home,' she went on, trying to sound positive. 'I—I can't keep him away for too long.'

'But he also has Breton blood,' Tante said. 'Another important heritage.'

And one that I dare not tell him about, thought Allie, her throat tightening.

She pinned on a smile. 'But you haven't told me yet where you're planning to live after this?'

Tante was vague. 'Oh, I have not yet made a final decision.' She yawned. 'There is no great urgency.'

And no pressing reason for me to stay either, Allie told herself as she lay in bed that night. But Tante would be terribly disappointed if I left before the end of the week, especially as I know I'll never be able to come back again. Or not with Tom, anyway. The risk is far too great.

So I'll return to England as planned, but until I go I'll just have to stay firmly around Les Sables. That way, there's no possibility of meeting Remy again. Or anyone else I'd prefer to avoid.

Because, looking back, she was almost certain that it *had* been Solange driving the blue pick-up that afternoon.

And if I saw her, she may well have seen me, she thought grimly.

She sighed to herself. She should never have come here, she thought with quiet desolation.

Nothing had turned out as she'd expected. And, while she was eternally grateful that Tante wasn't suffering from some life-threatening condition, she couldn't understand why the older woman hadn't immediately put her mind at rest.

She knew what I was thinking, so why didn't she tell me? she wondered. And what is she still not saying now? Or am I just being paranoid?

She sighed again, and turned her mind to the immediate future. She had to admit that returning to Marchington Hall held no attraction for her, and nor did the inevitable battles with her mother-in-law that lay ahead. But they'd be worth it, she told herself determinedly, if they secured for Tom the happy childhood he deserved, rather than Grace's rigid regime. She had to believe that, because she had nothing else to cling to. Nothing to hope for either.

So she would go back and take her rightful place as the new, improved Lady Marchington. She would concentrate her energies on fighting Grace and winning, and forget there'd ever been a girl who'd found Paradise in a man's arms and dared to dream of a different life.

And when these final days that she would ever spend in Brittany were over, she would ensure that, whatever her own feelings, she left only happy memories behind her.

'I am going to the hairdresser in Ignac,' Tante announced over lunch the next day. 'Do you wish to accompany me, *chérie*? You have shopping, perhaps?'

Allie pretended to consider the proposal. 'Not really—and I think, if you don't mind, that Tom would be much happier playing in the garden,' she returned, then suddenly smiled. 'Do you know, he insisted on having all his new animals in bed with him last night?'

Tante smiled too. 'He is an enchanting child, Alys. But he needs a masculine influence in his life—a father figure.' She gave her great-niece a penetrating look. 'I hope the disaster of your first husband has not turned you against the idea of a suitable remarriage.'

Allie shrugged. 'Perhaps—one day. But I don't meet that many people, and besides it would take a very brave man to get past Grace and the hedge of thorns she's built round Marchington to enshrine Hugo's memory.' She pulled a self-deprecating face. 'I think most guys would prefer a more accessible woman.'

'A problem.' Madelon Colville finished her last morsel of cheese and rose. 'But perhaps you should attend first to the thorn hedge around your own heart, *ma chère*,' she said gently. 'Then all else might follow.'

And left Allie gasping.

It was a gloriously hot afternoon. Allie, bikini-clad, lay on the rug, propped on an elbow as she watched her son playing, pushing his animals around on the grass with ferocious concentration, quacking and mooing at what he felt were appropriate moments.

Sometimes, she thought tenderly, he even got it right.

Wearing only his nappy, and an over-large cotton hat, he looked like an adorable if grubby mushroom. And he was happy. Also a little too pink, Allie thought, sitting up and reaching for the high-factor cream.

But Tom was enjoying himself too much to stand still while she applied it, and set up a wail of protest, his wriggles dislodging the sunhat.

'You'll have good reason to cry if you get burned,' she warned him with mock severity as he tried to pull away from her. Then suddenly he was still, his attention apparently riveted by something over Allie's shoulder, his thumb going to his mouth as it did when there were strangers about and he felt shy.

Strangers. There was a sudden tingle between her shoulder-blades, and she felt the fine hairs lift on the nape of her neck.

Even before she looked round, Allie knew who was there. Who it had to be.

She hadn't heard his approach. He'd simply arrived as he always had in the past, skirting the side of the house unannounced. And now he was standing there, just a few feet away, his hands clenched into fists at his sides as he stared at them both.

Allie was in shock. Instinctively she drew Tom closer, her grip tightening, startling a small indignant yowl from him.

She said 'What—what are you doing here? What do you want?'

His voice was hoarse, almost unrecognisable. 'I—I came—because…'

His gaze was fixed on Tom. He looked like someone who had suddenly turned to find himself face to face with his own reflection in a mirror. She saw a muscle move convulsively in his throat.

Dry-mouthed, she said, 'Remy, I'd like you to leave.'

Instead, it was Tom who moved, his small, slippery body evading her slackened clasp as he set off across the grass towards the tall, silent newcomer, grabbing a handful of denim trouser leg to steady himself, and laughing up into the rigid face above him.

And Remy bent, lifting him into his arms and holding him there, his eyes closed and a tanned cheek pressed against the small dark head.

She was trembling violently as she stretched out her arms. 'Remy,' she said huskily. 'Remy—give him to me—please.'

She realised that she was kneeling, what it must look like, and scrambled to her feet, wishing desperately that she had slightly more covering than a few square inches of black fabric.

She said again, 'Remy…' And her voice broke on his name.

There was an endless, breathless pause. She could hear the thunder of her own heart. Then he raised his head slowly and looked at her, and she took a pace backwards, recoiling from what she saw in his eyes, putting up her hands as if to ward him off, although he hadn't taken a step.

His voice was quiet. 'So I have a son.' He paused. 'And when, precisely, *madame*, did you plan to tell me this?'

She felt sick with fear, and a mixture of other emotions, but she managed to lift her chin defiantly. 'I didn't.'

'Ah,' he said. 'A little honesty at last. I congratulate you.'

'Because,' she said, 'I thought I'd never see you again— if you remember?'

'I have forgotten nothing. I recall in particular that you *did* see me, only yesterday.'

'Yes.' Allie set her jaw.

'And still you did not tell me.' The statement simmered with pent-up anger.

'No.'

'But why? Why did you not speak?' His voice rose, and Tom lifted his head from the curve of his father's shoulder.

'Maman…' he whimpered.

'We're frightening him.' Allie put out a hand. 'Give him back to me, please.'

'He is also tired,' Remy said curtly. 'But you are right. He should not be here—for this. Show me where he sleeps.'

Allie hesitated, then reluctantly led the way into the house.

We were lovers, and you used to carry me up these stairs to this very room. Now you're carrying our child, and we're enemies.

For a moment Remy paused on the threshold as he recognised where they were, and she saw his face harden as he glanced fleetingly towards the bed.

Then he recovered himself and walked forward. He put Tom gently down in the cot, in spite of his drowsily bad-tempered objections, murmuring to him softly in his own language until the little boy seemed to accept the situation, his thumb returning to his mouth.

Allie turned away, feeling her throat tighten as she grabbed almost blindly for her robe and put it on. She couldn't afford to be half-naked in front of him. It made her vulnerable, and for this confrontation she needed all the barriers she could get, she thought, hastily knotting the sash round her waist.

Remy looked round as he straightened—and she moved hurriedly towards the door, stumbling a little as her foot caught in the trailing hem of her robe.

His mouth curled contemptuously. 'You are trembling, *madame*. You think you are in some kind of danger? That I want, perhaps, to kill you for what you have done?'

'No.' There were, she thought, far worse things than death. Abruptly she left the room, leading the way downstairs and out once more into the small furnace of the garden. Where she faced him, eyes wary, hands clenched beside her.

'What is his name?' The question was almost conversational in tone, but she wasn't deceived.

'Thomas,' she said clearly. 'Thomas Marchington. *Sir* Thomas, if you want to be strictly accurate.'

His brows snapped together. 'He has your husband's title?'

'Yes,' she said. 'And the house, and the land, and the money. He—he's a very wealthy little boy.'

'*Mon Dieu.*' He whispered the words. For a moment he was silent, then he said slowly, as if the words were being torn from him in some terrible way, 'So you deliberately deceived this man—your husband—you let him think the baby was his—for gain—?'

'No.' She cut across him, her voice shaking. 'I didn't—I swear it. You have to believe me.'

'Why should I believe anything you say?'

She swallowed. 'There isn't a reason in the world, and I know that. But Hugo—couldn't have a child of his own. Not after his accident. He knew it, but because he wanted an heir—a son for Marchington—he wouldn't admit it. Ever.'

She looked away. 'Instead, he said it was my fault. Because I didn't know what to do in bed—how to perform the miracle that would finally arouse him and make me pregnant. Only it was—impossible. And he hated me for it.'

She ran her tongue round her dry lips. 'Eventually, I was at desperation point—worn out with being ignored all day—and then, at night, having to deal with his anger and frustration—the names he called me. I—I had to get away.'

'And so you came here, and found me.' His short laugh was like the lash of a whip across her senses. 'A willing stud to solve the little problem with your bloodline, *enfin.*'

'No-o-o!' It was a tortured sound, wrung from the depths of her. 'It wasn't like that. It was never like that.'

'We had unprotected sex, Alys, because you told me that there was no problem.' His voice was inimical. 'That was another lie.'

She looked at him incredulously. 'You mean you were just

enquiring if I was on the Pill?' She pressed her hands against burning cheeks. 'I—I didn't understand. I thought stupidly that you were asking if you'd hurt me—if I wanted you to go on.'

'A convenient mistake for someone who needed so badly to have a baby.'

'Yes,' she said. 'Perhaps so—if I'd been thinking that clearly. But I wasn't. You see—it was the dream.'

'What is this?' he asked harshly. 'Another excuse?'

'I don't think I even know any longer.' Ally turned away, leaning against the trunk of the tree, feeling the bark scraping her skin through the thin robe. One pain, she thought, to cancel out another. 'But, that's how it seemed then—being with you—being happy and loved. Loving you so much I thought I'd die with the joy of it. And feeling safe—from that other dreadful existence. From Hugo and his mother, and everything waiting for me back in England.'

She stared down at the grass. 'I knew I should tell you that I was married, but that would have forced me to face reality again. And I—I didn't want my dream to end. It was too precious. The one marvellous, shining thing in the mess I'd made of my life, and I was terrified I'd lose it—that I'd lose you.'

Her laugh cracked in the middle. 'And then I did anyway. But at least I had my memories—everything you'd said—everything you'd done. Or that's what I told myself—until I realised I was going to have a baby.'

'And still you said nothing.' His voice was grim. 'Sent me no word.'

'I wanted to.' She didn't tell him about the phone call to Trehel, his father's dismissal of her. What good could it do now? she thought wearily. Just make more trouble. 'But you were thousands of miles away, gone from my life for ever, or so I thought. I had to assume sole responsibility for our child. And part of that was being honest with Hugo. I went to him— told him I was pregnant, fully expecting that he'd throw me out—divorce me. But instead he—he just—pretended that the baby was his. That I'd finally done my duty by the family. And by him. That everything was perfect.'

'And you allowed this?' He was incredulous. 'You—went along with this delusion?'

'I had a choice,' she said stonily. 'To struggle as a single parent or know that my child would be brought up with every material advantage—his security guaranteed for his entire life.'

She bent her head. 'He was all I had, Remy, and I—I wanted the best for him. At the time it seemed—the right thing to do.'

'The *right thing*?' His voice bit. 'To let him live a lie? Or did you plan to tell him one day that he had a real father—a true family?'

'You want the truth?' She turned to face him, eyes glittering in her white face. 'I don't know, Remy. I just don't know. That's something I'll have to decide when the time comes.'

'The time is already here, Alys.'

'What do you mean? He's far too young. He couldn't possibly understand.'

'You are the one who must understand,' he said, and his voice chilled her to the bone. 'Thomas is my son, *madame*, and I want him. And this English estate and its money, and the title, can all go to hell. Because the lying stops now.'

The blue eyes burned into her. 'Our child will stay here, Alys. With me. Where he belongs.'

There was a stunned silence, then she said hoarsely, 'No, Remy. You don't mean that. You—you can't...'

'And who will stop me?'

'I shall,' she said. 'And Lady Marchington. Do you really think she'll let her grandchild go? She'll fight you every step of the way—and she can afford it, even if it goes to court. Because that's what it will mean. Down to the wire.'

He looked at her scornfully. 'You think I cannot match her? You are wrong, Alys. My mother was her father's only child, and he was a very rich man. Through her, his money has now come to me. I work in medicine because I wish, not because I must.

'But it will never come to court,' he added. 'The simplest DNA test will prove my son's paternity. This lady will not proceed, because she will not wish the truth to be known. And nor, I think, will you.'

'But what about you?' She spread impassioned hands in a pleading gesture. 'I admit—I never meant you to know. Because—yes—I was afraid of what you might do. But also I couldn't see what good it could possibly achieve.'

'Are you quite mad?'

'No,' she said. 'I'm trying to be sane—for both of us.' She paused. 'Oh, Remy—think. What will people say—how will they react—your family—your patients—when they discover you have an illegitimate son? The—the wife you may take in the future. What about her? Will—will she want to take on the responsibility of another woman's child?'

Solange—Solange would not even be kind. Instinct told her that.

She tried again. 'Wouldn't it be better to leave things as they are? I'll be leaving soon. Can't we please stop hurting each other and get on with our lives?'

'It is kind of you to concern yourself with my reputation, *madame,*' Remy said coldly. 'But I find the well-being of my son infinitely more important than any local gossip. And, for the moment, I have no wife.'

She took a step forward. 'Remy, If you take Tom, then I'll have nothing left in the world.'

'Then you too will know what that is like.' His tone was bleak. 'How it was for me, out in that stinking rainforest, lying awake at night, not knowing whether I would ever see another day's dawn, and realising I did not care. Because I had nothing left either, Alys. You took it all.

'And when I returned I heard that you had had a child—that you had carried another man's seed inside you. I thought that was bad, but now I know the truth—and that, believe me, is so much worse.'

He added quietly, 'So this time, Alys, it is I who will take everything—from you.'

'What do you want me to do,' she asked tonelessly. 'Go down on my knees and beg?'

'And after that—what?' His brows lifted. 'The offer of your body, perhaps? After all, it would not be the first time—in this garden you have given yourself to me. It might even be here that Thomas was made. That would have a certain irony, I think.'

He saw the colour rush into her pale face, the uncertainty in her eyes, and his smile was mocking.

'*Alors, ma belle,* what do you say?'

'Is—is that what you want?' She stared down at the grass.

He gave a slight shrug. 'I could, perhaps, be tempted.'

Her hands went slowly to her sash, fumbling with the knot until it was loose. She shrugged the robe off her shoulders and let it fall.

Not the first time, no. But always before it was part of the dream. Whereas everything had changed now. They were different people. And this—this was brutal, mind-numbing reality.

The silence around them seemed suddenly heavy—pulsating.

Allie unhooked the top of her bikini. Removed it.

It occurred to her that she'd never had to do this before. Not stand in front of him and—simply strip. Being undressed by him—kissed and caressed out of her clothes—had always been part of the pleasure. She realised that even now she was expecting him to move—to come to her and take her in his arms. Complete the task for her...

Only he didn't. And somehow she found she dared not even look at him.

Awkwardly, she slid down the tiny briefs and stepped out of them.

Stood, arms at her sides. Waited.

He'd seen her naked often, yet here, at this moment, she felt sick with self-consciousness, wanting to cover herself with her hands.

She found herself wondering how, in this blaze of sunlight, she could feel so cold.

His hand moved, gesturing her courteously towards the

rug. She walked over and sat down, trying not to curl too obviously into a ball.

The red and white horse was lying beside her, wheels in the air. She picked it up and placed it carefully at a distance. *Oh, Tom...*

She saw Remy reach into the back pocket of his jeans and extract his wallet. For one dreadful moment she thought he was going to offer her money, and braced herself for the shame of it. Then she saw the tiny packet in his hand and realised.

He must have heard her slight indrawn breath, because he looked at her, his mouth twisting. 'This time you have no husband to act as fall-guy,' he told her unsmilingly. 'So we must put safety before passion, hmm?'

Passion? Her dazed brain repeated the word. Is that what this is?

He walked across and knelt beside her. His hand brushed her body, passing lightly from her shoulder, over the tip of one pointed breast and down to her belly. He parted her slender thighs, his fingers questing almost insolently to ascertain her readiness.

He said, with a faint inflection of surprise, 'So, in spite of everything, you want me. *Alors...*'

He did not attempt to undress, merely unzipping his jeans. Then she was under him, aware that he was adjusting the condom before he entered her without preliminaries—just one swift, deep thrust.

She realised he was not even looking at her as he drove into her, his body moving in its usual easy, fluid rhythm. And she closed her eyes so that she would not have to see him—endure the hurt of him not looking at her.

Not looking, not smiling, not murmuring. Not loving...

Nor did he prolong the encounter, his body swiftly almost clinically attaining its climax.

'*Merci.*' His voice was cool as he lifted himself away from her. 'Your body is still an exquisite adventure, Alys. One would never think you had given birth to a child.'

She sat up slowly, numbly, reaching for her robe. Almost unable to comprehend what had just transpired between them. Feeling as if the strong inner core of her had crumbled.

'But I regret that you have humbled yourself in vain,' he went on. 'Your charming acquiescence has made no difference to my plans. I *will* have my son.'

He got to his feet, refastening his jeans, while she huddled the robe round her, aware that her teeth were chattering. As he turned away she scrambled upright too, and ran to him, catching his arm.

'Remy—please.' There was anguish in her voice. 'Oh, God, if you ever loved me…'

He took her hand, detaching it from his sleeve with a kind of terrible finality.

'And what love,' he said softly, 'could possibly survive what you have done to me? Tell me that—if you can.'

He paused, adding flatly, 'My lawyers will contact you, *madame.*'

Standing silent and bereft, she watched him walk away.

Knowing that, this time, it would be for ever.

And unable even to cry.

CHAPTER ELEVEN

ALLIE poured shower gel into her cupped hand and began to work it into her skin, wondering as she did so if she would ever feel loved again.

She'd been used, but not abused, and whatever violation there'd been was of her heart, not her body.

He'd taken her quickly and casually, as if demonstrating that although she might still appeal to him physically she had no hold over his emotions.

But what else could she expect? Had she really believed that offering herself sexually might change Remy's mind, or soften his attitude towards her?

If so, she'd made a desperate mistake. All that she'd done was make him despise her even more. And, once again, she had no one to blame but herself, she thought wearily.

Except—except that the hand asserting its dominant sweep down her body had seemed to tremble a little. Or was that simply a forlorn hope?

It certainly did nothing to alleviate her sense of shame. Of failure. Or the agony of regret that clawed at her even now. The realisation of all she had lost.

'I should hate him,' she whispered to herself. 'I have every reason in the world to do so. But I can't—I can't... And, God help me, I never shall.'

She rinsed the gel from her body, and the shampoo from her hair, then towelled herself dry, trying to get her thoughts under control. To make some kind of coherent plan for the immediate future.

She could not, of course, tell Tante any of it. She could not distress her like that. Although if Remy carried out his threat to fight for Tom's custody then her great-aunt would have to know, and sooner rather than later.

She sighed unhappily. Well, she thought, sufficient unto the day and all that…

In the meantime, everything had to appear as normal as she could make it. Just as if she'd actually spent a peaceful afternoon playing with Tom without a care in the world.

She put on a pretty blue and white floral skirt in floating georgette, adding a scoop-neck white top. She combed back her still-damp hair, and tucked it behind her ears.

Leaving Tom still asleep, she went down to the garden and collected up the rug and her bikini, bundling it all, together with her robe, into the washing machine housed in an outbuilding. Then she went back for Tom's hat, the sun lotion and the wooden toys. She found the cow and the duck readily enough, but there was no sign of the red and white horse.

It's probably up in his cot, she thought with a shrug as she walked back into the kitchen. And found herself stopping dead.

Solange Geran was standing in the middle of the room, arms folded across her body, the pretty face distorted by sullen anger.

Allie gave her a level glance as she deposited the things she was carrying on the table.

'Bonjour, mademoiselle,' she said with cool politeness. 'I didn't hear you knock.'

'For that there is a reason,' Solange said rudely. 'I did not bother.'

'Madame Colville is not at home.'

'It was not her I came to see.' The other girl took a step nearer, glaring at her. Allie had to fight an impulse to retreat. 'I thought it was you I saw on the road yesterday. I want to know what you think you are doing? Why have you dared to come back here, when you must know you are not wanted?'

'I came to visit my great-aunt,' Allie returned quietly. 'It didn't take much daring.'

Oh, God, if you knew—if you really knew…

'But you would not, I hope, be stupid enough to think you could throw yourself at Remy again,' Solange challenged scornfully. 'Because you would be wasting your time. He finished with you long ago.'

Allie looked down at the toys. 'Not—completely, perhaps. There are still—issues…'

'You think Remy welcomes this new tie between you?' Solange almost spat. 'He does not. *C'est une affaire ridicule.*'

He must have gone straight to her, Allie thought numbly. Told her everything. Or perhaps not—everything…

She threw back her head. 'Then why doesn't he simply—walk away?'

'Because he is devoted to his grandfather,' Solange said pettishly. 'Even when the old man is determined to make a fool of himself—and at his age too.' She snorted. 'My mother says it is disgusting.'

'His grandfather?' Allie stared at her. 'What are you talking about?'

Solange shrugged. 'The wedding, *naturellement.*' She paused, her eyes widening. 'You mean you do not know? But perhaps Madame Colville thinks it will be less embarrassing for both families if you do not attend.' She laughed unpleasantly. *'Elle a raison, bien sûr.'*

Allie's mind was reeling. 'You're saying that Tante Madelon is going to *marry* Remy's grandfather? Oh, I don't believe it.'

And yet, she realized, shocked, many of the things that had bewildered her were now beginning to make a horrible kind of sense.

That's why Tante got me here, she thought. So that she could break the news, slowly and kindly. Only she's found it harder than she thought…

'Believe—do not believe.' Solange shrugged again. '*Ça ne fait rien.* Who cares what you think? It will be good when you have returned to England and can trouble us no more.'

'And Remy's against—this marriage?'

'*Certainement.* What else?'

'But Tante's his patient.' Allie shook her head. 'I thought— I had the impression—that they—liked each other.'

'They have a professional relationship.' Solange pursed her lips. 'But he would hardly wish for a relative of *yours* to live at Trehel. *C'est une embêtement.*'

A nuisance was putting it mildly, thought Allie. It sounded like a nightmare waiting to happen. Tante—and Georges de Brizat! It didn't seem possible. Although she knew that in other circumstances she'd have been happy for them. Cheered them on.

'But at least Remy lives in his own house, and we will be able to keep our distance when the time comes,' Solange added with airy dismissal.

Allie's throat tightened. She said quietly, 'I'm sure that will be a relief to my great-aunt too—if the marriage ever happens, of course.'

Solange's eyes narrowed. 'You will try to prevent it?'

'By no means. But—things happen.' And there's a time bomb waiting to explode in this relationship, she thought wretchedly. When Remy makes his intentions public. Would he take this into consideration, or would he see it as something of a bonus—an opportunity to rid himself of a potential embarrassment? Could he be that cruel?

I just don't know any more, she told herself with sadness. She looked back at Solange. 'I won't be waiting around for the wedding—if that's the assurance you've come for, *mademoiselle.*'

'I also wish to be sure that you will not contact Remy. That you accept you have nothing to hope for from him.'

'No,' Allie said, after a pause. 'I have no hopes at all. And now I'd like you to go.'

Solange gave her another glare and turned away, but as

she did so there was a sleepy wail from upstairs. Tom had woken up.

Solange checked, frowning. 'You have a child? I did not know.'

Allie lifted her chin. 'Perhaps it wasn't considered any of your business, *mademoiselle*.' Although it may concern you sooner than you expect, she thought with sudden anguish. Oh, Remy, what are you doing to me? Of all the women in the world to be Tom's stepmother…

She mastered herself with an effort. Looked the other girl calmly in the eye. 'Please close the door behind you.'

She waited for the pick-up to drive off before she flew upstairs, where Tom was crying properly now—cross, red-faced, in tears as he shook the bars of his cot. She lifted him out, holding him to her so tightly that he struggled in protest.

Allie talked to him soothingly as she changed him then dressed him in shorts and tee-shirt, coaxing him out of his bad mood.

'Did you have a bad dream, my love?' she whispered. 'Because I feel as if I'm living through the worst possible one. But I can't let myself cry—not yet. I don't think I can even afford to be scared.'

She'd regained some of her composure and Tom was in his highchair, dealing with a beaker of milk, when Tante returned, her silver hair swept into an elegant swirl on top of her head.

'Very chic,' Allie approved. She paused, forcing an approximation of a teasing smile. 'Is that how you're going to wear it for your wedding?'

'You know?' Tante's expression of dismay was almost comical. 'But how?'

Allie looked back, deliberately expressionless. 'I had a visit from an old friend—Mademoiselle Geran.'

'That one!' Tante's tone was outraged. 'With her finger in every pie. What was *she* doing here?'

'She came to—warn me off.'

'*Mon Dieu.*' Tante took a sharp breath. 'What insolence.'

'Clearly she thinks she has the right.' Allie managed a shrug. 'She wishes me to vanish, never to return, and maybe in her shoes I'd feel the same.'

Tante snorted delicately. 'Perhaps her pursuit of Remy has not been as successful as she first hoped.'

Allie's gaze sharpened. 'You implied they were going to be married.'

'That has certainly always been her intention,' Tante said drily. 'And his father favours the match because he wishes to see him settled, and therefore unlikely to go on his travels again. *Alors*, with Remy himself one can never be sure.' She pursed her lips. 'But sometimes all that is needed is persistence, and Solange Geran is a pretty girl, who wants him, which is always flattering.'

She paused, her eyes reflective as she studied her great-niece's pale face. 'Besides, *ma chère*, he is young and very much a man, and it must be lonely for him at Trehel in that house he created for love.'

'Don't.' Allie's voice broke. 'Oh, please, don't…'

She turned away, burying her face in her hands, and *madame* moved to her, putting her arms round the slender shaking figure and soothing her quietly.

'Go to him, *ma chère*,' she urged. 'Tell him how you feel. What have you to lose?'

Allie shook her head. 'I—can't. It—it's much too late for that.' *And I've lost already—disastrously.*

'I should not have brought you back here,' Madelon Colville said with a sigh. 'Except that I thought—both Georges and I hoped—' She broke off, shaking her head. 'But one should never interfere.'

Allie lifted her chin, a smile nailed in place. 'Let's talk about something else, shall we? Your good news? How did it all happen?'

'We knew each other from childhood. Georges says that I was his first love.' *Madame's* half-shrug was deliciously cynical. 'But I was certainly not his last. We happened to meet one day—after Remy had gone away—and we talked a little.

The next time we talked more, and our meetings began to be arranged. *Et—voilà.*'

She shook her head. 'It was not what we had ever expected, you understand. And there are many who would say we are too old. But love is good whenever it is found. And I am happy again in a way I did not dream was possible. But I am angry that Solange should have come here to make mischief,' she added roundly. 'She must know that I wished to tell you myself.'

'I wish you had.'

'I wish it also. But I too was waiting only for the right moment, and once again it has gone wrong.' She sighed again. 'It has not been—easy, you understand. For Georges or myself. Remy's father took his departure very badly.'

Allie bit her lip. No one, she thought, had to tell her that. She said stiltedly, 'You shouldn't be blamed for my sins.'

'Mine too,' Tante said gently. 'I could have spoken, *chérie*. But I did not.'

Tom interrupted at this point, demanding vociferously to get down from his chair, his eyes fixed on his toys, still on the table.

'Here, darling.' Allie put them on the floor . 'But I don't know what you've done with your horse—unless you've eaten it.'

It was good to watch him playing, see him look up and laugh. But while she smiled, and clapped her hands, Allie was thinking hard.

Somehow she was going to have to talk to Remy, she realised with disquiet. Try and make him see that this marriage deserved a chance, persuade him to do some kind of deal.

Even if he hates me, he must love his grandfather and want his happiness, she told herself.

And I must do this for Tante's sake—no matter what the cost may be.

She shivered.

It was market day in Ignac, and Allie threaded the baby buggy carefully through the crowds thronging round the stalls as she crossed the square towards the medical centre.

She'd bought extra tee-shirts for Tom, which had been her excuse for the trip.

Now she had to fulfil the real purpose of the exercise.

She hoped she'd got her timing right. She'd found a leaflet with instructions about surgery hours, and figured that Remy would have dealt with his morning patients and be about to start on his visits. So she made her way to the small car park at the rear of the building and waited.

Ten minutes later he appeared, striding through the glass doors, his medical case in one hand, turning to call something over his shoulder as he emerged.

Swallowing, Allie moved forward to intercept him. 'Remy—can we talk?'

He checked instantly, his brows snapping together as he looked down at Tom. 'Is the baby sick?'

'No, he's fine. But there's something I need to say—to ask you.'

'And you chose here?' He glanced around him, his mouth twisting. 'You would not prefer to find somewhere more private, where your powers of persuasion might have—more scope?'

'No,' she said, steadily. 'I don't think so.'

'A pity,' Remy drawled insolently. 'I enjoyed the reminder of how delightful you are naked.'

She felt her face warm. Had to force herself to stand her ground, as the blue eyes moved down her body, mentally stripping her, she realised, all over again. And quite deliberately.

She said, 'I learned yesterday that Tante Madelon is to marry your grandfather.'

He shrugged. 'It seems so,' he countered brusquely. 'What of it?'

'This is a good time for them—a happy time. I wouldn't want anything to spoil that.'

'Ah,' he said softly. 'I begin to see. You think to appeal to my sentimental side, *ma belle. Pas de chance.*'

He walked past her, using the remote control to unlock his car.

'Remy—listen—please.' She turned desperately. 'They've—

found each other. After all these years. They want to spend the time they have left together.'

'And your point is?'

'If there's a court case over Tom it will force them to take sides. It could ruin their hopes for the future.' She took a step nearer. 'Isn't punishing me enough for you? Do they have to suffer too? Please think about what you're doing before it's too late.'

His laugh was harsh. 'Since when, *madame*, have you cared so much for the feelings—the happiness—of other people?'

Her chin lifted in challenge. 'And since when have *you* cared so little—Dr de Brizat?' She paused. 'If you—leave Tom with me, I swear that you'll still see him. As often as I can arrange. Once Tante and your grandfather are married, no one will think it strange if I visit Trehel.'

His brows lifted. 'Occasional visits?' he questioned jeeringly. 'More pretence? I don't think so. But there does not have to be a court case. You may, if you wish, voluntarily grant me custody of my son. A private matter between us, with no vulgar publicity. I might even allow you to visit him sometimes—if I am offered sufficient inducement,' he added softly.

There was a silence, then Allie said bitterly, 'I would never have believed you could be so cruel.'

His smile was hard. 'Everything I know, I learned from you, *ma belle*.' He glanced at his watch. 'I must go. Let me know if you wish to—negotiate terms.' He walked across and bent over the buggy, kissing the top of Tom's head. '*Au revoir, mon brave*.' He straightened, his eyes meeting hers. 'When you have a moment, you might teach him to say Papa,' he told her mockingly. '*A bientôt, Alys*.'

She stood gripping the handle of the buggy, watching him drive away.

That did no good at all, she thought wretchedly. In fact I've probably made things a damned sight worse.

She began to make her way back to where her own car was parked, so lost in her unhappy thoughts that she never noticed

the figure standing motionless in the shade of the building.
Or realised that Solange Geran's gaze was following her like
a dark, malignant shadow in the sun.

'Are you really returning to England at the weekend?' Tante
asked sadly. 'Can I not persuade you to stay for a little longer?
Thomas so loves it here,' she added persuasively. 'He is a different child since he came. He is walking well, and he talks all
the time—although it is not always certain what he is saying,
of course. And he laughs and plays, and is not shy with anyone.'

'He's been transformed,' Allie admitted, her eyes travelling to her son, who was chasing a butterfly between inter-
vals of falling over amid squeals of delight. 'And it's
wonderful. But—the ferry's all booked.'

She leaned back in her chair, a hand shading her eyes from
the sun dappling through the leaves of the tree. 'Besides, it
would be better if I went as planned. I feel that, at the very
least, I—I'm something of an embarrassment.'

'But there is so much still to be resolved,' her great-aunt
protested. 'How can you leave—feeling as you do for
Remy—and not tell him?'

'Because it wouldn't be something he wants to hear,'
Allie said tonelessly. 'Too much has happened that he can't
possibly forgive.'

Tante looked at her gravely. 'But you have given him a child,
Alys.' She saw Allie's eyes widen in shock, and nodded. 'Let
us now speak openly, *ma mie*, and forget this myth that Thomas
is a child of the Marchingtons. One has only to look at him to
know the truth. Ask Madame Drouac, if you do not believe me,'
she added drily. 'And Remy has a right to know this.'

Allie bent her head. She said in a low voice, 'He knows
already. He came here unexpectedly a few days ago and—saw
Tom.'

Tante gasped. 'Remy was here?' Her voice was incredulous. 'But why?'

'I don't know. He simply—arrived.'

'*Mon Dieu.* And you said nothing?'

'I didn't know how to tell you.' Allie shuddered. 'It was a nightmare. We—quarrelled terribly, because I'd kept the baby's existence from him along with everything else, and now he hates me more than ever.' She closed her eyes. 'In fact he's so angry he's threatening to take Tom away from me. Assume sole custody.'

There was a horrified silence, then, 'No—and no,' Tante declared strongly. 'I do not believe it. I cannot. To part a young child and his mother? Remy would not do such a thing.'

Allie's smile was bitter. 'Maybe he thinks I'm not fit to be Tom's mother.' She sighed. 'He's changed—and I'm afraid that's my fault.'

'Not in his heart, *chérie*.' Madame's voice gentled. 'That is impossible.' She paused. 'Remy has the de Brizat temper, but, like a summer storm, it is soon over. Once he is over the shock of knowing he has a son, he will listen to reason. Agree to—some compromise. I am certain of it.'

Allie shrugged unhappily. 'All the same, I'm just waiting to hear from his lawyer,' she said. 'Expecting the axe to fall, but not knowing exactly when.' She bit her lip. 'I thought that if I wasn't around, if I went back to England, he might become a little less angry, perhaps.'

She took a deep breath. 'And, of course, somehow I have to break the news to Lady Marchington. God knows what *her* reaction will be.'

Tante looked austere. 'It can hardly be any surprise to her. She must have known the truth would emerge one day.'

'No,' Allie said. 'I—don't think she ever did. She wanted Hugo's son to carry on the Marchington name—and together they invented this fantasy that Tom was Hugo's child. Only for Grace it's become a reality, and she'll fight to keep it. In fact, I dread to think what she might do.'

She sighed again. 'Oh, God, what a mess I've made of everything.'

Tante patted her hand. 'It has not been completely of your making, *chérie*. That marriage of yours—a disaster. If your father had lived, he would never have permitted it. Never! But your mother—all she could see was the title, the money, and the grand estate. Nothing else concerned her.'

And all I could see, Allie thought sadly, was a man in a wheelchair who said he needed me. Whose very survival seemed to be somehow my responsibility. So I put on my idealist's hat and walked into the trap.

'I should have stood up to them when I knew I was pregnant,' she said slowly. 'Instead of going along with this—madness. I should have walked out there and then. Made my own life.'

'Perhaps. Yet it is not so easy when there is a child to consider. It is a woman's instinct to protect, I think. To do what is necessary for the well-being of her baby, even if there has to be sacrifice.'

Sacrifice, Allie thought with a shudder. That's a terrible word.

Tom came trotting over to present her with a handful of grass and a pebble. She admired them and thanked him for them with due solemnity, and was rewarded by his father's slanting smile before he toddled off.

She watched him go, her heart twisting uncontrollably.

I've lost the only man I ever loved, she thought. If I lose my baby as well, what will I do? How can I live if I have nothing? *Nothing?*

And prayed that she would never have to find out.

CHAPTER TWELVE

A DAY passed, and then another, but there was still no word from Remy. No communication from a lawyer. No request for Tom to be subjected to any form of test.

This is what it must be like to be standing in the dock, thought Allie. Waiting for the judge to pass sentence. Knowing that no plea of mitigation—no appeal—is going to make the slightest difference.

'I feel as if I'm living on a knife-edge,' she told Tante restlessly. 'I can only suppose he's biding his time. Waiting until I get back to England. I don't know what the legal procedure is in cases like this.'

She paused. 'Does anyone at Trehel know what he's planning? Has—has anything been said?'

'Not one word.' Tante shook her head. 'And if Georges knew, he would have told me.' Her face was strained. 'After all, Thomas is his great-grandson. He could not have kept such a thing to himself.'

Allie bit her lip. 'When he finds out—will it make trouble between you? Because that's the last thing I want.'

Tante sighed. 'That, *mon enfant*, is in the lap of the gods. But life must go on,' she added briskly. 'And I have business in Ignac. Do you wish to come with me?'

Allie shook her head. 'Tom's in a scratchy mood. I think he's cutting another tooth.' Or maybe he's picking up on my tensions, she thought. If I just knew what I was up against. If only something—anything would happen…

But there was nothing like coping with a fractious toddler for taking your mind off your problems, she thought a couple of hours later, when Tom had finally fallen asleep on her lap after a heavy-duty session with his favourite nursery rhyme book.

She'd sung the old verses to him over and over again until she was practically hoarse, letting her voice sink lower as his eyelids drooped.

She eased him gently into the corner of the sofa and got up, stretching, to make herself some coffee. She was waiting for the kettle to boil when the telephone sounded shrilly.

'Wake Tom, whoever you are, and I'll kill you,' she muttered under her breath as she flew to answer it.

'Alice, is that you?'

She'd almost forgotten how icily autocratic Grace Marchington could sound—even at a distance. And this was a reminder she certainly hadn't bargained for.

She said slowly, 'Lady Marchington—this is a surprise. Is there something I can do for you?'

'Yes,' Grace Marchington said. 'I'd like you to bring my grandson home where he belongs. At once.'

'I'm afraid I'm not prepared to do that,' Allie returned. 'We'll be returning at the weekend, as arranged.'

'But it should be perfectly possible to book an earlier crossing—this evening or early tomorrow—and I require you to do that.'

Alice took a deep breath. 'Lady Marchington, you seem to have forgotten I came to spend some time with my great-aunt.'

'Ah, yes.' There was sudden venom in the other woman's tone. 'The famous sick woman who has, in fact, nothing wrong with her at all. Quite the contrary, I'm told. I suppose this was a scheme you cooked up together—to get Thomas away from me? Well, it won't work. You are to bring him back immediately, Alice. After which I shall consider your position very carefully. So be warned. The child belongs here—with me.'

Allie stiffened. The point of no return, she thought, had finally been reached.

'No,' she said quietly. 'He doesn't. And you know that as

well as I do. I should also warn you that his real father knows it too, and intends to sue for custody.'

There was a silence. Then, 'My dear Alice,' said Grace Marchington. She sounded almost amused. 'You have either been drinking or had too much sun, because you are clearly delusional. My beloved Hugo was Thomas's father. And that is the end of the matter.'

'No,' Alice said strongly. 'It's just the beginning. And all this pretending has to stop. You have to see that. Remy wants his child, and he'll do whatever it takes to get him.'

'Remy?' the older woman said slowly. 'I suppose you're referring to that wild-eyed young Frenchman who appeared here one morning after your last ill-advised trip to Brittany, demanding to see you. Claiming he wished you to accompany him to—Brazil, perhaps? I did not pay much attention.'

'Remy came to Marchington Hall?' For a moment Allie felt as if her heart had stopped beating. 'And you sent him away—without letting him speak to me?'

'Naturally. You were my son's wife. I told him that you were not there. That you had confessed everything to Hugo and been forgiven, and that you had both gone away for a few days. A second honeymoon to enable you to put an—essentially trivial piece of foolishness behind you.'

She paused. 'I may even have hinted that it was not the first time you had—strayed, but that in the end you would never seriously jeopardise your comfortable lifestyle in England. That you would always know which side your bread was buttered.'

She gave a light laugh. 'A vulgarity, but he seemed to understand what I meant, and left without further protest.'

'Oh, dear God.' Allie's voice was hushed with shock. 'He came for me, and you told him—all that?'

'I would have done more,' said Lady Marchington. 'To prevent our family name being tarnished by a slut like you. And you have not changed. Because now, it seems, you are using my grandchild in a pathetic attempt to get your former lover back. Using any lie, any subterfuge, to rekindle your *affaire* with him—just as she said.'

'*She* said?' Allie repeated. 'What are you talking about? Who is *she*?'

'I had a hysterical phone call from a young woman—a Mademoiselle Geran. It appears she once read some magazine article about your wedding to Hugo, and remembered our name. Traced me because of it,' she added with distaste.

'Solange?' Allie found she was fighting for breath. 'Oh, God—I don't believe it.'

'I suppose I should be grateful to her. She said you were pursuing this man—throwing yourself at him—although she was on the point of getting engaged to him herself. She told me that she had seen you together, and she was convinced you were trying to make him believe Thomas might be his by pretending that some—superficial resemblance meant more than it did. She thinks you should be stopped. And I, my dear Alice, tend to agree with her.'

Alice felt sick. She said curtly, 'I can't speak for Mademoiselle Geran's relationship with Remy, but there's no question of my being reconciled with him. Quite the opposite, in fact. And he saw Tom completely by accident and drew his own conclusions, so she's wrong about that too.'

'But you—you stupid little bitch—you told him the truth?' Grace's voice was a menacing snarl.

'Grace—modern science will provide him with all the proof he needs.' Allie spoke wearily. 'Denial was totally pointless. And, anyway, I wasn't prepared to lie to him. Not now, or in the future when—if—it goes to court.'

'Thomas is my grandson.' The older woman's voice rose furiously. 'A Marchington, and the last of his name. I will admit nothing different, and I will *not* allow this Frenchman to have him. Now, you will bring the boy back to England within twenty-four hours. Do I make myself clear?'

'As crystal,' Allie flung back at her. 'But it doesn't change a thing. Tom is my child, and Remy's his natural father. And, the way things are, I stand to lose him too. So I'm fighting for myself here, Grace. Not an inheritance to which my son isn't entitled, and which doesn't really matter a damn.'

She paused. 'No doubt the lawyers will be able to come up with some long-forgotten distant cousin to take his place, and you'll just have to bite the bullet and retire. You've played and lost, Grace, and you have to accept it. My only regret is that I ever let you do it. I must have been crazy.'

And she replaced the receiver and stood for a while, staring into space, her arms wrapped tightly round her body.

So, she thought, it's all out in the open at last—and that has to be totally the right thing. So why am I feeling more scared now than I've ever been before?

And she shivered.

'I've decided to go back to England, but not to Marchington Hall,' Allie said quietly as she and Tante sat together that evening. 'That's quite impossible. There's no point in turning to my mother either, so I'll try and find somewhere cheap, look for a day nursery for Tom, and get a job before what money I have runs out.' She forced a smile. 'I'm sure Grace will already have taken steps to cancel my allowance from the estate.'

She added with difficulty, 'If you could just make it clear to Remy that I'm—not running away or hiding. Just trying to get my life in order. And that as soon as I have a permanent address you'll pass it on to him, so that things can be settled— one way or the other.'

'No, Alys.' Tante's voice was anguished. 'I cannot let you do this. Remy would never wish it, I know. You must stay here, so that you can meet with him and talk calmly. Decide what is best for your child. That is the only way.'

'I don't think Remy and I can do calm.' Allie tried to speak lightly. 'Too much has happened. But perhaps if I'm not around, and he has time to think—to weigh up everything involved—perhaps there could be—some kind of compromise.'

She shook her head. 'Otherwise it means a court case, scandal and tabloid headlines. All the sordid details. And I don't want that kind of stigma attached to my son. Because he won't be a baby for ever, and one day he'll know. And I— I couldn't bear that.'

'It will not come to that,' Madame Colville said fiercely. 'It cannot.'

'That,' Allie said sadly, 'is what I'm trying very hard to believe.'

She was restless the next day, unable to settle to anything, her mind in turmoil. And Tom was in full grizzling mode over the new tooth, one reddened cheek advertising his discomfort.

Between us, we're the pair from hell, Allie thought wryly.

'I think I'll drive into Ignac,' she announced. 'Go to the pharmacy before it closes, and see if they can recommend something for him.'

And maybe, she thought, give it one last shot with Remy before she departed for England.

It took all the nerve she possessed to walk into the medical centre and ask for him. But she was to be disappointed. The receptionist told her that Dr de Brizat had left for the day, and asked if she wished for an appointment for the following morning.

Allie thanked her, but refused.

I shall be packing tomorrow, she thought. And perhaps this wasn't such a good idea anyway.

She applied some of the teething remedy to Tom's sore gum, and gave him a spoonful of the pink medicine that had also been suggested, and he fell asleep halfway back to Les Sables.

About half a mile from the house, she saw a car parked on the verge, and realised that someone had stepped into the road and was waving frantically at her. To her astonishment, she saw it was Madame Drouac.

She pulled over and opened the window. 'What's the matter,' she gasped in French. 'Is it *madame*? Has something happened?'

'*Non, non,*' the other woman assured her. She pushed a folded sheet of paper into Allie's hand. '*Lisez, madame.*'

It had begun, Allie saw, as a shopping list, then abruptly changed.

Do not come to the house. Your mother-in-law is here, with a woman she claims is a psychiatric nurse. She says you are suffering a breakdown caused by postnatal depression and grief for your late husband, and she is here to take charge of Thomas. I am afraid for you, my child, and for your little son. Go to the Hotel du Parc in Ignac and I will contact you there when it is safe.

'Oh, dear God,' Allie whispered. She looked numbly at Madame Drouac. 'Will you go back to *madame*? Make sure she's safe.'

A warm, capable hand descended on her shoulder and patted it. *'Allez, madame. Allez vite.'*

Allie turned the car and set off. But after she'd gone about a mile she pulled into the side of the road and stopped. She was shaking and nauseous, her mind reeling.

She smoothed the crumpled paper and read it again.

Grace is mad, she thought. Completely mad. She has to be—to imagine she can get away with something like this.

Yet why shouldn't she? said a voice in her head. You were ill after Tom was born, so the medical evidence is there. And she's already discussed your 'problems' with Dr Lennard. Therefore, what's to prevent you being whisked into some convenient nursing home and kept there, under sedation if necessary, while she does as she wishes with Tom?

And somehow she'll make bloody sure that Remy never sees him again—even if she has to take him to the other side of the world.

While I—I'll have just—disappeared.

She shook her head. Oh, come on, she adjured herself. This is conspiracy theory gone berserk. People don't behave like this. Grace couldn't. She wouldn't…

She stopped. Forced herself to consider. To remember. Grace and Hugo, she thought. Hugo and Grace. Both single-minded, both suffering from tunnel vision where the Marchington name and inheritance were concerned. At what point, she wondered, did obsession tip over into something even darker? A place where ordinary rules no longer applied?

Had there always been some flaw—some genetic kink—that made them feel they were somehow immune from the demands of normal conduct? Had she secretly suspected this all along—which was why she'd originally decided not to marry Hugo? Because there was always—something?

Thank God Tom isn't his child, she thought. Thank God he belongs to Remy, who may have a temper, but who's also decent and dedicated, tough and vulnerable, passionate and gentle. And who once loved me so much more than I deserved.

And who would now love his son and protect him always. If he had the chance.

Allie raised her head, gazing sightlessly ahead of her through the windscreen.

Grace will find me, she thought. She only has to tell the police that I'm mentally incapable and I have a child with me, and they're bound to start searching. I thought I could deal with her. But that was before I realised the lengths she might go to.

I don't care what she does to me, but I have to stop her taking Tom. Destroying his innocence and his pleasure in life for her own twisted purpose. I have to find somewhere safe for him that she can't reach.

And I know now where I must turn. Because I realise that there's only ever been one place—one person.

What was it Tante had said? That a woman with a child had to do what was necessary, even if there had to be sacrifice?

The tears were hot and thick in her throat, but she choked them back. There was no time to cry now. She would weep afterwards. After she had done what she had to do. What was necessary.

She started the car and drove to Trehel.

Tom was still asleep when she got there, so she left the car quietly and walked to the door alone.

They said in Ignac that you'd gone home, she whispered silently. So be here. Please be here.

She knocked and waited. Then the door opened and he was standing there, the dark brows snapping into a frown.

'Alys?' There was a note of incredulity in his tone. 'What are you doing here?'

He was wearing close-fitting charcoal pants, and his white shirt hung open over them. His bare feet were thrust into espadrilles, and his hair was still damp from the shower. Her aching senses picked up the tormenting fragrance of soap and warm clean skin. Taunted her with them.

'I—I had to see you.' She hesitated. 'But I seem to have picked a bad time. Are you going out?'

'Later.'

'With Solange?' The question was uttered before she could stop herself.

Remy propped a shoulder against the door frame. 'No,' he said. 'There is a card game tonight at the Café des Sports.' His mouth twisted. 'Does that satisfy your curiosity?'

Her face was burning. 'I—I'm sorry,' she mumbled. 'It—it's none of my business.'

'No,' he said with a touch of bleakness. 'It is not.' He paused. 'What do you want with me, Alys? Why are you here?'

She stared at him across the abyss of her own making. The great pit of misunderstanding and bitterness that seemed to be widening—deepening between them with every moment that passed. Somehow she had to reach out to him. Not for her own sake—she had already forfeited all chance of that. But for Tom, who was precious to them both. For Tom...

Her voice was a stranger's, small and strained. 'I came to say that I—I'm giving you the baby.'

Once the impossible, the agonising words had been spoken, others came, in an urgent, stumbling rush.

'I've brought him to you. Our child—our little son. I want you to take him for me. To love him and keep him safe. Because I realise that you're the only one who can.'

'In the name of God,' he said. 'What are you saying?'

'I'm telling you I've changed my mind. Because we can't

fight over him, Remy. It's—wrong. He's part of you—part of me. We'd just be tearing ourselves in pieces.'

'Alys,' he said. 'Listen…'

'No, you listen—please. He'll have a good life with you. I know that. This is a wonderful place to grow up in. He won't be imprisoned here—or warped—or any of the things I dread might happen to him if I'm not around to protect him.'

She swallowed, her hands clenching into fists at her sides, her nails scoring her palms. 'If you—take him, I—I won't interfere. I promise. I won't be a nuisance, or make any demands. He'll be yours. But you said—once—that you'd let me see him sometimes.'

She spread her hands in a gesture of supplication. Of surrender. 'So you can impose any conditions you like. I—I'll do whatever you want—be whatever you want—if—if that's how it must be… But please—dear God—please let me come here occasionally—so he doesn't forget me.'

Her voice cracked, and with it the last remnants of her control. The tears she'd tried to dam back were suddenly smothering her. Crushing her. And she sank under their weight down to the ground at his feet and knelt there, her whole body shaking under the force of her sobbing.

Dimly, she heard him swear, softly and succinctly. Then she found herself being raised, lifted into his arms, and carried into the house.

A sofa received her, and she shrank into its softness, an arm hiding her blurred and swollen eyes. She was aware of him moving about. The chink of glass. Then a bunch of tissues being pushed into her hand and a tumbler held to her lips.

She winced away from the smell of spirits. 'What is it?' Her voice was drowned and shaking.

'Whisky,' he said. 'Drink it.'

She obeyed, choking a little. Felt warmth begin to penetrate the Arctic night within her.

Eventually, she dared to look at him. He was seated at the other end of the sofa, his own glass clasped between his hands as he gazed down at the floor.

He said quietly, 'You say you have—brought our child to me? Without warning—or discussion? But how could you do such a thing. And why?'

Mutely, she fumbled in the pocket of her skirt and passed him Tante's warning note. She saw him read it, then go back to the beginning and examine it again, his sudden frown deepening thunderously.

'How did you get this?'

She said tonelessly, 'Madame Drouac was waiting for me on the road. Tante Madelon must have pretended she was sending her shopping.'

She swallowed. 'My mother-in-law is a very plausible, very powerful woman. The family doctor in England is totally under her thumb, and I know she's already put the idea into his head that I need therapy. I—I didn't take it seriously at the time, but I do now. I also realise I'd have a problem protecting Tom from her in England. That she wouldn't hesitate to use him as leverage against me if necessary.

'So, I—turned around and came here. You see, I was desperate. I didn't know what else to do.'

'Ah,' Remy said quietly. '*Oui, je comprends.*' He downed his whisky in one swift movement and rose to his feet. 'You have left Thomas in the car?'

She nodded. 'He's asleep. He's been teething. I bought some stuff from the pharmacy. But I thought, as you're a doctor, you'll know what's best to do for him.'

'Will I?' His smile did not reach his eyes. 'I hope you are right.' He walked to the door and disappeared outside.

As Allie turned to put her glass on a table beside the sofa, her hand brushed something that moved, and she realised she was holding a little red and white horse on wheels. She stared at it for a long moment, then gently put it back where she'd found it.

It was some time before Remy returned, and he was alone. Allie reared up in alarm. 'Where is he? Oh, God—has something happened?'

'He is at the house,' he said. 'Being worshipped by my

father and grandfather. Also by Madame Lastaine.' His mouth twisted. 'He will need to be rescued before she attempts to feed him.'

She sank back against the cushions. 'I thought for one awful moment that Grace might have found him.' She shook her head. 'I'm still scared that she'll find a way of taking Tom from me and keeping him.'

'But Thomas is with me now,' he said. 'So that cannot happen.' He paused. 'It does not concern you that I might do the same?'

'Yes.' She did not look at him. 'But I have to risk that. Because Tom's safety and happiness are all that matters.'

His head lifted sharply. 'All?'

'All that can be allowed to matter, anyway.' She got to her feet, still clutching the damp ball of tissues. 'And now I'd better go back to Les Sables and face her. Convince her to give it all up as a bad job.'

'An excellent notion. But not yet,' Remy said. 'Now we need to talk. So sit down, Alys.'

She complied reluctantly. 'My great-aunt…'

'My grandfather has telephoned Madame Madelon, and all is well. But she has agreed to spend the night here at Trehel, and bring your clothes and those of Thomas.'

'Oh?' she said. 'And—Lady Marchington?'

'Your mother-in-law was at last persuaded to leave, on the grounds that guests were expected, but she intends to return tomorrow at ten o'clock. At which time we shall confront her together, you and I. Mother and father.' He paused. 'And husband and wife.'

She said swiftly, 'But we're not—husband and wife.'

'There is the matter of a ceremony,' Remy agreed. 'But that is no great obstacle. And a child should have two parents, don't you think?'

'And so he will,' she said. 'But we certainly don't have to— live under the same roof.' She added hastily, 'If that's what you're suggesting.'

'You asked me if I would let you see Thomas.' He

shrugged. 'If you stay, you can see him every day, and probably several times during the night also.'

She bit her lip. 'I—can't do that.' *I can't live in this house where we were so happy together. Not without love—or passion or tenderness. I can't lie beside you at night and know that I'm just—a convenient body. Because it would kill me.*

I'm not just Tom's mother—I'm the woman who adores and needs you—and I won't settle for some sterile limbo of an existence. It would turn me into some kind of shadow person, and that's no good for Tom either.

I don't want him to grow up knowing that I'm simply—tolerated for his sake.

'No?' He did not sound particularly concerned. 'You have some other plan?'

'Naturally.' She forced an insanely bright note into her voice. 'I have to go back to England and look for a job, somewhere to live. Start to make a—a new life for myself. That—was the original deal, I think.'

'But circumstances change.' Remy paused. 'The Marchington woman—you are not afraid she will seek to be revenged on you in some way?'

'She's going to have her own troubles,' she said. 'Anyway, knowing that I'm homeless and penniless will probably be enough to satisfy her.'

'And that is the life you would choose rather than be married to me?' He sounded politely interested.

'Yes,' Allie said baldly. *Because it won't be as hard or as lonely as living here on sufferance. Wanting you, but having to guard every word—every look.*

'A pity,' he said. 'It means I will have to find a nanny for Thomas. Do you wish to help with the choice of a suitable candidate?'

'No,' she said, smarting under the pain of his careless words. 'Thank you. I'm sure you'll choose the right person.'

'So,' Remy said softly. 'You trust me in something at last.'

Anguish clawed at her. She said with difficulty, 'Don't—

please. For Tom's sake we have to put everything that happened behind us. Try to forget.'

'And you can do this?' Remy's voice was suddenly raw. 'I congratulate you, *madame*. Because I am not so fortunate. I, *tu comprends*, I cannot forget. It is not possible.' He drew a harsh breath. 'When I opened the door earlier, and saw you, for one moment I allowed myself to hope that you had come to me. That you wanted me. But I was wrong. You spoke only of Thomas.'

He shook his head. 'How could you—ask me to take our child without you? Do you truly think so little of me? Am I really such a monster? Do you think I can live only seeing you—sometimes? And that just for the sake of our baby?'

His voice rose. '*Mon Dieu*, Alys, how many more times are you going to break my heart?'

She stared at him, feeling hope tremble into life inside her, but hardly daring to believe it. 'You—love me?'

'Always—always.' He moved, sitting beside her, taking her hands in his and holding them tightly. He said, 'When I reached Paris two years ago, I was hurt and bitter, but I already knew that leaving you was a terrible mistake. That, in spite of everything, you were the only girl I would ever love, and that I should go back, and make you see this. Fight for you, whatever the cost.'

'You followed me to England,' she whispered. '*She* told me that—and what she'd said to you. Second honeymoon! I was probably upstairs—throwing up.'

'Ah, *mon ange*. But I did not know what to believe. It seemed that maybe you had been making a fool of me after all, and that I should go, try to put you out of my mind for ever.'

He raised her hands to his lips, kissing them reverently. 'But I could not. You were there in my mind—in my heart—wherever I went, whatever I did. I could not escape the memory of what we had shared. I also had a dream, Alys, of you as my wife, and the mother of my children. A life together here in this house. As that seemed impossible, I thought—Stop running. Go back and make another life.'

She looked down. 'With Solange?'

'What are you saying? Are you mad?' Incredulity mixed with horror in his voice. 'You think I would involve myself with the woman who gloated over the destruction of our happiness? I swear to you that I have never given her a moment's encouragement.'

'But she thinks—'

'Then that is her problem,' he said. 'Not ours. Because this house held only memories of you.'

'Yet when we met you didn't seem very pleased to see me.'

Remy groaned. 'I was terrified. Because it had occurred to me that your life could have changed so completely that there was no longer any place in it for me.' His smile was wry. 'When you exist for so long on a thread of hope, Alys, you have no wish to see it broken.

'And then, as I feared, you told me that it was over. And I—I reacted badly. I make no excuse for that. But I could not sleep that night for thinking of the touch of your lips, the sweetness of your body in my arms. And I knew I could not—just give up. That I had to try once more to get you back.

'When I came to Les Sables the next day, it was to tell you that I loved you and ask you to be my wife. Then I saw Thomas, and it was as if you had taken all that I felt for you and thrown it back in my face. I felt you must hate me very much if you could have borne my child and not told me.

'And just for a moment I wanted to take him away from you. To destroy your happiness as you had destroyed mine. But when I heard him call you Maman I realised that, although I might threaten, I would never do it. I could not.'

'Is that why you took his toy—the little horse?' Allie asked gently.

'Yes,' he said. 'A gift that you had touched. That he had played with and loved. A small part of something I thought I would have no share in.

'But I still wanted to punish you for trying to hide Thomas from me. I thought if I treated you with equal contempt it would be no more than you deserved.' His mouth curved ruefully. 'But I did not expect my bluff to be called—never believed that you would offer yourself as you did.

'I kept telling myself— She will not go through with this. She cannot. At any moment, she will stop. But you did not. And then—I—could not…'

'But you were so cold,' Allie whispered. 'So—businesslike.'

'I wanted you too badly,' he said frankly. 'I was near the edge—scared of what I might do. I told myself I could not afford to lose control in case I hurt you.' He looked at her remorsefully. 'And I did hurt you, *mon amour*, but in a different way.'

'Did you?' Her eyes were shining, her face transfigured by love. 'I—really can't remember.' She paused. 'But I did try and tell you I was pregnant. Truly.'

'Yes,' he said. 'So you said, and so my father confirmed that night. I had to confide in someone about Thomas or go mad, and we have always been close. But when he heard me speaking so bitterly he said that perhaps I was unjust. That you had once telephoned here, begging to talk to me, and maybe that was what you had wanted to say. Only he had refused to listen, or help. And that if he had been more understanding our lives could have been so different.'

'He was trying to protect you,' she said gently. 'Just as I knew you would always protect your son. And why I could trust you with the rest of his life.'

'And will you trust me with yours?' he asked quietly. *'Mon ange—mon coeur.'*

'Yes,' she said. 'If you still want me. Oh, Remy—*Remy*.'

Then she was in his arms and his lips were on hers, and they were murmuring brokenly to each other between kisses.

Allie wanted the consummation of their love. She wanted to sink down with him to the rug and offer the surrender of her body for his adoration. But Remy was drawing back with a faint groan.

'We cannot, *mon amour*,' he told her breathlessly. 'Thomas may be getting fretful after all this time. Also, I promised Liliane that I would get my old cot from the attic so that she can clean it for him to sleep in. And my grandfather thinks it would not be *convenable* for Madame Madelon to sleep over at the house before they are married, so she must stay here, and her room needs to be prepared.' He looked at her, his mouth rueful, his eyes brimming with sudden laughter. 'Welcome to family life, *ma belle*.'

'It has a nice ring about it,' Allie said, her own lips twitching. 'So we shall just have to wait until tonight, my darling.'

He took her hand. Kissed it. 'Last time, to my eternal shame,' he said quietly, 'I took and gave nothing. Tonight it will be very different. So, will you forgive me, Alys, and lie with me in our bed?'

'Yes,' she told him huskily. 'Oh, yes.' She looked at him from under her lashes, a world of promise shining in her eyes. 'Although poor Tom is teething, remember?' she murmured. 'We could be—disturbed.'

Remy kissed her again, his lips lingering on hers. 'He is my son, *chérie*,' he told her softly. 'And no Frenchman would ever do that to another.' His smile caressed her. 'We shall have our night, I promise you.'

And so, with joy, tenderness and a sweet and soaring passion, they did.

THE ENGLISH
ARISTOCRAT'S BRIDE

BY
SANDRA FIELD

Although born in England, **Sandra Field** has lived most of her life in Canada; she says the silence and emptiness of the north speak to her particularly. While she enjoys travelling and passing on her sense of a new place, she often chooses to write about the city which is now her home. Sandra says "I write out of my experience; I have learned that love, with its joys and its pains, is all important. I hope this knowledge enriches my writing and touches a cord in you, the reader."

CHAPTER ONE

HER sister lived in this house. The sister she had never met, whose existence she'd discovered a scant four weeks ago.

Karyn Marshall stepped deeper into the shadows of the trees. Should anyone glance out of one of the tall windows set in mellow, rose-pink brick, she was safely hidden from view. Skulking like a common thief, she thought with a shiver. Watching and waiting.

It wasn't just a house. It was a mansion. Wisteria drooped its delicate blooms all the way up to the second story; there were stables to one side and a four-car garage with a cobbled driveway. Every detail was perfect, yet served only to increase her unease.

She was afraid. Far too afraid to announce her presence.

Her twin sister and only sibling, Fiona Talbot, lived in this house, whose name was Willowbend. For Fiona, Willowbend was home, along with a luxury beyond Karyn's imagining. Karyn glanced down at her plain linen slacks and tailored shirt, clothes she'd thought would be entirely adequate for this meeting. An evening dress would have been more appropriate; not that she owned one.

She'd given away all her dresses after Steve had died.

Karyn shrank back against the tree trunk as a woman in a glowing red gown suddenly appeared in one of the windows. An older woman; even at this distance, Karyn could discern the twinkle of diamonds encircling her throat. Was this Clarissa Talbot, Fiona's adoptive mother? The woman turned her head to speak to someone in the room, then disappeared. A moment later, a uniformed butler drew long curtains across the window.

A butler. Karyn bit back a quiver of hysterical laughter. This was an English country mansion. Of course they'd have a butler.

Why, oh, why, hadn't she written first, to tell the family of her existence? That way, she'd have been an expected guest who could have walked confidently up the driveway and knocked on the front door.

She hadn't written because she'd worried that the Talbots would tell her to stay away. To leave the past where it belonged, buried and forgotten.

If only she wasn't so desperate to meet her unknown twin, to assuage some of the terrible loneliness of the last few months…

Behind Karyn, something rustled in the undergrowth. She whirled, her heart leaping like a startled rabbit's, every nerve on edge. A twig snapped. She strained her eyes, trying to penetrate the dense tangle of shrubs and trees, and to her dismay saw a darker shadow climbing the little slope that led up to the garden. Coming her way.

A man. Whistling softly under his breath, finding his way through the gloomy woods with the ease of familiarity.

Her eyes flicked around her. She could have tried to hide, ducking behind the nearest oak tree and hoping for the best. But her raincoat was light beige, as were her trousers, and the odds of remaining unseen far too small. So she stood her ground, lifting her chin. She might look like a thief. But there was no need to behave like one.

The man was only a few feet away from her. He was tall, with hair black as night; dressed casually in jeans and a sweater, he moved with a feline grace that added one more layer to her fear. She'd read about poachers who prowled the woods after dark. Was he one of them? A lawbreaker? She should have hidden. Or run. While she had the chance.

Then, suddenly, the man saw her. He stopped dead in his tracks, his eyes, dark as his hair, trained on her face. "Fiona," he said softly, "what are you doing out here?"

Karyn's breath had lodged in her throat; she couldn't have said a word to save her soul. At the inn where she was staying in the village of Droverton, the landlord on his first sight of her had called her "Miss Fiona," and his initial disbelief had been all too obvious when she'd said she was Karyn Marshall, a tourist from eastern Canada. He'd looked, she remembered quite clearly, downright suspicious; and hadn't behaved with any of the friendliness she'd expected to find in a little village inn.

Now the man who'd appeared out of the woods was confirming what the landlord's behavior had suggested: she and Fiona must be identical twins. Must look so very much alike that one of them could be mistaken for the other.

The man had stepped a little closer. He was well over six feet tall, broad-shouldered and long-legged, making Karyn feel both feminine and fragile in a way she didn't care for. Although his face was shadowed, she could see that it was strongly hewn, handsome and full of character. Character? Much too wishywashy a word, she thought breathlessly. How about ruthlessness? Power? Charisma? Cemented together with a compellingly male dose of sexiness. It took all her pride not to step back, and all her willpower to keep her eyes from fastening on the carved sensuality of his mouth.

Think, Karyn. Think.

Her throat might have closed as though a hand was clamped tight around it. But she didn't have to shut her brain off as well. The man had called her Fiona, not Miss

Fiona. So he knew her sister well. Perhaps, just perhaps, he'd be her way into Willowbend.

She might succeed, after all, in meeting her twin this very evening; and if she had to use this black-haired man to do so, she would.

Rafe Holden had been thinking about Fiona as he wended his way through the trees. He'd hoped to make it to Willowbend in time for dinner that evening; but his flight from Athens had been delayed, and he'd phoned Clarissa to tell her not to expect him.

Then, breaking into his thoughts as he climbed the slope, something had alerted him to another presence in the woods. When he glanced up, he saw Fiona immediately; she was standing against the oak tree that the pair of them had often climbed as children. He, seven years older and always the leader; and always protective of his little blond, blue-eyed neighbor.

"Fiona," he said, "what are you doing out here?"

As he waited for her to answer, his feet sank gently into the rich humus of last autumn's leaves, new ferns brushing his knees. His gaze sharpened and he stepped a little closer. She looked frightened. More than frightened, as though something had knocked her right off balance, striking her dumb. If Clarissa had been at her again, there'd be hell to pay. He'd see to that.

He closed the distance between them in three swift strides and took her in his arms. Her body was taut. Her scent was new, more complex and more sensuous than he was used to. He liked it. Liked it very much. Her hair was different, too. Astonishingly different. For as long as he could remember, Fiona had obeyed her mother's strictures to let her hair grow all the way down her back; she often wore it pulled away from her face in a long braid. Virginal, he'd occasionally thought. Untouched. Just as Clarissa wanted Fiona to be.

But now her hair was cut short, feathered to her face in soft curls that made her look like another woman. A more sophisticated woman; and again that word sensuous came to Rafe's mind. Her decision to lop off her braid intrigued him, and he was certainly into encouraging any rebellions on her part. He said, bending his head to kiss her cheek, "I like the haircut—what made you do it? I bet that got your mother's goat."

He liked holding Fiona. It was like coming home to all that was familiar, to the friendship they'd shared for years, their bonds of a shared history and a deep love of the landscape where they'd both grown up. He rubbed his cheek gently against the softness of her hair, wanting only to soothe her. Clarissa Talbot on the warpath was a force to be reckoned with.

Then, to his astonishment, her head shifted and almost inadvertently his mouth found hers. Her lips were cool, their touch tentative; her slender frame, in a raincoat he'd never seen before, felt as rigid as the ghastly Greek nymphs Douglas Talbot had stationed throughout the azalea garden. Against her mouth, he whispered, "It's okay…you can relax now. I'm here, and I'm on your side."

One of his hands was cupping her nape. Wisps of blond hair, soft and silky, teased his fingers. She made a tiny sound in her throat, and almost insensibly her mouth softened under his. There were layers upon layers to her scent, each of them encouraging him to explore further.

Which was something he'd never thought of doing before. Certainly never felt driven to do. For wasn't Fiona his oldest friend? Only once in his life had he known the fire and recklessness of a passion that had swept him off his feet, and the results had devastated him in a way he'd never forgotten, and had no wish to repeat. For him, Fiona's strongest attraction was how she represented all the comforts of familiarity: the ease, the lack of demand and the total trust.

He could live without passion. Once burned, twice shy. Or, more accurately in his case, once burned, permanently shy.

By now her body had softened, too, her shoulder under his palm fractionally less tight. Still with infinite care, Rafe drew her closer, sliding his hand under her coat to find her shoulder and knead it gently through the folds of her shirt. She even felt different, he thought in an unquenchable shaft of excitement. All of a sudden he didn't want the feel of fabric; he wanted her skin to his. Heat to heat.

His kiss deepened, the pressure of his mouth seeking more from her. In a sunburst of shocked delight he realized she was giving him exactly what he was asking, opening to him, yielding. Her hands were pressed to his chest, their warmth penetrating his pores. Slowly, as though she were savoring every moment, her palms slid upward to encircle the back of his neck, where her fingers buried themselves in his hair. He was the one who should have got a haircut, Rafe thought dimly. He'd planned to, but the meetings at his new hotel had taken longer than he'd expected.

Then he stopped thinking altogether as he felt the first, swift dart of her tongue to his. Instantly he met her, feeding on the wet, slick heat of her mouth, enticed by its sweetness. He wrapped his arms around her, pulling her toward him, her pliancy like a flame in his arms, her startled gasp of pleasure potent as the roar of a waterfall on the fells. How could he possibly have guessed that so much ardor was hidden under her delicacy, beneath that air she wore of remoteness and untouchability?

She'd never shown it to him before.

His groin had hardened with fierce intent; he shifted away from her, afraid she would withdraw from fear or shyness. However, in a fierce mingling of gratitude and sheer lust, he felt her press her hips into his, as though she, too, craved to do away with the barriers of clothing and civilized restraint. Yearned to belong to him in the most primitive of ways.

Desperate to touch her, Rafe tugged her shirt from her waistband and thrust his hand under it. Her skin was like the finest silk, her ribs impossibly fragile. When he found the swell of her breast, firm and warm under the sheerest of lace, its tip was hard as a small stone. She moaned again as he teased her nipple; all the while his tongue played with hers, their lips locked together in a searing commitment to give each other pleasure.

From a long way away, he was aware of her tearing at his shirt; then felt the dizzying heat of her fingers flat against his chest, tangled in his body hair. His heart was pounding like a farrier's hammer; his own nipples hardened to her touch. He nibbled at her lower lip, his teeth scraping her tongue, his emotions churning as she trembled in his embrace in mute and total surrender. Could he die of such ecstasy?

He wanted her here. Now. On the ground, against the tree, he didn't care. Had he ever felt such explosive desire, such hot, fierce hunger?

But he couldn't take her here. Not Fiona. Not in sight of Willowbend. His breath sobbing in his chest, Rafe said urgently, "Come home with me now, to Stoneriggs. I want to make love to you, Fiona." His voice warmed with laughter. "In a bed. Not on the ground under the oak trees—you deserve better than that."

Make love to you. As though the shaft of an arrow had pierced her to the heart, Karyn went utterly still in the man's arms. Although, she thought distantly, nothing could have stopped the air heaving in her lungs, the pulse throbbing in her ears. Or the pangs of desire, unrelieved, that ached in her belly.

In a kiss that seemed to have gone on forever, she'd traveled to a place she'd never been before. She, Karyn Marshall.

Not Fiona Talbot.

"I know you want me," the man whispered, running his fingers down her cheek and tracing the soft curve of her lips until she gave another of those unquenchable shudders of response. "You want me as much as I want you."

Distraught, horrified, Karyn struggled to get her breath under control, to find her voice amid the turmoil in her body. What had happened to her? How could she have let a simple kiss go this far without blurting out who she was?

But before she could even find the words, let alone speak them, a chorus of excited barking split the silence of the woods. From the undergrowth a pack of dogs burst into the open and hurled themselves joyously on the man who was still clasping her in his arms. Their weight threw him sideways. Seeing her chance, Karyn yanked herself free. Obeying instinct, she whirled and raced for the woods.

"Get down, Sandy! Randall, down! For God's sake, when are my parents ever going to teach you any manners? Charlotte, off!"

If Karyn had learned one thing during that devastating kiss, it was that this man took what he wanted: he wouldn't be delayed for long. She ran for her life, tumbling down the slope and leaping over a stream that roiled between rocks slippery with moss. The woods were thicker now, and the sun had set. Seeking the shadows, jumping over fallen trunks, she ran on, deeper and deeper into the trees.

She was headed in the general direction of the village, that much she knew, and for which she was pitifully grateful.

"Fiona! Fiona, come back."

His voice was fainter, masked by the leaves, the rattle of the stream and the barking dogs. Desperately Karyn increased her pace, until her ribs hurt and her chest was starved for air. Branches lashed her coat, her hands warding them from her face. Would the dogs follow her? Lead him to her?

Then what?

It was her nightmare all over again, she thought with sudden, sickening clarity: the nightmare that had recurred with ominous regularity ever since her husband Steve's death. In it she was running for her life through the darkness...

All too abruptly, the woods thinned and with a whimper of fear she burst into an open field. A stone wall loomed ahead of her, curving around to the left; sheep were huddled like small boulders on the other side.

The road to the village, she remembered, ran alongside this field. If she could cross the road, she could follow the woods on the far side until she came to the cluster of houses. Once she was at the inn, she'd be safe.

Safe from what? A nightmare? Or from the man in the woods?

He hadn't exactly attacked her. She'd been the one who'd gone on the attack. Who'd laced her tongue with his in open invitation and pushed her hips against his.

With a moan of despair Karyn scrambled toward the nearest wall which, she now saw, edged the woods all the way back toward Willowbend. A metal gate was inset where the wall met the field. The harsh whine of hinges scraping her nerves, she unlatched the gate, swung it open and eased through, carefully shutting it behind her. The sheep paid her no attention whatsoever.

The road was empty, its grassy verges fragrant with wild-flowers. Her lungs still fighting for air, she crossed it as quickly as she could, easing into the shrubbery on the other side and scurrying toward the lights of the village. The man who'd kissed her had come through the woods; at least he didn't have a car in which to pursue her.

She'd kissed him with a seductive intimacy that Steve, even in the early days of courtship, had never elicited from her. Yet she didn't even know the man's name.

What difference? She didn't need to know his name. She just had to make sure she never saw him again.

She'd reached the first house, stone like so many of the houses here, its tiny front garden jammed with a riot of delphiniums, foxgloves, daisies and poppies. After drawing her coat tighter around her, Karyn pulled her headscarf from her pocket to cover her hair and as much of her face as she could.

The sidewalk, to her great relief, was empty: to have been mistaken for Fiona for the third time that day would have been more than she could bear. To her greater relief, the dour landlord of the inn was nowhere in sight when she pushed open the door; the wood-paneled counter with its tarnished collection of horse brasses was deserted, although she could hear the echo of laughter from the pub. She sneaked up the stairs, unlocked her door and slipped into her room. Quickly she snubbed the latch. Then she leaned back on the panels, letting out her breath in a shuddering sigh.

Her knees were trembling from her flight. Her trousers were flecked with bracken and dirt. She felt both exhausted and horribly wired. But she was alone. And she was safe.

She'd learned two things this evening. That Fiona lived

a privileged life amid surroundings of exquisite beauty; and that her sister had a lover, a black-haired man who had—under the assumption that Karyn was Fiona—kissed her as though there was no tomorrow.

No, Karyn thought sickly, levering herself away from the door and dragging off her coat. She'd learned three things. She'd learned that passion, which she'd thought had died within her long before she was widowed, wasn't dead after all. It had taken just one kiss from a total stranger to show that her sexuality, far from being dead, had merely been slumbering. Waiting to be reawoken.

Never again, she thought. Never again. Sinking down on the old brass bed, Karyn buried her face in her hands.

It took Rafe nearly five minutes to get the six dogs sitting in a circle at his feet, gazing up at him adoringly, their pink tongues flopping from sharp-toothed jaws. "You're idiots," he said coldly. "I love my mother dearly, but on the subject of dogs we differ. I'd have paid ten times over for obedience classes, and will she do it? *Oh darling, they listen to me, and that's what counts.*"

Right. They listened to his mother when she had a pocketful of dog biscuits, that's when they listened. In a resigned voice Rafe went on, "Okay, we're going to Fiona's. I'm locking you in the garage and I'm expecting you to keep your big mouths shut. Have you got that?"

Charlotte flopped down on her belly and rolled over. With an exasperated sigh Rafe headed for the house. In a way, he was almost glad of the six dogs now trooping at his heels as though they'd never leaped up on him and stopped a kiss that had overturned his world. What would have happened next? Would Fiona have gone with him to Stoneriggs and made love with him in his big bed?

Maybe not, he thought with a touch of grimness. After

all, hadn't she pulled free and run for the woods as though all the hounds of hell were after her? Had she so quickly regretted that surge of passion, wishing it had never happened?

He could have gone after her. But the dogs would have liked nothing better than another mad dash through the trees, and the odds of finding her were slim. Besides, he couldn't bear the thought of chasing her down like a fugitive.

His whole body was one big ache of frustration. His jaw set, Rafe marched past the perennial garden and across the forecourt of topiaried yews and formal clipped boxwood. He loathed topiary. Clarissa's gardener was never going to get within a mile of Stoneriggs.

He ushered the dogs into the garage and shut the door firmly, ignoring their downcast faces. He'd walk them home once he'd seen Clarissa and done his level best to find out what had upset Fiona. The haircut. He'd be willing to bet it was the haircut.

What had brought about that particular rebellion?

After cursorily rapping the large brass knocker against the door, Rafe let himself in. His boots were muddy from the stream, and his jeans wouldn't meet with Clarissa's approval; but he'd needed the exercise of walking over here from Stoneriggs after the day he'd had. He shucked off his boots, and heard Clarissa call from the dining room, "Is that you, Rafe?"

"Sorry I'm so late," he called back, and walked into the vast living room with its array of Victorian ceramics, several of which he'd been tempted to knock—accidentally, of course—off their pedestals. There was only one person in the room. She was standing by the fireplace with a Spode cup in her hand; emerald earrings shot green fire as she turned her head.

Fiona.

Her long hair was drawn into an elegant twist on the back of her head. Her dress was a slim pencil of leaf-green.

Rafe's breath hissed through his teeth. Was he losing his mind?

Not stopping to think, he strode across the room. Taking the cup from her hand, he plunked it down on the priceless Chippendale table, took her in his arms and kissed her hard on the mouth.

No flame of response. No flick of her tongue. No matching heat, body to body.

No surrender.

Only her jerk of shock and sudden withdrawal, her hands warding him off. The sweet naiveté of lilies of the valley drifted to his nostrils, rather than subtle layers of scent that teased all his senses. As he wrenched his mouth free, Fiona gasped, "Rafe! Whatever's wrong with you?"

Before he could think of a word to say, she added in genuine horror, "What if Mother had seen us?"

"Even your mother must know that old friends kiss each other on occasion."

"That wasn't just a friendly kiss!"

"Maybe it's time for a change."

"But you've never kissed me like that. Ever."

He had. Only minutes before, under the shadow of the oak tree. Hadn't he?

His head whirling, Rafe said, "I need a drink."

"The coffee's freshly brewed." Her cheeks bright pink, Fiona indicated the ornate sterling pot on a tray by the hearth.

"Whiskey," he said tersely, and poured himself a triple from the crystal decanter on the sideboard.

"What's the matter?" Fiona said, distressed. "I don't

understand why you're behaving like this. Didn't Athens go well?''

He swallowed a hefty gulp of Glenfiddich, gazing at her broodingly. Fiona, well-known friend of so many years. Slim, beautiful, exquisitely groomed, her blue eyes like the delphiniums in the garden, her brows arched like the wings of birds. And her hair, in its thick coil on the back of her head, its wheaten gleam under the chandelier.

It wasn't Fiona he'd kissed under the trees. Obviously.

So who had he kissed? And where had she gone, that woman who'd looked enough like Fiona to be her sister, yet who'd responded to him as though she was his soul mate? Meant for him, and for him alone, calling to his blood as though he'd known her all his life.

He'd never seen her before this evening. He might never see her again.

"Darlings!" Clarissa said, sweeping into the room in a rustle of taffeta.

"Hello, Clarissa," Rafe said, and dutifully kissed her expensively scented cheek.

"Lovely to see you, Rafe." She smiled charmingly at his jeans and socked feet. "Even in deshabille. How was Athens?"

He'd recently opened a new resort several miles south of the city, one more addition to the international chain of luxury hotels that he owned and managed. "Ironing out a few wrinkles," he said casually. "Well worth the trip. You're looking lovely, Clarissa."

From the doorway, Douglas Talbot said bluffly, "I bought her that dress in London. It suits her rather well, don't you think?"

If Clarissa had the brittle beauty of a Dresden statuette, Douglas was a Toby jug. Rotund, outwardly hearty, Douglas was also, as Rafe knew all too well, a rabid social climber with a tendency to bully. Yet he adored his wife and would have done anything for her.

Rafe said smoothly, "A delightful dress, Clarissa, to which you more than do justice. Little wonder you have such a beautiful daughter."

Fiona's smile was almost natural; quite plainly, she'd decided Rafe's kiss was best ignored. Douglas poured himself a drink, asking a shrewd question about the political situation in Greece, and the evening proceeded along its predictable path. A couple of hours later Rafe took his leave, for once unamused when Fiona's parents tactfully left him alone with her. Clarissa and Douglas wanted much more than friendship between himself and their daughter; they wanted him to marry Fiona. Douglas, to put it bluntly, was applying the crudest of pressures toward that end.

He, Rafe, wasn't going to be pushed around by Douglas. Although, at the time, hadn't that kiss under the trees made the thought of marrying Fiona a lot more plausible?

Except for two small details. The woman hadn't been Fiona and the kiss had gotten way out of hand.

He was going around in circles, he thought furiously. Like a dog chasing its tail. Striving to sound casual, he said, "Am I taking you shopping tomorrow, Fiona?"

"In Coverdale, if you don't mind."

"No problem. I'll pick you up around ten?"

"That'd be lovely." With the shyness that normally Rafe found endearing, she reached up and brushed her lips to his cheek. "I'll see you tomorrow."

His pulses didn't even stir. Nothing. Absolutely nothing. Rafe patted her on the shoulder and let himself out. The dogs surged out of the shed, and he set off across the gardens behind the house. After closing the gate behind him, he took the path that meandered from Willowbend's more civilized surroundings to the open fells. The moon had risen over the trees, Venus a small steady light just below it.

Venus, goddess of love.

He loved Fiona, Rafe thought soberly. She was a dear friend he'd known all his life. But he wouldn't even have entertained the idea of marrying her if it hadn't in many ways suited him. He was thirty-three years old, ready to settle down and raise a family, and who better to do that with than Fiona? She'd never betray him as Celine had done all those years ago.

He'd bet every one of his hotels on that.

If he married Fiona, he'd also be rescuing Douglas from a series of disastrous investments. His eyes narrowed. A little financial leverage wasn't a bad thing to have should Douglas become his father-in-law. Rafe was several times smarter than Douglas and could be ten times as ruthless, and he'd have no hesitation in using any weapon at his command to free Fiona from her parents' smothering hold: a hold Fiona was too sweet and trusting to see, let alone counter.

He hadn't yet mentioned the word marriage to Fiona. He'd needed time to think about it first.

The path left the trees for the open fields. To the west Rafe could see the turrets and spires of Holden Castle, where he'd grown up. Eight years ago he'd had it extensively renovated as a five-star hotel and installed his parents as managers, to their enormous gratification. If Joan and Reginald Holden added a certain eccentricity to the castle, so be it. The customers didn't seem to mind.

He'd take the dogs back to his mother, then head home to Stoneriggs.

The moon had disappeared behind a cloud. But Rafe knew every footstep of the way, and walked confidently westward, Charlotte demurely trotting at his heels as though she'd never heard of misbehavior.

Why hadn't the woman, whoever she was, told him she wasn't Fiona? Why had she been hiding in the grounds of Willowbend in the first place? And why had she kissed him until he hadn't been able to think with anything except his hormones?

He swore under his breath. Rafe was no stranger to women throwing themselves at him; he was, after all, filthy rich and—so he'd been told—sexy to boot. But the woman couldn't possibly have known he'd be coming through the woods toward Willowbend. He hadn't even known it himself until after his flight delay.

He didn't like being made a fool of.

Didn't like the fact that passion could still take him unawares? Was that the crux of the matter?

He didn't want passion. Its betrayals were too cruel.

Tomorrow afternoon, after he'd taken Fiona home from the shopping expedition, he was going to get some answers to all his questions. In a village the size of Droverton, it shouldn't be difficult to find someone who so closely resembled Fiona. She had some explaining to do, that unknown woman. She owed him that much.

Maybe he would marry Fiona, he thought trenchantly, rounding a crag where a stream fell in a series of gurgling waterfalls. Assuming she'd have him. Marrying Fiona would ensure his personal life was entirely and happily predictable. Unlike the tempestuous ups and downs of his affair with Celine.

Unlike the tempestuous kiss in the woods?

There'd be no repeat of that, he thought grimly. He'd make it his business to forget the blond-haired witch who'd woven a spell around him under the shadow of the oak trees.

The sooner the better.

CHAPTER TWO

THAT night Karyn slept about as badly as it was possible for anyone to sleep. She did sleep. She knew that, because all too clearly she could remember fragments of dreams whose eroticism horrified her in the cool light of morning. But she also spent far too long wide-awake, her body on fire with needs she was determined to deny. Tossing and turning, she'd found every lump in the mattress and had heard every creak as the old building was buffeted by the night winds.

At some point in the middle of the night, as she stared wide-eyed at the low ceiling, Karyn had finally admitted to herself that being kissed, in all good faith, by the man who was Fiona's lover had further complicated her own compulsive need to meet her sister. Wasn't it all too likely that in meeting Fiona she'd meet him as well? How would she ever face him? Shake his hand and say *How do you do, so nice to see you again?* She groaned aloud, wishing with all her heart that she'd been rational and sensible and four weeks ago had written a letter to Fiona about her proposed visit.

She hadn't. So what was she going to do instead? Phone the Talbots this morning and ask for a meeting? Or write a letter and have it hand-delivered to Willowbend? She had to do one or the other. She couldn't just hang around the village on the off-chance that she'd bump into Fiona on the street; that wouldn't be fair to either of them. And she'd come too far at too great an expense to simply turn tail and flee.

What was she, a coward? No way. She was going to meet her sister, no matter what it took.

A bath in rather tepid water, choosing her most becoming summer dress and applying makeup all helped to restore Karyn's spirits. Okay, so last night had been a disastrous beginning to her quest. This was a new day, and she was going to begin afresh.

She snacked on an apple and some granola bars she'd stashed in her luggage, not wanting to face the landlord or any of the villagers now that she knew about the resemblance between herself and Fiona. In the little desk by the window she found a pad of yellowing notepaper and some envelopes. She sat down, took out her pen and, her tongue caught between her teeth, began to write.

It took several false starts before Karyn was satisfied with her letter. She folded it carefully and stuck it in one of the envelopes. Just as she got up from the desk, stretching the tension from her shoulders, someone rapped on the door.

She gave a nervous start, staring at the door in horror. The black-haired man from the woods was standing on the other side. She knew it. Who else could it be?

The landlord. Of course. Come on, Karyn, smarten up.

She marched over to the door and pulled it open. The man glaring at her in the hallway was almost a caricature: scarcely an inch taller than herself, round as a barrel, clad in a tweed suit with a tweed hat clasped in his pudgy hands. But, she realized rapidly, there was nothing remotely funny about the look in his eyes. Her smile dying on her lips, she said, "Yes? Can I help you?"

"My name is Douglas Talbot. You are, I presume, Miss Karyn Marshall?"

"Yes." He looked ready to give her a hard right to the

chin, and somehow this freed Karyn's tongue. "Although I'm not sure how you know my name."

"I wish to speak to you in private. May I come in?"

Her heart hammering in her rib cage, Karyn said calmly, "Of course, Mr. Talbot," and gestured him toward the chair by the desk. Quickly she picked up the letter and tossed it on the bed before closing the door. Then, there being no other option, she sat down on the bed and folded her cold hands in her lap.

The chair creaked ominously as Douglas Talbot sat down. He put his hat on the desk. "You can start by telling me exactly what you're doing here."

Karyn said pleasantly, "I'd be pleased to. But first I'd like to know how you got my name."

"The landlord phoned me last night to tell me you'd booked into the inn, and that you looked exactly like my daughter, Fiona. I want to know what game you're up to."

Karyn clamped firmly on her temper; losing it wouldn't advance her cause. "I'm sure you know why I'm here," she said. "I'm Fiona's twin sister. I—"

"Balderdash."

With a faint flicker of humor, Karyn realized she'd never actually heard anyone use that word before. She said flatly, "You asked why I was here. I'm trying to tell you. But if you won't listen, we're wasting each other's time."

Calculation flicked across Douglas's red face; clearly he hadn't expected any argument from her. "Then why don't you tell me your story? I'm sure you've had lots of time to concoct it."

"I'll tell you the truth," Karyn said.

As Douglas gave a rude snort, she tried to organize her thoughts. Douglas Talbot deserved the facts, yes; but none of the emotions that went along with them. She said coolly, "My mother died last winter. When I was going through her papers a month ago, I found a letter telling me I'd been adopted in England as a baby, twenty-six years ago. My twin sister had been adopted at the same time by a couple called Douglas and Clarissa Talbot, from Droverton in Cumbria.'' She paused, fighting the tightness in her throat. ''I hadn't known I was an adopted child. To cut a long story short, I decided to come to Droverton to meet Fiona. A long-overdue meeting, as I'm sure you'd agree.''

She seemed to have run out of words. She'd give her soul for a cup of hot, black coffee.

His voice laced with sarcasm, Douglas said, ''A charming story—and not a word of truth in it. Fiona was not adopted. So that's the end of it.''

''You can look at me, and deny every word I've told you? Fiona and I—we're identical twins. Of course she was adopted!''

Douglas leaned forward. ''Let me tell you something that I'm sure you already know. I have a considerable position in the business world and in society. A very considerable position.'' He gave the shabby little room a disparaging look. ''It would be greatly to your advantage to ally yourself with our family.''

''I couldn't care less—''

''But that's not all. My daughter is intimately associated with one of the richest men in England, an association that's moving toward marriage. You're telling me it's coincidence that at a time when an announcement is imminent Fiona's identical twin appears out of the blue? Come, come, Miss Marshall, you strain my credulity. And my patience.''

The black-haired stranger in the woods… ''Rich?'' Karyn faltered.

''Rafe Holden of Holden Enterprises. I'm sure even in the wilds of Canada you've heard of him.''

Karyn had certainly heard of the Holden chain of hotels, although she'd never stayed in one of them. Their cheapest rooms would have blown her budget for months. She said roundly, "I had no idea when I flew over here that Fiona was about to get engaged, let alone to whom. Nor would it have made any difference if I had."

"The kind of money Rafe Holden commands? I have no doubt it inspired your story from beginning to end." Douglas levered himself up from his chair. "You'll leave Droverton today, and you'll stay away from my daughter forever. Should you disobey me, there will be severe legal consequences—I will not tolerate any disturbance to my family's peace of mind, especially by a little upstart like you. Do I make myself clear?"

Karyn got to her feet, pink flags of fury in her cheeks. "I'm Fiona's twin sister. She was adopted by you and your wife twenty-six years ago. Don't you dare try to bully me."

His eyes looked as though they might pop out of his head. "Get out of Droverton today, Miss Marshall—you'll regret it if you don't."

He marched to the door, swung it open and slammed it shut behind him. Through the panels she could hear his footsteps clumping down the stairs. She went to the window that faced the street. A few minutes later, Douglas Talbot stalked over to a shiny silver Jaguar and barreled down the road in the direction of Willowbend.

So much for any fantasies she'd cherished of being warmly welcomed into the bosom of the family. How could Fiona stand having such a horrible father?

She stayed at the window, gazing down at the street. There was a cold lump in the vicinity of her heart. All along, she'd blithely assumed that Fiona knew she'd been adopted; that Fiona's parents hadn't chosen the same course as the Marshalls of keeping their child in ignorance. But

Fiona didn't know. As far as Fiona was concerned, Douglas and Clarissa were her only parents and there were no shadows around her birth.

Was she, Karyn, to be the one to tell Fiona the truth? She could remember as clearly as if it were yesterday how the discovery of her own adoption had shocked her to the core, causing her to look at her parents with new eyes. How could she expose Fiona to the same doubts and confusion?

She couldn't. Which meant she was barred from meeting Fiona now or ever.

Stay away from my daughter forever...

Lanced by pain, Karyn moved away from the window. Now that it had become totally impossible to approach her sister, she realized how much she'd been counting on meeting her, finding out what it was like to have an identical twin.

Both her own parents were dead, and she was an only child; she was alone in the world. What a cliché, Karyn thought with an unhappy twist to her lips. But how lonely those words made her feel; and how understandable that she'd come all the way from Prince Edward Island to Cumbria to find her sister.

She looked around the little room with sudden loathing. She couldn't stay here one more minute. If Willowbend was out of bounds, then she'd go somewhere else. Because, of course, it wasn't just Fiona who was on her mind.

Rafe, she thought. Rafe Holden. It was a name that suited him, that dark-eyed man who'd kissed her under the trees thinking she was Fiona; and to whom she'd responded mindlessly and with the total abandon of desire. Even now, she could remember the strength of his arms around her, the sensitivity with which he'd stroked her breast, the way he'd invited her to his bed.

Douglas Talbot had confirmed that Rafe and Fiona were lovers. Lovers who were soon to be married.

Shivering, Karyn paced up and down, the floorboards groaning underfoot. When she'd looked up Droverton and its environs on the Internet, she'd read about Holden Castle, an exclusive retreat west of the village. The man who'd kissed her owned it, along with dozens of other internationally-known luxury resorts.

He'd spoken to her so gently, thinking she was Fiona. He'd tried to soothe her fears, and he'd wanted her to enjoy his bed and his body. Tears filled Karyn's eyes. Steve had never cherished her in that way.

She clamped down viciously on thoughts of Steve; the only way she knew how to deal with those memories was to repress them. However, when she transferred her attention to her present predicament, Karyn felt just as unhappy. She had to leave Droverton for Fiona's sake, certainly. Rafe Holden was the other reason, equally pressing, that she must get away from here. She couldn't risk meeting him again. It would be too humiliating, too upsetting.

Her quest was over before it had begun.

Impulsively Karyn grabbed the little folder supplied by the inn and flipped through it. Picking up the antiquated phone, she dialed the number of the nearest car rental agency. To heck with her budget. She'd go nuts if she sat in this room all day.

Late that afternoon, Karyn was driving back along the narrow roads toward Droverton. She'd tramped the fells, rented a rowboat on one of the lakes, lunched in a pub and seen innumerable shaggy sheep. On the outskirts of Coverdale, she'd had a calorie-laden tea sitting on a balcony overlooking tree-clad hills and velvet-green fields neatly edged with stone. She felt, marginally, better.

She'd also made a decision. She was going to leave Droverton today. She had no other choice. She couldn't risk hurting Fiona in any way.

As she coasted down a hill on the approach to the village, she caught a glimpse of a rose-brick mansion tucked among the trees. Impetuously she pulled over onto the verge and got out of her car. Crossing the road, she leaned on the stone wall and gazed down at Willowbend.

It might as well have been on the other side of the world.

Another car was approaching. Studiously she kept her gaze trained on the view, doing her best to look like one more tourist admiring the scenery. But the other vehicle pulled up behind hers; as the engine was turned off, the distant bleating of sheep sounded very loud in the silence. Furious with the intruder, Karyn turned to see who was disturbing her privacy.

Rafe Holden was crossing the grassy verge toward her, his hands jammed in his pockets. It was the first time she'd seen him in daylight. Rapidly she skimmed his face with its broad cheekbones, strongly modeled jawline and hard-set mouth. His black hair was thick, glossy as a raven's wing; his dark eyes stormy.

He was taller than she remembered. Taller than Steve, she realized with an inward judder of her nerves; and more powerfully built. His whipcord trousers were snug to his hips, while his open-neck shirt revealed a physique wholly and disturbingly masculine. Would she ever forget that devastating kiss under the oak tree?

For a moment her gaze flicked to his hunter-green sports car. She didn't know much about cars, but she'd be willing to bet this particular one represented five years of her salary.

Somehow this gave her the courage to go on the offensive. She said coldly, ''Why don't you get back in your car

and drive straight to Willowbend? It's where you belong—
and you're the last person in the world I want to see right
now.''

''In that case, why did you station yourself on a public
road overlooking Fiona's house?''

''I don't owe you any explanations!''

''That's where you're wrong,'' Rafe said with dangerous
softness. ''I want to know who you are and what you're
doing here—and I'm not leaving until you tell me.''

One of Steve's legacies to Karyn was a fear of large
angry men. For Rafe Holden was angry, she was in no
doubt about that. But they were standing in the open, and
what could he do to her, short of bundling her into his car
or tossing her over the wall? She retorted, ''I don't respond
well to threats.''

''I don't like women who trespass on other people's
property and run away without explaining. Why don't we
start with your name?''

While he didn't look remotely like an ally, neither did
he look at all like Douglas Talbot. Wasn't Rafe Holden her
last chance to reach Fiona? Maybe Douglas had been lying
and Fiona did know she was adopted; as Fiona's lover, Rafe
was in a position to know the truth.

What did she have to lose? Nothing.

''My name is Karyn Marshall,'' she said. ''I'm from
eastern Canada, a place called Heddingley in Prince
Edward Island.''

''That explains the accent…you're a long way from
home. What brought you here? And take your time, I'm in
no rush.''

Trying to ignore the sarcasm in his voice, Karyn looked
out over the peaceful valley. ''This all began when my
mother died six months ago. Unexpectedly. It was a huge
shock to me.''

Rafe stood still, watching every change of expression on her face. Her profile was Fiona's. But her hair clung like a gold helmet to her head, emphasizing the elegance of her cheekbones and the slender line of her throat. Her eyes were bluer than Fiona's. Or was it just that they were more direct?

She was slimmer than Fiona, he saw, as the breeze molded her flowered dress to her body; fiercely he quelled a flame of desire, and, almost hidden beneath it, a flicker of fear. He'd assumed, in the middle of the night, that daylight would bring with it a return to sanity, burying passion where it belonged. "What happened to your mother?" he asked brusquely.

"An aneurysm. She died instantly." Unconsciously Karyn was smoothing the rock beneath her fingers. "It took several months before I could bring myself to sort through her belongings. My father died ten years ago, and I have no brothers or sisters. So there was only me."

Her fingers were slender and ringless; delicate shadows lay in the hollows under her collarbone, while her face was thin, as though she had indeed been through some hard experiences. Hating himself for feasting on her like a starving man, Rafe forced himself to listen. "Four weeks ago," she was saying, "I found some papers in her jewelry box. Among them was a letter to be opened by me only in the event of her death." She bent her head, picking at a clump of moss with her nails, fighting the tightness in her chest. Then she looked full at him, all the blue of the sky shimmering in her eyes. "I have that letter with me now. I'd hoped to show it to the Talbots."

"What does the letter say?" Rafe asked noncommittally.

"My parents were both English. They met in Sheffield and married there—they loved each other very much, that much I've always known, and they wanted children. But after my mother had three miscarriages, they decided to adopt. I was only two weeks old when they were notified about me. My birth mother, so the letter said, was a single woman who'd refused to divulge my father's name and who later moved to Australia. She died in an accident in Sydney when I was just a year old.''

Again Karyn bent her head, wishing she didn't find this recital so painful. ''You can imagine how I felt,'' she said in a low voice. ''But there was more. The letter went on to say that I had a twin sister. Although my father had done his best to adopt both of us, another couple had put in a prior claim on my twin. Through a bureaucratic foul-up, my father was sent the adoption certificate for Fiona by mistake. Douglas and Clarissa Talbot, from Droverton in Cumbria—my mother had written down every detail she knew.'' She glanced up, noticing for the first time that Rafe's eyes weren't black, as she'd thought last night, but the darkest of blues. Like a lake at dusk, she thought, full of secrets. ''That's why I'm here, Mr. Holden. I came to meet my twin sister, Fiona.''

''So until a month ago, you knew none of this?''

There was an edge to his voice. Karyn flushed. ''That's right. The letter ended by describing my parents' mutual decision to keep the truth from me about the adoption.'' *We only wanted to spare you pain, darling, and we couldn't have loved you more had you been born to us,* her mother had written. *In all the ways that count, you are indeed our dearly beloved daughter.*

The words were inscribed on Karyn's memory; she'd remember them, she was sure, for the rest of her life. But they were too intimate to share with Rafe Holden. Clearing her throat, she went on, ''At first I was paralyzed by shock. I felt ungrounded, as though the world had rocked on its foundations and everything I'd taken for granted had been

a lie. Then I got really angry that they'd never told me."
She bit her lip. "I don't know why I'm telling you this. I
haven't told anyone. I couldn't at the time, it was too painful."

The fragility of her wrists, the strain in her voice: Rafe
was almost overwhelmed by the urge to take her in his arms
and comfort her. Or was he fooling himself? Maybe all he
really wanted to do was kiss her senseless.

Passion. He'd sworn off it years ago. So what was it
about Karyn Marshall that drew him like an eagle to its
mate?

Whatever it was, he resented it deeply.

He said with brutal honesty, "I grew up in Droverton,
and I've known Fiona all my life. If she'd been adopted,
I'd have known."

"You'd only have been a child at the time."

"Seven years old. Old enough to know about village
gossip. In all the years I've lived here there's never been a
whisper of anything you've so touchingly described."

"So you think I've made it all up," Karyn said, feeling
cold creep into her bones.

"What else can I think?"

"And why would I bother spending money I can ill afford to cross the Atlantic on a fool's errand?"

"How would I know? Although if you're that strapped
for cash, Willowbend would look pretty good."

She wouldn't lose her temper. She wouldn't. Karyn said
tightly, "So, according to you, even the resemblance is
coincidence."

"What else can it be? Douglas might be a thoroughly
unpleasant man at times, but one thing I know—he wor-
ships the ground Clarissa walks on and he'd never have
been unfaithful to her. Nor she to him. So, yes, it's coincidence."

"You're so logical, so cold-blooded," she cried. "Don't you have any room for emotion? I don't give a damn about money! All I want is to meet Fiona. My sister."

"When I kissed you last night," Rafe grated, "I wouldn't have called either one of us cold-blooded. Why didn't you tell me then who you were? You had the chance. Instead you played me like a fish on the hook, trying to insinuate yourself into Willowbend in any way you could. I hate being made a fool of. Particularly by a woman."

"I didn't do it on purpose! It just...happened."

Something in her pinched face infuriated him. "You expect me to believe that?" he rasped. "Let me tell you something else. Fiona and I have been friends for years. I'm a very rich man, Karyn Marshall, and you've just admitted your circumstances are straitened. So quit trying to convince me of the purity of your motives."

"You're despicable," Karyn seethed. "No better than Douglas, with whom I had a delightful interview this morning. Stay away or I'll put the legal sharks on you—that was the gist of his little speech."

Rafe's eyes narrowed. "Douglas came to see you? I didn't know that."

"Oh, yeah?" she said rudely.

How dare she compare him with Douglas? "I'm telling you the truth," Rafe said in a staccato voice.

"What do I care? For the last ten minutes you could have saved your breath—I've already decided to leave Droverton and stay away from Fiona, because she doesn't know she's adopted and it's not my job to tell her. To hurt her. But of course you're not going to believe me—I'm just a lying bitch who's after your bucks. You can keep them, Rafe Holden! I don't want them."

She looked so furious, so utterly convincing. But Fiona hadn't been adopted; he'd have known if she was. So Karyn

Marshall's whole story was fabrication from beginning to end. "You belong on the stage," Rafe said coldly, "you could make a fortune. Much as I hate to ally myself with Douglas, I'm going to repeat him. Leave here today and don't come back. Or you'll be sorry."

"I can't get out of here soon enough."

Karyn pushed herself away from the wall. But some rocks that had fallen from the wall were hidden under the grass; her sandal skidded on one of them. As she lurched sideways, Rafe automatically reached out to save her, one arm around her waist, the other steadying her shoulder.

For a moment that was frozen in time, Karyn sagged against him. The hard wall of his chest, the latent strength of his fingers, their burning heat through her dress: she was pierced by a knife of desire so sharp that she almost cried out. As though she couldn't help herself, she looked up, plunging into the dark depths of his eyes where she saw desire reflected, meeting her own, magnifying it. Briefly his arms tightened, so briefly that she wondered afterward if she'd imagined it. Then he thrust her away so hard that she staggered.

Trembling in every limb, Karyn fought for balance, all her distress and confusion rushing to the surface. "Last night you could be forgiven, because you thought I was Fiona. But today you know I'm not. You wanted to kiss me a moment ago, didn't you? I know you did! How dare you kiss Fiona one day and me the next? As though we're interchangeable."

Rafe stood still, her accusation throbbing in his brain. Karyn's body, so suddenly and unexpectedly in his arms, had struck him to the core. How could he deny it? How could he have prevented it? It had been elemental, instinctive, utterly beyond his control.

If he was going to marry Fiona, it was also totally against his principles.

He took refuge in anger. "Was that another of your clever little ploys—let's see if I can get him to kiss me again? What's next on the list?"

She paled, looking suddenly older than her years. "I'm not going to stand here and be insulted by you any longer. I'm only sorry for Fiona—her father's a bully, and you wouldn't recognize the truth if it was right under your nose. I never want to see either one of you again."

In a swirl of skirts she stumbled through the long grass, crushing wildflowers underfoot. After glancing both ways, she ran across the road, opened the door of her car and got in. Although her fingers were shaking, she finally got the key in the ignition. Dirt grinding from her tires, she drove away; and the whole time was aware of Rafe Holden standing like a statue by the wall. Making no move to stop her.

Rafe watched her go, his blood pounding in his ears. Years ago, Celine had been unfaithful to him, destroying his passion, his trust and his love as carelessly as if he'd meant nothing to her. Less than nothing. Today Karyn Marshall had accused him of infidelity toward Fiona. And wasn't it true? He was pulled toward Karyn as inexorably as the moon pulled the tides.

He had to find out if she'd been lying to him from the first moment he'd laid eyes on her, or if she'd been telling him the truth. He had to.

He'd go out of his mind if he didn't.

CHAPTER THREE

WHEN Karyn reached the inn, she parked her car, tied a headscarf over her hair and jammed on dark glasses. Then she hurried inside. The landlord was standing behind the counter in a wrinkled green shirt. He said, not bothering to hide his sneer, "Ah, Miss Marshall. I'm glad you're back. I will, unfortunately, be needing your room tonight for other guests. Would you settle up now?"

"That would give me great pleasure," she said, snapping her credit card on the counter. When he handed her the slip, it also gave her pleasure to put a long slash through the space for the tip. Then she looked up. "You can phone Mr. Talbot now and tell him I've left," she said sweetly. "Goodbye."

Ten minutes later she was driving out of the quadrangle behind the inn. She had no idea where she was going. Nor, at the moment, did she care.

For the last time she wound along the narrow road through Droverton, past the little shops and the stone cottages with their beautiful gardens. A few minutes later she passed the driveway to Willowbend.

Her throat tight, her eyes aching with unshed tears, Karyn drove on. It was early evening, the golden light a mockery to all her hopes, her sister receding with every turn in the road. Although, deep in her heart, she knew she was doing the right thing, that she couldn't have lived with herself had she done otherwise, she only wished it didn't hurt so abominably.

37

Then she saw, to her right, a layby tucked under the trees. Quickly she pulled over and got out. Her eyes sharpened. A little path led down the slope. After changing from sandals to walking shoes, Karyn locked the car and set off down the path.

If she walked for an hour or so, she'd feel better.

She took off her dark glasses and thrust her headscarf in the pocket of her dress. No more need for disguises. No need to hide. Just the distant chuckle of a woodland stream and her own thoughts.

Ten minutes later, the woods opened out in one of the vistas characteristic of this northern countryside: gentle hills blending into granite crags that faded blue into the distance. Always, somewhere, there was the glitter of water.

The landscape called to her, beckoning, almost as though she belonged here.

Not a train of thought she wanted to follow.

Karyn started climbing, feeling the pull on her leg muscles. When she came to the crest of the hill with its screen of gold-starred gorse and piled boulders, she stood still, her eyes widening in shock. Below her, edged by a tumble of rocks and the lazy curve of a river, were the battlements of a castle. Even from here she could see the formal gardens that surrounded the castle, the bright turquoise of a large rectangular pool, and lawns so green they made her eyes ache.

Holden Castle, she thought. Ancestral home of Rafe Holden.

As though she couldn't help herself, her gaze was dragged farther westward. Nestled in open fields edged with trees was a huge two-story stone house with south-facing wings, a glassed solarium and, again, the gleam of an outdoor pool. Its slate roofs were dark as shadows, its outbuildings surrounded by white-painted fencing. For all its civilized accoutrements, the house faced the fells and tarns, the rocky crags of the moor, and was perfectly suited to the wildness of its surroundings.

She squinted into the dying sun. Wasn't that a dark green sports car parked in the courtyard?

Rafe's car. The house must be his, too. A house so beautiful it made Karyn's heart ache. A house Fiona must know inside and out; she'd be mistress of it when she and Rafe married.

Into Karyn's mind came an image of the little clapboard house her mother had left her, where Karyn had grown up. The comparison was laughable.

Except she didn't feel like laughing.

Abruptly Karyn tensed. From her left, approaching fast, she heard the clump of hooves on the grass. Instinctively she ducked behind the line of boulders and gorse. The hooves slowed. A woman's voice said softly, "Well done, Sasha. What a glorious sunset."

With painstaking care Karyn peered between the stiff green branches. Horse and rider were perhaps thirty feet below her; the Arabian mare was tossing her head so the bridle jingled as the woman looked out over the peaceful valley. She was slim, clad in well-fitting jodhpurs, a white shirt and a black hard hat. A thick coil of blond hair was pinned at her nape.

When she turned her head to the east, toward Willowbend, Karyn saw, as though in a mirror, her own profile with its straight nose and high cheekbones.

Hadn't she known, from the moment she first heard the sound of hooves, that the rider would be Fiona?

Her heart was thumping so hard in her breast that she was afraid Fiona would hear it. She sank lower behind the bushes, knees trembling from the strain. So near and yet so far. So unutterably far.

Fiona said cheerfully, "We'd better get going, Sash. Mother's invited that dreadful old snob, Emily Fairweather, in for drinks and I'm expected to put in an appearance. Let's go down the hill and have a good gallop through Fenton's field—we'll jump the wall, how about it?"

Sasha blew through her nostrils, and as Karyn risked another glance, Fiona squeezed her knees and the horse trotted down the hillside. Within a couple of minutes horse and rider were out of sight. To her dismay Karyn realized she was weeping, a flood of silent tears streaming down her cheeks. She'd seen her sister, her twin. That one glimpse had to be enough for the rest of her life.

She cried for a long time, until she had no tears left. Then, blowing her nose and wiping her wet cheeks, she stood up. As though she couldn't help herself, her eyes were drawn once more to the stone house on Rafe's estate. In its mixture of the sophisticated and the untamed, wasn't it just like the man himself?

A man she'd never see again.

She started tramping back the way she'd come. Fiona, she could only assume, had been visiting Rafe...and why not?

They'd probably been in bed together.

She'd been very quick to accuse Rafe of infidelity toward Fiona. But hadn't she, Karyn, betrayed her sister as well, first in that incendiary kiss by the gardens of Willowbend, and then again this afternoon in that wild leap of her blood when she'd stumbled into Rafe's arms by the wall? How could she have responded with such passionate intensity to a man who was her sister's lover?

It was unforgivable. The only way for her to make amends was to vanish from both their lives.

Her steps quickened. At least she'd seen Fiona, Karyn thought stoutly. Once only, and all too briefly, but she'd been granted that much. In time, she was sure, she would be grateful for that small crumb of comfort.

The trees welcomed her into their embrace, and her vehicle was exactly where she'd left it. She climbed in, checked for other cars and pulled out onto the road.

By eight o'clock the next morning, Rafe was on the phone to one of his assistants in the London head office. "Vic? I want you to do something for me. Fast. Ready?"

Vic was from Manhattan and knew all about *fast*. "Right on," he said agreeably, focusing so he wouldn't miss the smallest detail. He liked working for Rafe Holden. Sure, the man was both demanding and exacting. But he was also fair, he didn't stand on ceremony and he paid extraordinarily well.

"This is confidential," Rafe added in a clipped voice.

"Understood."

"I want a thorough investigation on the following person, and I want results by the end of the day. Pay for the top people. Got that?"

"Yep. Go ahead."

"Karyn Marshall." Quickly Rafe gave the particulars of her rented car. "Find out where she's spending the night tonight and have her followed. I also want you to investigate a possible adoption twenty-six years ago of identical twins…" Speaking with crisp precision, Rafe gave every detail he'd learned from Karyn, along with the relevant information about the Talbots. He finished with the name of Karyn's hometown in Prince Edward Island. "Check how she earns her living, her marital status, anything at all."

Vic said imperturbably, "I'll set it in motion right away, and e-mail you as soon as anything turns up."

"Thanks, Vic."

Rafe put the phone down. He'd done it. Rightly or wrongly, he was going to find out whether Karyn had been telling him the truth, a partial truth, or a pack of lies. Maybe then he could put her out of his mind and get on with his life.

Running upstairs, he showered and shaved; he didn't look that great, he thought dispassionately, staring at himself in the mirror. Two sleepless nights in a row were taking their toll.

Had a chance meeting with a blond, blue-eyed woman made any thoughts of proposing to Fiona an utter impossibility?

Out of control, he thought savagely. That's how he felt. As though the course he'd been mapping for his life had been totally derailed. Was he wrong to want a peaceful domestic life? To opt for a well-marked track rather than the crags and peaks of passion?

Passion, betrayed, had ripped him apart.

Marriage to Fiona would never do that.

It was Douglas who'd put the idea of marriage in his head, five days ago in the oak-paneled study at Stoneriggs. Douglas wanted Rafe to rescue him from some ill-considered investments, that information had come out right away. But he also wanted Rafe to marry Fiona. How had he put it?

"You owe me, old man. Nothing Clarissa and I would like better than to welcome you into the family."

"Owe you?" Rafe repeated sharply.

"Remember when you turned twenty? Your mother gave you enough money that you could buy your first three properties. Get your start. She told you the money was left to her, an old great-uncle who'd died in the highlands of Scotland." Douglas gave a hearty laugh. "Balderdash! I loaned her the money. I had you taped as someone who'd rise to the top, and I was right. So now I'm calling in the loan, Rafe. I want you to marry Fiona.''

''I can't believe the money came from you!''

''Just ask your mother,'' Douglas said smugly.

''You can be sure I will.''

''So what's your answer, Rafe?''

''You're not getting one right now,'' Rafe said, steel in his voice. ''I'll need a month to think about it. In the meantime, you're not to say a word to anyone—least of all Fiona—or I won't touch your debts. Is that clear?''

With bad grace Douglas agreed, and took his leave. Rafe then drove as fast as he could to the castle. ''Darling, your father and I would have done anything to get you away from here,'' Joan Holden said. ''Don't you remember what it was like the whole time you were growing up? Death duties to the eyeballs and the walls falling down around us.''

Rafe remembered all too well. In a twisted way he did owe Douglas a debt of gratitude: those first three properties had started him on the road to fortune. But Douglas hadn't loaned the money all those years ago out of the goodness of his heart. Oh, no. Douglas desperately wanted an alliance with Holden blue blood, and had gambled on Rafe as the means to achieve this.

Rafe loathed the prospect of being manipulated like a chess piece by a player as crass as Douglas. But the more he thought about it, the more he realized how ready he was to settle down, and how deeply he wanted to avoid the intensity of emotion Celine had evoked in him. He'd known Fiona all his life, and would have trusted her with his life. Besides, Fiona would be all too happy to settle at Stoneriggs, for, like himself, she loved the hills and dales of his estate.

He'd been rather pleased with these conclusions. But

then he'd met Karyn, and had discovered that the passion he'd thought he'd outgrown was very much alive.

One kiss was all it had taken.

The phone rang at five past eleven that night in Rafe's study. He barked his name into the receiver.

Picking up on his boss's tone immediately, Vic said, "I've sent you an e-mail filling in the details. The rundown's like this. Karyn Marshall left Droverton late yesterday and booked into the Warm Hearts Bed and Breakfast in Hart's Run for two nights. She and Fiona Talbot are identical twins, adopted at age two weeks by the Marshalls and the Talbots respectively. Karyn's employed as a veterinarian at the Heddingley Clinic near Charlottetown, Prince Edward Island. Her husband, Steven Patterson, died a year ago. No children from the marriage." Vic paused. "You hadn't authorized investigation of peripheral people, so we didn't follow up on the husband."

Husband…his head reeling, Rafe said, "That's fine. I'll check the e-mail and get back to you if I have any questions. Good job, Vic, thanks."

The e-mail described Karyn's childhood, schooling, university degrees, marriage and career. Facts, facts and more facts. One of particular interest was that twenty-seven years ago Douglas had taken his wife to Italy for a year; when they returned to Droverton via London, they'd brought a baby with them. So that, thought Rafe, was how they'd avoided village gossip.

He got up from his chair and walked over to the windows that overlooked the crags he'd climbed as a boy. The main points in Vic's report he'd already known, because Karyn had told them to him. She hadn't lied. She'd told the truth from beginning to end.

Although not the whole truth. She hadn't said anything

about being widowed. As clearly as if she were standing in front of him, he could remember her slim, ringless fingers.

Either way, he'd accused her of social climbing, avarice and deceit. Well done, Rafe. You're going to have to work damn hard to jam your foot any further down your throat.

What are you planning for an encore?

Wasn't that the issue? What *was* he going to do for an encore? He had two choices. Delete the e-mail, pay the bill for the investigators and forget Karyn Marshall existed. Or get in touch with her and bring her and Fiona together.

He started pacing up and down the room, his emotions roiling. The easy course was to do nothing. Let the secrets of many years remain secrets. Karyn had already left Droverton and would—he knew in his heart—stay away. She wouldn't risk hurting Fiona as she had been hurt by her own parents' deception. She'd told him that, her blue eyes meeting his unflinchingly. And hadn't he just been given proof that every word she'd spoken had been trustworthy?

If he took the easy way out, he'd never have to see Karyn again. The fierce attraction she'd exerted on him simply by existing would fade from his memory and from his body, becoming part of the past, a temporary madness.

Eclipsed by his marriage to her sister?

Fiona. Even as a boy, Rafe had understood that the heart of Fiona's rich and comfortable life harbored an acute loneliness. She had no brothers and sisters, and her parents, while they loved her, were controlling and manipulative in ways sweet-natured Fiona was only rarely aware of. Was it fair to keep her in ignorance of her sister's existence?

Karyn, although she was Fiona's identical twin, had been differently molded. She wasn't rich: when she'd sold the house that had been in her dead husband's name, she'd used the money to pay off a substantial student loan. Which brought Rafe back to the fact he'd been trying to avoid. Karyn had loved a man enough to marry him, and had suffered from his death. When she'd been standing by the wall in the sunlight, Rafe had been achingly aware of the character in her face, her features honed by experiences he'd chosen to disparage. Now he had some idea of what those experiences had been.

Fiona might learn what she herself was capable of from the woman who was her identical twin. Who better as a teacher? And was it up to him to prevent this from happening?

He had that power of prevention. He was a man used to wielding power. He could, single-handedly, keep the two sisters apart for the rest of their days.

Abruptly Rafe grabbed a jacket from the cupboard and opened the French doors to the stone patio. Hands thrust in his pockets, he set off through the garden toward the woods. He always thought better outdoors.

Temporary madness. That's what he'd called it and that's all it was, that kiss in the woods at dusk, that streak of lust when Karyn had fallen into his arms by the wall. He'd get over it.

From his left, deep in the trees, an owl hooted, a wild, plaintive cry that shivered along his nerves. Be honest, Rafe, he told himself caustically. The attraction went deeper than that. She'd felt it, too. Unarguably. Blood to blood and bone to bone.

Flesh to flesh.

How could he marry Fiona when he felt this overwhelming attraction toward a woman he hadn't known existed two days ago?

One thing at a time. His primary decision right now was whether he should bring the two sisters together. Because Karyn, he suspected, wouldn't hang around the area very long.

What was he going to do?

At seven the following evening, Rafe was navigating the narrow streets of Hart's Run, forty miles from Droverton. Fiona was sitting beside him in his adored green Ferrari. She said lightly, "You're being very mysterious, Rafe."

"There's someone I want you to meet, that's all," he said just as casually. Although he didn't feel casual. He felt as though he was playing God. A highly uncomfortable role and not one he aspired to.

"But who?"

"You'll see." He swung into the parking lot of the Hart Inn, where, so one of the investigators had informed him earlier today, Karyn had made a dinner reservation. Turning to face Fiona, he said, "Just keep an open mind, that's all. Promise?"

"*Very* mysterious." She gave him her sweet smile. "You know I'd promise you anything."

When he led Fiona into the dining room, Rafe saw Karyn immediately. His heart gave a great thud in his chest. Schooling his features to immobility, he took Fiona by the hand and threaded through the tables. Karyn was reading the menu. Then, as though she felt the pull of his gaze, she looked up, dropped the menu on the cloth and gaped at him. "Rafe?" she croaked.

He said easily, "I've brought someone to meet you," and stood aside so Karyn could see Fiona.

Shaken to the core, Karyn felt the color drain from her cheeks. Enough of a shock to see Rafe. But to discover in the space of seconds that he was accompanied by Fiona...she gripped the edge of the table, her knuckles white with strain, and said raggedly, "Hello...won't you both sit down?"

Fiona sank into the nearest chair, her eyes glued to Karyn's face. "I'd heard gossip in the village about a woman who resembled me," she said dazedly. "We're the image of each other—it's amazing!" She turned to Rafe. "Why didn't you tell me?"

Karyn's brain stumbled into action. So Fiona didn't know who she was. Rafe hadn't told her.

To her infinite relief the waiter appeared on the scene. "Will the gentleman and the lady be joining you, madam?"

"Er—yes," Karyn faltered. "At least, I hope so."

"I wouldn't leave for worlds," Fiona said, smiling at the waiter as he put two more menus on the table. When he'd gone, she turned that smile on Karyn. "You must tell me who you are—I don't even know your name."

One step at a time. "Karyn Marshall. My home's in Prince Edward Island on the east coast of Canada."

"We can't possibly be related then," Fiona said. "Yet we could be sisters, we look so much alike."

In desperation Karyn sent Rafe a hunted look. He was sitting across from her, the light from the window delineating his strongly carved features. But not penetrating his eyes, she thought with an inward shiver. They were like rooms locked against her. He said flatly, "Fiona, I want you to listen to me. Remember what I said in the car, about keeping an open mind?"

Fiona's smile faded. "I don't understand..."

"There's no easy way to tell you. You and Karyn—you look alike because you *are* sisters. Twin sisters."

As Karyn's jaw dropped that he could admit to a truth he'd so bitterly denied, Fiona frowned in puzzlement. "How can we be?" she said. "That's impossible."

"You were adopted," Rafe said bluntly. "You and

Karyn have the same birth mother. Douglas and Clarissa didn't tell you they'd adopted you, and Karyn didn't find out she'd been adopted until recently, after her mother died. That's why she came here—to find you.''

There, he thought. He'd done it. He'd altered, irrevocably and in a few words, the lives of several people.

"Adopted? You're saying I'm *adopted?*''

"That's right," Rafe said steadily, taking her hand in his and raising it to his cheek in a gesture that seemed to Karyn, distraught though she was, more like comfort between friends than intimacy between lovers. She shoved the thought away, concentrating on what Rafe was saying. "I know this is a huge shock to you, Fiona. But I didn't feel I could keep the truth from you, or rob you of your sister's presence in your life.''

Tears flooded Karyn's eyes; she blinked them back as Rafe went on, "All these years your parents have kept you from knowing the truth. And I have to be honest—when I first talked to Karyn, I didn't believe her story any more than your father did.''

Fiona looked straight at Karyn. "You've met my father?''

"He came to see me at the inn in Droverton, yes.''

Rafe said grimly, "He warned Karyn off. Told her to vanish and threatened her with severe repercussions if she didn't. Regrettably, I did the same thing.''

Fiona was sitting like a woman stunned. Karyn whispered, "Rafe, whatever made you change your mind?''

"I had you investigated, and found out that every word you'd said was true.''

As she winced, Fiona cried, "It can't be true! My parents wouldn't have deceived me—keeping me in the dark about my real roots. They couldn't be so cruel!''

Rafe grimaced. Still gripping her hand in his, he said

gently, "I'm afraid they did keep the truth from you. Maybe from the best of motives, who knows?"

She was glaring at him almost as though she hated him; then transferred that glare to Karyn. "I don't believe a word you've said to me, either one of you. If this is your idea of a joke, Rafe, I don't think it's remotely funny. I'm not—"

"Fiona, hiding your head in the sand—"

"I'm not sitting here listening to the two of you lie about my parents!" She shot Karyn a furious glance. "As far as I'm concerned you can go back to Canada on the first plane and stay there. I never want to see you again!"

She thrust her chair back, surged to her feet and hurried off between the tables. The conversation in their vicinity, which had dropped to a fascinated hush, hurriedly picked up.

"Hell and damnation," Rafe muttered. Then he, too, got to his feet. Without so much as a backward glance at Karyn, he followed Fiona out of the dining room.

Like magic, the waiter reappeared. "Is there a problem, madam?" he said politely.

Oh, no, Karyn thought hysterically, no problem. I've just been responsible for wrecking my sister's peace of mind and destroying all her illusions, that's all. "I'll be dining alone after all," she said. "Would you bring me a carafe of your house wine, please?"

"Certainly, madam."

He disappeared. Karyn stared out the window at the pretty garden that edged the river, while pain, dismay and, undeniably, gratitude battled for supremacy in her breast. Rafe had done his best to bring her and Fiona together; for that, she was truly thankful. However, despite his efforts, Fiona had repudiated her; and how that hurt.

The waiter poured her a glass of wine. She took the first sip, still gazing out at the peaceful scene on the other side

of the glass. There was another layer to her pain. Seeing
Rafe and Fiona together had also hurt. Hurt horribly, in a
way she couldn't possibly justify. Naturally, Rafe had gone
after Fiona rather than staying and comforting herself. His
allegiance was to Fiona: they were lovers. What right did
she, Karyn, have to be hurt?

Yet had she entirely misread their body language? Not
once had she gained any sense of sexual intimacy between
them, of the small, significant signals that bespeak the privacy of the bedroom and the sharing of a mutual passion.

Or was she fooling herself? Maybe she didn't want to
see those signals.

Because she was jealous? Karyn took another sip of
wine, briefly closing her eyes. It would have been far better
if she'd left Cumbria two days ago, after that one glimpse
of Fiona riding her Arabian mare on the grassy slopes near
Willowbend.

Better, too, never to have seen Rafe again.

CHAPTER FOUR

RIGHT after breakfast the next day, Karyn set off on foot down the main street of Hart's Run, a narrow, cobbled street lined with charming boutiques hung with baskets of fuchsias and geraniums. Yesterday she'd noticed a little wool shop there. When she was upset, knitting was very good therapy, although the results were unpredictable. She might be a dab hand at spaying cats, but she couldn't knit for beans.

Her eyes were scratchy from lack of sleep and her limbs felt heavy. She'd stayed in her room all evening, hoping against hope that either Rafe or Fiona might get in touch; but the phone had remained distressingly silent. Once she'd bought the wool, she was going back to her room, phoning the airline and heading south. She wanted to go home, to the known and the familiar.

If she was running away, too bad.

In the wool shop Karyn found a delightful shade of pink mohair and a pattern that appealed to her. She left the shop and walked back toward the inn. It was raining, a fine, misty rain that fell softly on her face, gathering in drops on her cheeks like tears. But she wasn't going to cry. Not for Rafe and not for Fiona. She was going home instead.

As she approached the bed and breakfast, a green sports car drew up alongside her. To her utter consternation Rafe got out, followed by Fiona. The bag of wool slipped from her fingers and plopped into a puddle.

Rafe bent down and fished it out of the puddle. "Good

thing someone invented plastic bags,'' he said with a crooked grin.

Quite rationally, Karen decided to lose her temper. In a gush of adrenaline she grabbed for the bag. ''Thank you,'' she snapped insincerely. ''Now why don't the two of you get lost? You'll be delighted to know I'm getting on the first available flight home and neither one of you will ever see me again. Rafe, give me the damned wool!''

He shook droplets of dirty water from the bag and passed it to her, his fingers lingering briefly on hers. ''Fiona has something to say to you.''

The touch of his lean fingers had surged through Karyn's body like a river in full spate. It did nothing to calm her. ''I'm not having a conversation with either one of you in the middle of the sidewalk. Or anywhere else. Too much was said last night and as far as I'm concerned, that's it.''

Fiona grabbed her by the wrist. ''Don't go! Please, Karyn, don't go…''

Karyn… To hear her own name in her sister's voice brought sudden tears to Karyn's eyes. She brushed them away. ''Fiona, I can't take any more of this, don't you see? If you don't believe a word I—''

''Rafe told me all about you on the way home yesterday. How you really were my sister and what he'd found out about you in the investigation.''

''He had no right to—''

''But I had to see my parents before I could take it all in. I had a terrible fight with them last night. I asked them if I was adopted and told them I'd met you. They denied everything, they yelled and screamed at me, it was awful. You were an imposter, they said, I wasn't ever to see you again. They went on and on until I thought I'd be sick.'' She shuddered. ''They were so upset, so adamant, that I knew they were lying. I just knew it. So I went over to

Rafe's first thing this morning and begged him to help me find you again.''

"Oh," said Karyn.

"I don't blame you for being angry," Fiona whispered.

"I'm not angry anymore," Karyn said truthfully, pushing down a wild hope that frightened her with its intensity.

"You see, I love animals, too. You're a vet and I volunteer at the local animal shelter—that's the only thing that's ever made me defy my parents. Can you sing?"

Karyn blinked. "Not a note."

"Can you paint or sculpt?"

"Nope. Hopeless." Karyn indicated the bag of wool. "Can't knit, either. Although I keep trying."

"Neither can I." Fiona gave her a watery smile. "We're very much alike—and I don't just mean looks. We really are twins!"

"You won't change your mind?" Karyn faltered.

"Oh, no. I know you're my sister." Impetuously Fiona flung her arms around Karyn. "Oh, Karyn," she sobbed, "I have a twin, I'm not alone anymore. I'm so happy, I can't tell you how happy I am—why am I crying?"

Tears were streaming down Karyn's face, too. She hugged Fiona as hard as she could, and within her the terrible loneliness that had been the legacy of her mother's death eased for the first time. "I'm happy, too," she mumbled. "I'm so glad we've found each other."

More moved than he cared to admit, Rafe looked away. Such emotion was private, even though he was the one who'd brought it about.

How could he possibly regret what he'd done? Yet his whole body was filled with foreboding. From now on, Karyn would—inevitably—become part of his life.

Fiona had been astonishingly brave to have withstood the combined rage of Douglas and Clarissa last night. She'd need his support on the home front more than ever now. As a friend, certainly; although if she could claim him as her fiancé, that would give her a lot more clout. He winced inwardly, because as he watched the two sisters locked in each other's arms, it was to Karyn that his gaze was drawn.

When Karyn and Fiona eventually disentangled themselves, scrubbing at their wet cheeks, he said curtly, "You know, it might be as well if you both had DNA tests. That way you can show your parents irrefutable proof, Fiona. It could help get them off your back."

"Good idea," Karyn said warmly.

Fiona gaped at her. "You mean you would?"

"Of course." Karyn spoke the simple truth. "I'd do anything for you, Fiona."

More tears spilled from Fiona's spectacular blue eyes. Which were, Karyn thought wryly, just like her own. She added, "We'll do it today, if you like."

"Why not?" Fiona said recklessly. She gave Karyn the full benefit of her smile. "I never knew I could be this brave. I actually yelled at my mother, can you believe it?"

"I'd love to have been a fly on the wall," Rafe said.

"For once, I didn't need you there—I managed fine on my own," Fiona said. "Although I'm sure I'll need your help when I go home today. Mother will have had time to replenish her arsenal, and as for Dad—" She gave a small shudder.

"I'll look after your father," Rafe announced.

Fiona looked back at Karyn. "If you can become a vet, I can do five days a week at the shelter."

Karyn laughed. "If you can stand up to your parents, I can ask for a raise when I get home."

"If you can ask for a raise, I can be late for dinner."

They laced their arms together, giggling like two little girls. Rafe said dryly, "I'm not sure the world's ready for you two. Let's go find some good strong coffee, how about it?''

Karyn stood tall, knowing there was something she had to say. Her blue eyes steady, she said quietly, ''Rafe, I can't thank you enough for what you've done. If it hadn't been for you, Fiona and I would never have found each other.''

A lump in his throat, Rafe said huskily, ''My pleasure.''

''It's true,'' Fiona quavered, and threw herself into his arms. ''Thank you, thank you. I owe you so much already, and now this as well…you're so good to me, Rafe.''

Karyn's nails dug into her palms as Rafe's arms went around Fiona's waist; although again she had that illusory sense that the embrace was compounded more of companionship and gratitude than anything as basic as sex. But what did it matter? Either way, Fiona was in Rafe's arms, where she belonged. Where Karyn never would. She looked away, her happiness stabbed by a shaft of pain so strong it appalled her. In a flash the implications of the last few minutes passed before her eyes. Rafe would be a part of her life from now on. Her sister's lover. Maybe even her sister's husband. Always there. Always out of reach.

So what, she thought fiercely. Rafe was nothing to her. Nothing. Nor was she going to allow him to ruin her new-found joy. Instead she should be happy for Fiona that she had such a strong protector in Rafe.

Steeling herself, she watched as Rafe's hold loosened and Fiona stepped back. She *was* happy for Fiona. Of course she was.

Half an hour later, sitting at a table that overlooked a small mist-wreathed lake, Karyn's resolve to be happy was severely tested. As they drank pungent Colombian coffee accompanied by sinfully rich pastries, Fiona said artlessly, ''Where do we go from here? Literally, I mean.''

"Not to the inn in Droverton," Karyn said. "I royally insulted the landlord before I left."

"I can't expose you to my parents right now," Fiona said. "Even if they'd agree to have you at Willowbend, which I doubt."

"Easy," Rafe drawled. "The two of you can stay at Stoneriggs."

"Wonderful!" Fiona exclaimed.

"No way," Karyn gasped.

"You can have adjoining rooms in the east wing. Lots of horses to ride, Karyn, if that interests you."

She loved to ride. "I scarcely know you, Rafe. I couldn't possibly come and stay with you." Expose herself to Rafe and Fiona's love affair at close hand? Every nerve in her body screamed revolt.

"I could stable Sasha at Stoneriggs," Fiona said eagerly. "Can you ride, Karyn?"

"Yes," Karyn said grudgingly. "But—"

"Then that's settled," Fiona said. "If we went right now, I could collect Sasha and we could ride after lunch. We can swim in the pool every day, too. Oh, Karyn, it'll be such fun!"

Karyn bit her lip. Short of stamping her feet and throwing a tantrum, she was trapped. "Just as long as you know I'll have to go home in a few days," she said.

"All the more reason to enjoy today," Fiona said, and drained her coffee.

Stoneriggs, close up, took Karyn's breath away. The house, its stonework dampened by mist, was so imposing, so exquisitely proportioned; the informal gardens such a riot of color and scent. The pool, the tennis courts, the moss-green lawns, all surrounded by the wildness of the fells: overwhelmed, she said softly, "It's incredibly beautiful, Rafe."

"The favorite of all my houses," he said casually. "I'm here whenever I can be."

Because of the house? Or because of Fiona? Quelling a shaft of pain, Karyn said, "I can see why."

He then took them on a tour of the stables, where Karyn was reduced to an entranced silence. She walked into stall after stall, rubbing flanks glossy with health, murmuring endearments to each and every thoroughbred: mare, stallion and gelding; bay, chestnut and palomino. Wistfully she said, "You've got the horses in Heddingley beat by a country mile."

"Fiona will help you pick your mount," Rafe replied, his eyes trained on her enchanted face. "Why don't we go inside so you can change? Then I'll drive Fiona over to Willowbend to get Sasha."

So he could be alone with Fiona for a few minutes. Karyn said brightly, "That sounds like a great idea."

Inside, Rafe had opted for simplicity of décor. Off-white paint, the clean lines of Finnish and Swedish furniture, and polished oak parquet scattered with richly hued Persian carpets that even to Karyn's uneducated eye screamed money. The few pieces of art had obviously been chosen with great care.

Of all this, Fiona would be mistress.

Feeling suddenly exhausted, craving solitude, she gripped the banister as she climbed the long curve of staircase to the second floor. Rafe said sharply, "Are you all right, Karyn?"

Hating him for seeing too much, she muttered, "Too much emotion, I guess."

Fiona put an arm around her sister. "Why don't you lie down for a few minutes? Rafe and I will take our time…it doesn't matter if we don't go riding until later. The mist's supposed to clear sometime this afternoon.''

So within minutes Karyn was alone in her bedroom. As Rafe closed the door, her shoulders sagged with relief. She hadn't anticipated the degree of strain it would cause her to be in his presence, on his home territory. Yet Stoneriggs was the logical place for her to stay.

She must make the best of it. Focus on Fiona, not Rafe.

Her bedroom was painted a soft apricot, with a thick-piled cream-colored carpet, silk draperies and delicate floral prints on the walls. The tall windows overlooked the rose garden; a frilly bouquet of peonies had been placed by the big bed. In which, of course, she would sleep alone.

Where would Fiona sleep? Next door? Or with Rafe?

Don't go there, she scolded herself, throwing her jodphurs and shirt on the pretty armchair. Then she fell onto the bed and within moments was asleep.

A sleep that twelve hours later Karyn regretted.

It was now midnight. The mist had cleared; stars jittered in the sky and her body ached with tiredness. She and Fiona had had a wonderful ride among the crags of the moor; they'd swum in the pool, eaten gourmet French cuisine in the informal dining room that led onto a stone patio, and picked armloads of roses and honeysuckle for the lounge that they shared on the second floor. They'd laughed a lot and talked. Talked endlessly, trying to catch up on twenty-six lost years.

Every moment they spent together confirmed the unconscious bonds of twinship and their growing ease with each other, and for this Karyn was deeply grateful. She was also grateful for Rafe's tact: most of the day he'd absented himself, as though he realized how important it was that the two sisters be alone to explore their new relationship.

And now she couldn't go to sleep. Restlessly Karyn

roamed up and down, her feet sinking into the carpet. Through the wall she could hear the small sounds of Fiona having a shower, then moving around her bedroom. A few moments later something dropped on the bathroom tiles. Karyn's nerves fluttered. She stopped dead beside her bed, her ears straining. Wasn't that the opening and closing of a door?

Feeling like a spy, yet unable to help herself, Karyn waited a few seconds, then very softly opened her own door. Fiona, in a long blue gown, was gliding down the hall. As Karyn watched, she turned the corner and disappeared.

Swiftly Karyn retreated. Why, oh why, couldn't she have fallen asleep at eleven, when she and Fiona had said an emotional good-night out in the hallway? But no, she'd had to stay awake, and be given incontrovertible proof that Fiona and Rafe were lovers. No matter that their body language said otherwise. No matter that Rafe desired her, Karyn. Fiona was even now in Rafe's bedroom, in his arms.

For the second time that day, tears flooded Karyn's eyes. Leaning against the wall, she fought them back. She had to accept the hard truth of her sister's relationship with Rafe. She had no other choice.

It was only Fiona who was important here, she thought fiercely. Not Rafe. She simply couldn't afford to let Rafe ruin the growing bond between herself and her sister.

Oddly enough, as the days passed, Karyn was helped in this resolve by Rafe. He flew to Paris one day, to Prague another. He rarely rode with them, and never joined them in the pool, pleading the pressures of work. At mealtimes, he was a charming, witty conversationalist who might just as well have been a chance acquaintance.

Karyn should have been happy with this state of affairs. Instead, against all logic, she was infuriated.

On the fifth evening, she and Fiona couldn't resist the flushed evening sky and went for a ride on the moors after dinner. When they got back, Karyn collapsed into one of the chairs on the patio, running her fingers through her tousled curls. "That was wonderful."

Fiona sat down beside her. Taking off her hard hat, she said with unusual hesitancy, "Karyn, there's something I've been wanting to ask you…"

"Go ahead."

"We've talked about so much—but not about your husband. You never even mention his name."

Karyn said shortly, "I don't like talking about him."

"I know it was only a year ago that he died…you must still miss him dreadfully."

As Karyn leaned over to rub dust from her riding boots, mumbling an indistinct reply, Fiona persisted, "What did he look like? Was he a vet, too?"

"He was an accountant with an international firm. Tall, blond and handsome," Karyn said with an attempt at lightness.

"You must have a photo of him?"

"I don't need one," Karyn said. "Fiona, I'm sorry. You mustn't take this personally—I don't talk about him to anyone."

"I just hope he was good to you," Fiona said fiercely. "My only standard of comparison is Rafe—I don't know what I'd do without him, I depend on him for so much." She sighed, tugging the ribbon from her braid and shaking out her long hair. "It only takes one look from Rafe and my father settles right down. Money talks, I suppose."

"Then I'm very glad you've got Rafe," Karyn said. She could have asked in just what capacity Fiona did have Rafe, for that, too, was a subject they'd never talked about. But didn't she already know the answer? "I think it's time for a shower."

"Me, too. What a drag—it takes forever to wash my hair." Fiona gave a wicked grin. "Maybe I'll cut it short, like yours."

"That'd get your mother's goat."

Karyn followed Fiona upstairs, going into her own room and staring out the window. Today Rafe had gone to London; she had no idea when he'd be back.

Restlessly she turned on the radio, wishing Fiona had never brought up the subject of Steve; even miles from home, memories of him had the power to disturb her. Then, as she looked around for the book she was reading, she realized she'd left it downstairs in the drawing room. Still dressed in her jodphurs, she headed for the back stairs.

Rafe was standing at the bottom of them. As her heart gave a great jolt in her chest, her socked foot slipped on the smooth wood. She stumbled, grabbed for the railing, missed it and fell forward, her knees banging against the next step. So fast she didn't have time to think, Rafe charged up the stairs and put his arms around her; her face was jammed into his chest. "Are you okay?" he demanded. "Did you hurt yourself? Karyn, answer me!"

Her own arms had gone around him in sheer reflex. Beneath her palms, through the thin cotton of his shirt, Karyn could feel the taut planes of his back, the hard curve of his spine. His heart was pounding under her cheek; his breath stirred her hair. Wasn't this closeness what she'd been desperate for? She wanted to stay here forever, she realized dazedly, and raised her head. "I—I'm fine. Silly of me to slip, I guess you startled me—I thought you were in London."

"I came back early..." His voice died away. His gaze

bored into hers as his hand rose to stroke a strand of hair from her cheek. His fingers weren't quite steady, each of them leaving a streak of fire on her skin. Unmasked, naked desire flared in his eyes, as vivid and dangerous as fire.

For the briefest of moments she yielded to that desire, her lashes drifting to her cheeks and her lips parting. Then, with a tiny sound of distress, Karyn shoved against Rafe's chest. Almost simultaneously, he pushed her away as hard as he could. Losing her balance, she gripped the banister, and from somewhere dredged up the shadow of a smile. "It won't help if we both fall down the stairs."

He was shaking his head like a man who'd just been struck a crippling blow. Or a man waking from a dream and finding himself in a harsh reality not of his choosing. "Hell's teeth," he muttered, "I swore that wasn't going to happen again."

He surged to his feet, pulling her with him, then holding her by the shoulders a careful distance from his body. "Are you sure you're all right?"

Her left knee hurt abominably. "This is unbearable—whatever it is that happens when I get within ten feet of you," she whispered. "Don't bother denying it, I know it happens to you, too."

"There's no point in denying it. I'm pulled to you every time I see you, I can't get you off my mind night or day—I wish to God we'd never met."

Because of Fiona, she thought wretchedly. Fiona, whom she already loved, and had unwittingly betrayed once again in that brief embrace on the stairs.

But wasn't there more, she thought with a sudden chill of her blood. Wasn't Rafe's charisma, his sheer sexuality, all too reminiscent of Steve? An icy hand clamped itself around her heart. Steve had swept her off her feet. Was she going to allow the exact same thing to happen again, this time with Rafe? "You can't wish we'd never met any more strongly than I do," she said in a stony voice.

"Okay, so we've got that much straight," Rafe said harshly. "We wish we hadn't met and we lust after each other. But we're not going to do one damn thing about it. If you hadn't fallen on the stairs, we—"

"So now it's my fault?"

"I didn't say that."

"But you were thinking it."

"For God's sake, Karyn, I don't know what's going on any more than you do! You think I like feeling this way every time I look at you? What's between you and me is an aberration. It'll pass. It's got to."

"Who are you trying to convince, myself or you?"

Her cheeks were pink with temper and her lips, those delectable lips, were pressed firmly together. "Both of us," he said with a wintry smile.

She said flatly, putting her suspicions into words, "There isn't any chemistry between you and Fiona. Not one spark."

"You let me worry about that," he grated, dropping his hands to his sides as though contact with her was poisonous. "Where's Fiona?"

"In the shower. She uses enough water for ten people, that's one thing I've learned about her." Recklessly Karyn pressed her point. "When you hug each other, it's almost as though you're brother and sister."

"We're the best of friends," he snapped. "Have you got a problem with that?"

How could she know? She'd assumed Steve was her friend as well as her lover, and had learned otherwise all too soon and with devastating consequences. Karyn bit her lip. "But if there isn't any passion—"

"Passion's overrated. I went that way once, and she

ripped the heart from my body. So I swore off it. As for Fiona, she's too innocent to know the difference.''

Karyn said raggedly, ''What you feel for me—is that passion?''

His jaw tightened; he looked like a man being tormented. ''There's no point in even talking about it.''

He was right. But when he was standing so close to her that she could feel herself sinking into the dark blue of his irises, desire made nonsense of reason. Aching to touch him, longing to lift her lips to his and taste him, she burst out, ''How can you be Fiona's lover if there isn't any passion between you? I just don't understand how you can do that.''

''Her lover?'' he repeated blankly. ''What the hell do you mean?''

Karyn's temper flared. ''The usual. Two people who make love. In bed. What did you think I meant?''

''Fiona and I have never gone to bed together.''

''Rafe, I saw her going to your room one night.''

''Fiona hasn't been anywhere near my bedroom.''

''Don't lie to me! The way you kissed me that night under the trees, thinking I was Fiona—''

Clipping off each word, Rafe repeated, ''I am not and never have been Fiona's lover.''

Karyn gaped at him. ''Then why are you going to marry her?''

''Who says I'm going to?''

''Douglas.''

Rafe swore under his breath. ''He told you that?''

''The day he came to see me at the inn, he said an announcement was imminent.''

''Have you said anything to Fiona?''

''No!''

''Thank God for that.''

"Oh, let's keep Fiona in the dark," Karyn flared. "After all, we're only talking about her life and her happiness."

Rafe said tautly, "Douglas wants Holden blue blood and Holden money in the family, and isn't above using a little leverage to get them. But he picked the wrong man to push around."

"So are you going to marry Fiona?" Karyn persisted, her chest tight.

Rafe jammed his hands in his pockets. "I told Douglas I'd think about it."

"If you have to think about it, you're sure not in any danger of succumbing to passion."

"Since when did you become the expert?"

She flinched. Hadn't her marriage proved she wasn't even remotely an expert? "I asked you a straightforward question about marrying Fiona," she retorted. "Yes or no—either answer will do."

"How about minding your own business?"

She had no part in his life. That's what he was saying. Torn between fury and an agony that would overwhelm her were she to let it in, Karyn muttered, "I'll be delighted to stay out of your business. But don't you dare hurt Fiona!"

"I have no wish in the world to hurt Fiona."

What more was there to say? Striving for normality, Karyn asked, "Were you coming upstairs to look for one of us?"

"You, as it happens…I came to tell you that Clarissa and Douglas are giving a formal dinner party next week to welcome you into the family."

Karyn's jaw dropped. "They are?"

"Don't ask how I did it," Rafe said, his smile almost genuine. "Just turn up."

To spend the evening watching Rafe and Fiona side by side? With Douglas and Clarissa eying her every move?

Karyn said tersely, "If you think I'm going to Willowbend after the way Douglas treated me, you're crazy."

"It's an olive branch, Karyn. Take it and be glad. Besides, you'll get to meet my parents."

Her eyes narrowed. "I don't like other people controlling my life. Back off, Rafe."

"You'll need an evening gown. You and Fiona could go shopping together."

"You don't get it, do you? I have a life at home, a job I have to get back to—I can't wait around until next week."

"Extend your holidays. Three or four days won't make any difference."

"I don't own the clinic," she said nastily, "I just work there."

"Then I'll—"

He broke off as Fiona's bedroom door opened and Fiona called out, "Karyn? Shall we raid the kitchen for tea and biscuits?"

"I haven't had a shower yet," Karyn called back, "so give me ten minutes." Then she turned back to Rafe, lowering her voice. "Don't you dare tell Fiona about the dinner—because it's not going to happen."

She hurried back up to her bedroom, giving Fiona a distracted smile. "Rafe's back, why don't you go and say hello to him?"

Then she went into the bathroom and turned on the water full blast. Hot water. She was under no illusions that cold water would be of any use whatsoever.

Fiona and Rafe had gone outside to sit on the patio under Karyn's window, where Fiona was trying to untangle her wet hair. "I've had such a wonderful time with Karyn, Rafe. I'm really getting to know her—I can't thank you enough for bringing us together."

Fiona made a beautiful picture as she combed out her hair in the last rays of the setting sun, a picture that left Rafe totally unmoved. Then she flipped her hair back so she could see him. "Well, except for one thing. Any mention of her husband and she spooks like a frightened pony."

"It's only a year since she was widowed."

"I think the hurt went so deep she can't talk about him."

But not so deep that she couldn't kiss me, Rafe thought savagely. The thought of Karyn in another man's arms, sharing another man's bed, nearly drove him out of his mind: not an insight he could share with anyone, especially not Fiona. "Perhaps she will when she's spent more time with you."

"Perhaps," Fiona said uncertainly. "Anyway, while she's in the shower, why don't we rummage in the kitchen for some of those chocolate-almond cookies, she loves them."

So when Karyn wiped the steam from the bathroom window, she saw Fiona and Rafe walking side by side across the garden. Knowing exactly what she was going to do, she wrapped herself in a towel and picked up the phone in her bedroom.

The secretary at the clinic answered, sounding as though she was across the room rather than across the ocean. Quickly Karyn asked for her boss. When he picked up the receiver, she said, "Dennis, it's Karyn. I was thinking I might come home a few days early, how would that fit in the schedule?"

"No kidding? Karyn, it'd be a godsend. Jim and Rita are both down with flu and the rest of us are trying to cover. Come as soon as you can, it'd be fine with me. Did you find your sister?"

Karyn gave him an edited version of events, rang off, called the airline and was lucky enough to get a cancellation for the very next evening. She booked a seat on the train, threw on some clothes and went downstairs to find Fiona and Rafe in the drawing room, with its gleaming cherrywood furniture and single vibrant Picasso. Fiona held out a plate of almond cookies coated in rich Belgian chocolate. "These are for you," she said. "Though if you felt like sharing them, I'm sure I could choke down a couple."

Feeling absurdly guilty, Karyn took one. "I'll have to take some of these home with me," she said lightly. "I called the clinic and they've had a flu outbreak. So I changed my flight and I'm going home tomorrow."

Fury flashed across Rafe's face, and then was gone as if it had never been. Fiona said in genuine dismay, "Tomorrow? Oh, Karyn, you can't go that soon."

"You can visit me, Fiona. Anytime."

"I could, couldn't I? But promise you'll come for Christmas. I'm sure by then Mother and Dad will be happy to see you."

Karyn wouldn't count on it. "That'd be lovely," she said.

"Mother always decorates with holly and hundreds of candles, it's so beautiful. And Rafe throws a huge party here at Stoneriggs on New Year's Eve, you'll have to come to that."

Maybe she'd break a leg the week before Christmas, Karyn thought wildly. Fall off a horse. Be trampled by a sick cow. "I don't have any fancy clothes."

"If you weren't going home tomorrow, we could go shopping in London," Fiona wailed. "It's much too soon for you to leave."

"I have to go. My boss has always been very good to me, and the least I can do is help out when they need me."

"In that case," Fiona said, "you and I are going to stay

up all night and talk. I don't want to waste a single minute.''

''I'm flying to Oslo early tomorrow morning, and I've got some paperwork to clear up before I go,'' Rafe said brusquely. ''So I won't see you again, Karyn—have a safe trip.''

Feeling as though her heart was being torn from her body, for the next time she saw him he might well be married to Fiona, Karyn said stiffly, ''Thanks for everything.''

''For heaven's sake,'' Fiona said impatiently, ''give her a kiss, Rafe. She's my sister!''

Praying that her wince of dismay had been invisible, Karyn stood as stiff as a china doll as Rafe chastely put his lips to her cheek. She didn't dare meet his eyes; she'd be finished if she did.

Rafe kissed Fiona on the cheek as well, and headed for his study as though pursued by a pack of wolves. By tomorrow night Karyn would be boarding a plane that would carry her four thousand miles away. Home, where she belonged.

He didn't want passion. So the sooner she went home, the better.

Four thousand miles sounded just fine to him.

CHAPTER FIVE

KARYN had spent the last couple of hours in the company of a cow with bloat. While the cow was feeling better for the encounter, it could by no stretch be called a romantic way to spend an afternoon. So why was she thinking about Rafe as she took the turn from the farmer's muddy driveway onto the highway?

She thought about him entirely too often, especially at night. Which wasn't romantic, either. It was painful and disturbing and made her very unhappy.

Rafe had awoken her body from its long sleep; and now, unfortunately, it wouldn't go back to its state of dormancy. Nor—so she'd discovered—could she substitute anyone other than Rafe. For the first time since she was widowed, she'd gone out on a couple of dates, one with another vet and one with a city planner from Charlottetown. Both were nice men, who'd kissed her good-night with enthusiasm; and both had left her cold. Rafe was the man she wanted.

Rafe was the man she couldn't have. So was she simply craving the forbidden?

She and Fiona kept in constant contact by e-mail. Often Fiona's e-mails mentioned Rafe's name; always they served as a reminder of him. Phrases stuck in Karyn's mind…*Rafe invited me to a dance at the castle last night, I wore a very classy silver dress…Rafe's off to New Zealand to check out a new hotel… Rafe's so incredibly good at keeping Mother and Dad off my back.* Even, occasionally, *Rafe says hello.* Upon which Karyn would grit her teeth and type back, *Hi to Rafe.*

At no time did Fiona say anything about Rafe proposing to her. Did that mean he'd decided against marrying her? Or that he was still thinking about it?

With a big sigh Karyn brought her attention back to the present. May had merged into June. The fields were green with sprouting corn and drills of potatoes; the cows looked sleek and well-fed. Then, as she wound down a long hill, her foot hit the brake. She always tried to avoid this road, but today her mind had been more on Rafe than on the route she'd chosen. To her right was the split-level where the Harveys lived with their young son, Donny. A bicycle was lying on the lawn; a red SUV was parked in the drive-way. Saving Donny Harvey from drowning had cost Steve his life…

Next door to the Harveys was the house she and Steve had shared, an attractive blue Cape Cod.

Behind both houses lay the sinuous curve of the river.

Her hands were clenched around the wheel so tightly her wrists hurt. Steve was going to walk out the door, she thought wildly, in his gray business suit and expensive trench coat, his eyes a cold, pale blue.

She braked hard, pulling over onto the shoulder of the road. Her forehead dropped to the wheel; she squeezed her eyes shut, trying to obliterate the surge of ugly memories. Steve's face contorted with rage. The cruel grip of his fingers. His voice hammering at her, his endless questions, his prying into every corner of her life.

Worst of all, the sensation that—no matter where she went—he was watching her.

Karyn could hear her own breathing harsh in her ears. She raised her head. No one was walking out of the door of the blue house, she thought dully. No one.

A wave of exhaustion washed over her. No wonder she'd

repressed the two years of her marriage; the alternative was too frightening.

As though a lightbulb had been turned on, she suddenly realized that it didn't matter whether Rafe got engaged to Fiona or not. Didn't matter at all. Even if he stayed as free as—as that crow flying across the road—she couldn't possibly get involved with him.

How had she described Steve to Fiona? *Tall, blond and handsome.* Wasn't Rafe tall, dark and handsome? Charismatic, like Steve. Sexy like Steve. Dangerous like Steve. Because Rafe, like Steve, made her lose her head and melt in his arms in all-too-easy surrender.

How stupid she'd been the past ten days not to have figured this out! Instead she'd moped around the house, allowing dreams and fantasies of Rafe to dominate her life.

No more, she decided militantly. She should have driven past Steve's house long before this; it had just taught her a salutary lesson.

She simply wasn't ready to get involved with anyone: city planner, veterinarian or one of the richest men in England. Maybe she never would be. There'd be no more dates, no more kisses on the front step; and no more mooning over a black-haired man she wouldn't kiss on the doorstep or anywhere else. In fact, if Rafe did get engaged it could be seen as a bonus, in case she backslid.

For the first time, she felt glad to be home.

It wasn't quite as easy as Karyn had anticipated to oust Rafe from her thoughts. She still dreamed about him regularly, waking with her body aching with unfulfilled desire. As well, his face would flash across her mind at the most inconvenient times; she'd want to share a joke with him, or tell him about the horse whose colic she'd cured. Instead she e-mailed Fiona with all the events of her day.

However, as time passed, Fiona's responses became less frequent, and stopped mentioning Rafe altogether. Stopped mentioning anything very much. With a perplexed frown, Karyn read a message from her sister that described the raspberry crop and the slugs in the lettuce in exhaustive detail. *I'm glad the raspberries are fine and the slugs aren't,* she e-mailed back, *but how are you?* For four days she didn't hear a word. Then, as she entered the house after work one afternoon, tired from a nine-hour shift, the phone was ringing. She wasn't on call. But she'd better get it anyway.

"Karyn? It's Fiona."

"Are you all right?" Karyn demanded. "I've been worried about you."

"Oh, Karyn, I can't tell you how happy I am! I've fallen in love. Head over heels in love."

With Rafe, Karyn thought with a sick jolt in her chest. And why not? The lack of chemistry between Fiona and Rafe, which Karyn had noticed and Rafe hadn't denied, was because Fiona hadn't been in love with her friend of so many years. But now she was.

"It happened so suddenly," Fiona burbled on, "between one moment and the next—just like in the books. Love at first sight... I don't care if it's a cliché, it's absolutely true and so wonderful I don't even know how to describe it."

She had to say something. Injecting as much warmth in her voice as she could, Karyn said, "Congratulations... although I'd hardly call it love at first sight."

"He's such a lovely man, why didn't I ever notice that before? Oh, Karyn, I suppose I shouldn't say this, but he kisses like a dream. Absolutely delicious..."

Karyn knew he did. Her heart congealing into a cold lump in her rib cage, she muttered, "Perhaps you were too close to him to really appreciate him before this."

"I don't know what you mean—I'd only seen him a couple of times."

Karyn frowned. "What are you talking about? You've known him all your life."

"All my life?" Fiona repeated in a puzzled voice. "No, I haven't. Although it feels like I've been waiting for him all my life." She gave a delighted giggle. "I'm going away with him this weekend and I'm not even nervous about it. He just feels so right, Karyn. So absolutely perfect."

Karyn said faintly, "Are you or are you not talking about Rafe?"

"*Rafe?* Goodness, no, whatever gave you that idea? I couldn't possibly fall in love with Rafe! I'm talking about John."

Karyn sat down hard on the floor, wondering if she was going out of her mind. She said evenly, "Fiona, will you please begin at the beginning? I thought you meant you'd fallen in love with Rafe."

"You must be joking," Fiona said blithely. "Rafe's like a brother to me. He's never been remotely like a lover."

Sounding like a robot, fully aware that Rafe had already given her this information, Karyn said, "You've never been Rafe's lover."

"Nope—not even close." Fiona sighed. "Mother and Dad would love me to get engaged to Rafe, they've been dropping very broad hints in that direction lately. They're not going to be too happy when they find out I'm passionately in love with someone else and want to marry him instead...but they should have known Rafe was never in the running."

"So tell me about John," Karyn mumbled, her emotions in a turmoil.

"John Settler. Fourth son of an earl, so that's all right. And he's got more than enough money for the two of us, although nothing like what Rafe has, of course. Because he's not content to live off his inheritance, he apprenticed as a cabinetmaker, and now he makes the most beautiful furniture that he sells at outrageous prices. I'd seen him around town once or twice, but we'd never connected. Then Mother invited him to the house to see if he could design a wardrobe for her bedroom, and that was that. Game over. We were head over heels in love.''

How ironic that Clarissa herself had precipitated what must have been a bitter blow to her. ''What does he look like?''

''Didn't I tell you? Brown hair and deep brown eyes and a beard, and he's the kindest man I've ever met.'' With a maturity new to her, Fiona added, ''I think kindness can go a long way, don't you?''

Steve had been anything but kind. ''I do, yes.''

''He thinks I'm wonderful and he makes me laugh. Karyn, I'm so happy!'' After a telltale hesitation, Fiona added shyly, ''We've been to bed together—that was lovely, too. I'd never done it before. I'm glad John was the first.''

''I—I didn't realize you'd never been to bed with anyone. We never talked about that.''

''There've been men who've kissed me in a loverlike kind of way. Trying it on, I suppose. Even Rafe did that once, one evening at Willowbend.'' Fiona paused thoughtfully. ''About the time you turned up.''

Karyn would be willing to bet Rafe had kissed Fiona right after a very different kiss under the oak trees. As Fiona chattered on, she struggled to pay attention. Fiona finished by saying with a touching new confidence, ''Even though I haven't told my parents yet, John and I will be getting married this summer. You'll be sure to come for the wedding and be my maid of honor? Floral colors in chiffon, I thought, and lots of sweet peas and garden flowers. Don't you think that sounds pretty?''

"Beautiful," Karyn said, and asked the critical question. "Will you invite Rafe?"

Sounding shocked, Fiona replied, "Of course I will. I couldn't get married without Rafe being there."

"Does he know about John?"

"Oh, yes. I tell Rafe everything. He was a bit taken aback at first, and who can blame him? So was I! But he's really happy for me." Again Fiona paused. "Almost relieved, in a way that I don't quite understand. Maybe he'd been worrying about my single state...by the way, did I tell you how sweet John is with the animals at the shelter?"

"You didn't, no." With heartfelt warmth Karyn said, "Fiona, your news took me by surprise, too. But I'm delighted for you...I wish you and John years of happiness together. And guess what—I get a new brother-in-law out of the deal."

"The best one in the whole world. Promise you'll come to the wedding?"

"All right," Karyn gulped, "I promise...let me know the date, won't you? I'll talk to you soon. Love you."

"You, too. 'Bye, Karyn."

Karyn scrambled to her feet, replaced the receiver and stared blankly at the wall.

Rafe was never going to marry Fiona, because Fiona had—in all innocence—fallen in love with someone else. She, Karyn, would never have to cope with Rafe as her sister's husband, or as the father of her sister's children.

For a moment sheer relief transfixed her. She felt as though a huge weight had been lifted from her shoulders, leaving her light and suffused with unthinking happiness; as though she could dance around the kitchen.

But in all too rapid succession, that thought was followed

by another. What she'd come to view as a safety net was no longer in place. Rafe was a free man. He'd even been relieved to hear Fiona was in love with someone else.

Why had he been relieved?

Why did it matter? After driving past Steve's house a couple of weeks ago, she'd decided Rafe's marital status was immaterial to her; because of the long shadow Steve had cast, she wasn't even ready to date anyone.

She'd believed her own assertions, wholeheartedly. For exactly fourteen days.

Now they were wavering like flags in the breeze.

Thank heavens Rafe lived four thousand miles away. All she had to do was pray that he stay there.

As the golden light of evening streamed through the window, it seemed obvious to Karyn that Rafe would stay safely in England, where he belonged. A man of enormous wealth, he'd just been supplanted by a cabinetmaker, the fourth son of an earl. No, Rafe wouldn't hightail it to a small island across the Atlantic in hot pursuit of Fiona's twin sister.

A ridiculous prospect. Besides, she shouldn't flatter herself she was that important to him.

But that night, when the stars were glimmering coldly through the skylight over her bed, Karyn wasn't so sanguine. She remembered with searing clarity every moment she'd spent with Rafe, from the spark that had leaped between them on that first encounter in the woods, to the heat of his body when he'd shielded her on the stairs at Stoneriggs.

None of this had been trivial. She couldn't pretend that it had been: to minimize his feelings or hers would be an insult to both of them. She burrowed into the pillow, wishing with all her heart that she'd never met him.

If she hadn't, she'd never have met Fiona; who'd enriched her life so immeasurably.

When Karyn did finally fall asleep, she didn't dream about Rafe, as she'd expected to. She dreamed about Steve. It was the same dream that had haunted her ever since his death; a dream saturated with a terror all the more powerful for being amorphous. It was only at the end of the dream, after she'd been running through endless dark alleyways, her breath sobbing in her ears, that she burst out into the open and saw, right in front of her, her husband, Steve. He had a gun in his hand, and was slowly lifting it to point at her heart.

She always woke up just as his finger tightened on the trigger. Tonight was no exception. Her pulses racing, her body rigid, Karyn stared up at the night sky and knew she had her answer. It didn't matter what Rafe did, whether he got engaged to ten different women or moved to Antarctica. He wasn't for her.

Everything that could go wrong the next day did. An elderly dog Karyn had been medicating against kidney failure succumbed to the disease, leaving her with the unenviable task of breaking the bad news to the dog's equally elderly owner. One of the other vets called in sick, doubling her workload in the clinic. This was followed, four hectic hours later, by an emergency call. A farmer's flock of sheep was threatened with an outbreak of orf, a disease as nasty as it sounded; she and another vet labored long and hard for the rest of the day in the open fields to vaccinate the whole flock. It was backbreaking work, which left her covered in mud and physically exhausted. But at least her shift was finished. Over two and a half hours ago, she thought wryly as she drove home, an old tarp between her trousers and the car seat.

A hot bath and a Greek pizza with extra feta and black olives. That'd fix her up.

She turned the last corner and drove down her street; her mother's house, which she'd inherited, was at the very end of the road, enclosed in a small grove of birches. The Camdens' garden halfway down the street was in full bloom; one of Karyn's plans, when things slowed down at work, was to tackle the garden. Peonies, maybe, and lots of Shasta daisies. Fiona liked peonies.

A car was parked in her driveway. She slewed to a stop.

It looked just like Steve's car.

A whimper of fear burst from her lips. Wasn't that what the dream was about? And wasn't that, irrationally, still her living nightmare? That, somehow, Steve hadn't really died. Instead he'd been lying in wait for the last year, playing with her, cat and mouse. Wanting her to build a false sense of security before he knocked it to the ground and engulfed her once again.

There was a man standing in the shadow of the lace vine that had entwined the front porch. As he sighted her, he walked down the steps toward her.

A man with black hair. Not blond. It wasn't Steve. It was Rafe.

Very slowly Karyn climbed out of her car.

Rafe took one look at her face and grabbed her by the arm. "Karyn! For God's sake, what's wrong?"

His voice, the breeze flattening his shirt to his chest, the concern in his face: had she ever forgotten anything about him? "I—I thought you were someone—I mean, it startled me, seeing you there."

His eyes narrowed. "Who did you think I was?"

She tugged her arm free and took refuge in anger. "Nobody! What are you doing here, Rafe Holden? I don't recall inviting you for a visit."

He suddenly grinned at her, a boyish grin so full of charm and so laden with male energy that she took an instinctive step back. "You didn't. I figured if I asked, you'd say no. So I came anyway. Just like you with the Talbots. That worked, didn't it?"

"You're so right—I would have said no."

"I'm taking you out for dinner." He looked her up and down, from the toes of her mud-caked, steel-toed boots to the streak of dirt on her cheek. "Not many restaurants would let you in the door right now."

"Some of us work for our living."

His grin widened. "You can't insult me that easily, Karyn."

"I'll work on it."

"You do that." Before she could duck, he reached out and ruffled her hair. "It's great to see you."

It was a huge effort not to smile back. "I wish I could say the same. You realize you've turned up one day after Fiona told me she's going to marry John."

"No sense in wasting time."

"Are you looking for sympathy?"

"I'd already decided I couldn't possibly marry Fiona."

"I'm supposed to believe that?"

"I'd prefer you did...it happened the first time I saw Fiona and John together. They looked so gloriously happy, so wrapped up in each other." He hesitated. "I figured if Fiona could break every one of her parents' rules, I could damn well drop in to see you. So here I am." He looked her up and down, laughter lurking in his dark blue eyes. "Did you spend your day mud-wrestling?"

With an exasperated sigh, Karyn straightened her aching back. "I vaccinated thirty-three sheep, not one of whom wanted to be anywhere near me or the syringe. You should try it sometime. It's a humbling experience."

He laughed outright. "Looks as though they won."

"There was one ewe who nearly did." She wouldn't smile. She wouldn't. "I'm going inside, having a hot bath and ordering a pizza. You can drive right back to the airport and fly home."

"That's not very hospitable of you."

Now she did smile. "You can't insult me that easily, Rafe."

"I can't fly home. I have pictures of Fiona and John. She'd never speak to me again if I didn't show them to you."

"Pass them over. Then vamoose."

"Not a hope," he said. "We're going out for dinner, I have it all planned." He glanced over his shoulder. "This was your mother's house, wasn't it?"

"My neighbor, Bob Camden, used to be a fullback. If I tell him you're bothering me, he'll turn you inside out."

"I scarcely think so. Have you heard of a black belt in karate? Oh Karyn, you look so cute when you're angry."

"Don't patronize me!"

"You also look worn-out." He took her by the arm and steered her toward the house. "Where are your keys?"

His fingers burned through her shirtsleeve, and briefly her mind went blank. How could she think when all she really wanted to do was fling her arms around him and kiss him until she couldn't breathe?

She fumbled in her backpack for the house key and inserted it in the front door with a clumsiness that horrified her. In a wash of the same terror that had overwhelmed her the night before, she looked up at him and said with raw truth, "Rafe, you scare the life out of me. I can't afford to be hurt again, I just can't!"

So she was still grieving her husband, Rafe thought; vehemently he wished it were otherwise. "The last thing I want to do is hurt you."

"Then go home and leave me alone."

"No. Not yet," he said, a note in his voice she'd never heard before, and that terrified her with its implacability.

"What are you doing here anyway?" she cried.

"Waiting for you to get ready so we can eat. It's four hours later for me—I'm hungry."

She let out her breath in a hiss of fury. "There are lots of restaurants in Charlottetown that'd be delighted to feed you. Then you can get the first flight to Halifax and catch the red-eye to England—you've got plenty of time."

"I traveled in my own jet," Rafe said calmly, "it's at the Charlottetown airport. While you're unlacing those godawful boots, I'll start a bath for you."

"Pardon me, of course you'd have your own jet," she snarled. "And they're very practical boots—you try being stepped on by a 1,700-pound bull."

She dumped her pack on the porch floor. It was just as well Rafe didn't know that underneath her green man-tailored shirt and her taupe canvas pants—work clothes that served her well when she had to wrestle sheep—she was wearing an ivory silk bra lavishly decorated with lace. Sexy underwear was her one indulgence—that, and her scent. She'd always loved frivolous underclothes. But Steve hadn't approved of them; in one of his vicious flares of rage, he'd accused her of being on the make when she went to work at the clinic with lace hidden under her work clothes.

As if she'd had the time or the inclination to look for another man. But to keep the peace she'd put away all her pretty underwear, wearing cotton jockey shorts and grey cotton bras instead.

"You're a long way away," Rafe said.

Her lashes flickered. "Oh. Yes. Sorry."

"What were you thinking about?"

"I'm tired, that's all," she said shortly, and bent to undo her laces.

Light as gossamer, Rafe's lips slid across her nape. Before she could react, he walked away from her, crossing the hall and starting up the stairs. Of its own accord her hand reached up to cup the back of her neck and her eyes closed. Nothing had changed. She still wanted him.

Although *wanted* didn't seem in any way to express the tumult of longing and desire that had flooded her at that briefest of caresses. She could add panic to the mix, she thought helplessly. The man scared her out of her wits.

Steve had scared her out of her wits. Oh God, what was going on?

After unlacing her second boot, she lined it up on the mat with the first one. She could hear footsteps overhead, then the sound of water filling the tub, ordinary domestic sounds that reignited her fury. Okay, so Rafe had taken her by surprise, and she'd thought he was Steve. But she'd had time to recover and be damned if he was going to have it all his own way.

She marched up the stairs. The bathroom was engulfed in steam and the glorious fragrance of freesias. She read the label on the bottle standing on the vanity, and said blankly, "Where did that come from?"

"I brought it with me."

"That stuff costs the earth."

"Hardly."

"You can't go giving me expensive presents!"

"Wear something casual," he said. "You'll like where we're going."

In a low voice Karyn said, "Rafe, don't ride over me

like that. As though I don't exist." Wasn't that what Steve had done, time and time again?

Rafe stood still, gazing at her. She looked exhausted, he thought with compunction. When she'd first seen him this evening, she'd been terrified; he'd swear to that in a court of law. So was he in danger of hurting her just by being here? Leaning over to turn off the taps before he had a flood on his hands, he said, "I have more money than I know what to do with, and that's a very small gift. All I want is to give you pleasure, Karyn—and don't ever think you don't exist for me."

She didn't know what frightened her more, his gentleness or his willpower. "Where were you planning to eat?"

"Will you trust me enough to put yourself in my hands?"

"That's one heck of a big question," she said with a flash of defiance.

"I only meant as far as dinner's concerned," Rafe said with very little regard for the truth; and to his relief saw her slow nod of agreement. If only he knew more about Karyn's husband; then maybe he wouldn't have the sensation that with every move he made, he was stepping into a minefield.

Surely her husband wasn't anything to do with the white-faced terror with which she'd greeted him?

Now that he was here, he was going to make it his business to find out about Steven Patterson. While he could have set his investigator on Steve a long time ago, something in Rafe had shrunk from such a course. Yes, he'd needed to investigate Karyn, for Fiona's sake as well as his own. But he wanted Karyn herself to tell him about Steve. "I'll wait for you downstairs," Rafe said, and suited action to word.

He didn't want to be waiting downstairs, Rafe thought

as he wandered through the pleasant, unpretentious living room to the small dining alcove that overlooked the birch trees and a field of new corn. He wanted to be in Karyn's bed. But all those years ago when he'd been learning to ride cross-country, hadn't he been warned never to rush his fences? It was advice he should take to heart right now.

He glanced around at the eclectic collection of books and magazines, at the brightly colored cushions and the few carefully chosen ornaments. On the stereo-stand there was a photo of a smiling couple in their forties: Karyn's adoptive parents, he'd be willing to bet. But although he prowled through the whole downstairs, he didn't find a single photo of the man who'd been Karyn's husband.

One more piece of evidence that Karyn was so deeply sunk in grief she couldn't bear to be reminded of Steve.

Feeling restless and unsettled, Rafe went outdoors to wait for her.

CHAPTER SIX

KARYN came downstairs ten minutes later. Her hair was an aureole of soft curls around her face; her brief blue denim skirt was topped by a figure-hugging sweater in soft pink mohair. Her legs were bare, her feet in flat, thin-strapped sandals. For a moment that was outside of time Rafe stared at her. For six years he'd had his defences firmly in place. He'd dated, had brief affairs and had never allowed anyone to tap the deep well of passion that Celine had desecrated. Everything easy, and according to his own rules.

The woman standing in front of him could breach those defences all too quickly. Or had she already done so?

Karyn said uncomfortably, "Am I too dressed up?"

Rafe pulled himself together. "You look beautiful," he said. "Isn't that the wool you bought in Hart's Run?"

"I unraveled the sweater the first time, it would have fit me if I'd been pregnant with triplets. The second time it came out a bit small, but I couldn't be bothered to try again."

"I like it just as it is," he said, and managed to keep his gaze above the level of her breasts.

She blushed, lowered her eyes and muttered, "I just wish I knew why—"

"Dinner first," he said. "We'll talk later. I want to go in the general direction of Stanhope."

As she got in his rented car, she thought out various routes, instantly discarding the one that went past the house she and Steve had lived in. "I'll navigate," she said. "Have you made a reservation in Stanhope?"

"You'll see." He got in the driver's seat and took an envelope out of the dash. "Fiona sent this. With her love."

The envelope was tied with pink ribbon, smelled faintly of lilies of the valley and contained several photos. In each one, Fiona looked radiant, her arm linked with a pleasant-faced, bearded man not much taller than she, who also looked extremely happy. Karyn spoke without thinking. "I've never seen Fiona look like that…he must be quite a guy." Then she added awkwardly, "I didn't mean that you—"

"Thinking I could marry Fiona was a classic case of self-deception," Rafe said dryly. "You were the one who said there wasn't any chemistry between us, and you were right. Luckily Fiona met John. You can imagine Clarissa and Douglas's reaction—but Fiona stood her ground as though she'd been defying her parents since the day she was born."

"She said you helped."

"I pointed out a few basic facts to Douglas—but Fiona took him on first. All by herself."

"Good for her," Karyn said. "Anyone who can make an impression on Douglas Talbot has my undying admiration. Which doesn't include you," she added. "All you had to do was wave your money in front of him—that doesn't count."

"Pity," Rafe said, his smile crackling with energy. "I'd like to have your undying admiration."

"For someone who'll never have it, you look entirely too pleased with yourself."

For someone who didn't know what the hell he was doing, he felt entirely too pleased with himself. And with her. Deciding to keep that piece of information to himself, Rafe said, "I love Fiona. I've known her since she was a babe in arms, I taught her how to climb trees and jump her first pony over a stone wall, and I'm delighted she's found someone she adores. John's a fine fellow—they're admirably suited."

"I wired her a huge bouquet of flowers," Karyn said. "I do so want her to be happy."

"She will be, I'm sure. What's the name of this river?"

Karyn started describing the countryside. Rafe's questions were penetrating and his interest unfeigned; she expanded, forgetting how angry she was with him, allowing her intelligence full rein, and hearing herself being wittier than usual. Before she knew it, they'd reached the north shore with its miles of sand beaches and red cliffs. Instead of turning toward the restaurants in the area, Rafe parked alongside the beach. Karyn got out, watching as he took a large wicker hamper from the trunk. "Picnic," he said economically. "Let's find a table where we can see the water."

"A picnic?"

"Is that okay?"

"It's a wonderful idea—I love picnics!"

She looked as entranced as a little girl on Christmas morning. Rafe turned away, wanting to kiss her so badly his whole body was on fire with need. He slammed the trunk shut and walked along the boardwalk. Some picnic tables had been set on a grass verge overlooking the long stretch of surf; he dumped the hamper on the furthest one. "Let's eat."

Karyn unlatched the lid and peered inside, lifting out one of the delicate china plates with its hand-painted pattern of flowering herbs. "It's a work of art," she marveled. "Don't tell me those are lobster rolls—my favorite."

"There's caviar and chicken, as well, and an avocado salad. Not to mention dessert."

"Chocolate?" she said hopefully.

"Dark chocolate mousse with truffles and hazelnuts."

Karyn laughed out loud. "I've died and gone to heaven."

He took out two crystal champagne flutes and the bottle of champagne that had been wrapped in a towel to keep it chilled. "We'll start with this."

She raised her brows. "A high-class picnic."

"Not quite the best money can buy," he grinned, "but getting close."

The cork came out with a most satisfying pop, bubbles rising like foam on the shore. Rafe raised his glass and for a moment was tongue-tied. He knew what he wanted to say. At least he thought he did. But it was way too soon. He drawled, "May all the vaccinated sheep be as healthy as horses."

"I'll drink to that." Then she unwrapped a crusty roll crammed with lobster, crisp celery and a deliciously tangy dressing and began to eat.

Rafe dug into the caviar, enjoying her pleasure in what was, by his standards, a very simple meal. The wind from the ocean was playing with her curls; her eyes were a deeper blue than the sea, although just as full of mysterious depths. Color tinted her cheeks. Helping her to salad, Rafe began to talk about his newest hotel, located on New Zealand's South Island.

Eventually Karyn had eaten her fill. She licked the last smear of chocolate from her spoon. "That was incredible. If I ate like this every day, I'd be as fat as a barrel."

"You're too thin."

"You're supposed to say I'm perfect," she responded pertly. "This was a much better choice than a restaurant, Rafe, thank you so much. I feel like a new woman."

"You've got chocolate on your chin," he said, leaned forward and wiped it off with one finger.

His face was so close she could have counted his eyelashes. If she'd been able to count. "Rafe, why are you here?" she blurted.

He poured two demitasses of coffee from a thermos, taking his time. "To bring you Fiona's photos—much as she loves you, she can't tear herself away from John right now to give them to you herself."

"There's a marvelous invention called the post office. What's the real reason?"

He had no intention of giving his cards away too soon; he'd learned a thing or two about strategy over the years. "I'm checking out a possible hotel purchase in Toronto and thought I'd drop in on the way."

She gave a rude snort. "Toronto's 2,500 miles away. You can skip that one, too."

"It's for real," he said mildly. "I travel hundreds of thousands of miles a year, a detour like this is nothing. Besides, you're Fiona's sister, and I wanted to see how you were."

"So it's nothing to do with that kiss in the woods?"

"Only if we want it to be."

Karyn said with a careful lack of emphasis, "I like my life the way it is. Sure, we lust after each other—so what? We aren't going to do anything about it."

"You're right, we aren't," he said cheerfully. "So you won't mind if I hang around for a day or two."

"It's a free country—I can't stop you," she said coldly.

"We'll go for dinner somewhere fancy tomorrow. What time do you have to be at work the next day?"

"I'm on the late shift," she said, eying him suspiciously.

"Good. Pack a toothbrush."

"I'm not going anywhere overnight with—"

"I've never in my life taken anything from a woman that

she wasn't willing to give, and I don't plan to start with you.''

His jaw was a tense line, his eyes unsmiling. Karyn said slowly, ''I hurt your feelings.''

''Yeah, you did.''

She could have apologized. But hadn't she spent a great deal of time apologizing to Steve, often for things that weren't her fault? She said coolly, ''You're a big boy, Rafe, you can handle it. Where are we going for dinner?''

''It'll be a surprise. I guarantee you'll like it and that you'll have a good time—how's that for arrogance?''

''You took the word out of my mouth.''

He gave a snort of laughter. ''Wear your best dress. There's live music, too—do you like to dance?''

''Dance with you—no way!''

''Why not?'' he asked blandly.

''I'd jump on you on the dance floor,'' she said, her scowl deepening.

''Fine by me.''

''You've got a one-track mind.''

He said deliberately, ''Did you ever feel that way about Steve?''

She surged to her feet in a move from which all her natural grace had been stripped. ''I don't want to talk about Steve!''

''Then we won't,'' Rafe said, all his senses on high alert. ''Tell me about the clinic instead. Or the teacher you had a crush on in grade seven.''

Karyn was wringing her hands; he was almost sure she didn't know she was doing it. ''I have to be at work at eight tomorrow morning,'' she said, ''we should go back.''

''A ten-minute walk on the beach first. It's a glorious sunset.''

He was putting the food and plates back in the basket.

Feeling trapped and beleaguered, Karyn said choppily, "I'm not playing hard to get. I'm not interested in your money and I couldn't care less about your status."

Rafe knew the truth when he heard it. "Good," he said. "With regards to my money, you're in a minority of two— you and Fiona...I'll put the hamper back in the car and meet you on the beach."

So Karyn wandered down to the sand by herself, slipping off her sandals and letting the smooth grains slide between her toes. The surf's endless rhythms laved her ears; a pair of terns swooped in elegant curves over the white crests. I can handle Rafe, she thought in a surge of confidence, and walked down to the water's edge, letting the marbled foam wash over her feet. It was numbingly, bone-achingly cold.

With a tiny shriek she leaped backward. Into Rafe's arms.

She stood very still, watching the mosaic of orange and gold light dance on the sea as the sun's brilliant disc was slowly swallowed by the horizon. His hands were clasping her shoulders; he'd pulled her into his body, her back to his chest, his cheek to her ear. The heavy thud of his heart, the strength of his fingers, the waft of his breath in her hair, each was an astonishing intimacy, somehow bound up with the elemental powers of the ocean. Karyn closed her eyes, savoring every sensation, until her body was suffused with a liquid heat. Only then did she turn to face him.

The strong planes of his face were lit by the dying rays of the sun; his eyes, eyes that held the darkness of night, were fastened on her. She knew what was going to happen and welcomed it, opening to him before his lips as much as touched hers.

Rafe slid his arms around her, his hands stroking the soft wool of her sweater; he felt like a teenager before his first kiss, he thought dimly. He also felt as though he held the whole world in his arms.

She was a woman. Just a woman.

Then his mouth found the soft, delicious curve of her lips, and in an upwelling of pure sensation he stopped thinking altogether. Plunging with his tongue, savoring the fluid sweetness that was Karyn, he pulled her tight to him, molding her to his body. His groin had hardened instantly. Rather than pulling away, she pressed herself into him, trembling very lightly, her fingernails digging into his back.

He slid his mouth down the taut line of her throat, nuzzling the pulse in the hollow at its base where her blood was racing in tandem with his. Pushing her sweater aside, he found the silken curve of her shoulder, tasting, licking, nibbling until he wondered if he'd go out of his mind. The rise of her breast fit his palm perfectly; her nipple was as hard as a tiny shell. She moaned his name, cupped his face in her hands and pulled his mouth down to hers.

When he opened his eyes, hers, blazingly blue, were so close he could drown in them. Was drowning in them, he thought, and somehow found his voice. "Karyn, someone's coming—we've got an audience."

Another couple, hand in hand, was wandering toward them down the beach. She said dazedly, "Do we care?"

He wanted to protect her, he realized. From everything, including prying eyes. "I care," he said. "What's between us is private."

Karyn stepped back. The sand underfoot was both wet and cold, bringing her to her senses. "The only thing between us is old-fashioned lust," she said faintly.

"Even if that's true, it's still our concern. Not anyone else's."

He turned her to face the sea again, his arms wrapped around her body, hands linked at her waist. She leaned back, glad of his support because her knees felt as wobbly as jellyfish. She herself felt desired, sensual and fully alive, sheltered in the heat of Rafe's body. Had she ever luxuriated so instinctively in the pleasure of being held?

The sun had disappeared; the distant clouds were painted all the shades of pink and gold. She murmured, "I love the sea, don't you?"

"I own a little place in the Outer Hebrides, you can hear the surf through every window."

The other couple had passed them. Even though he yearned to continue a kiss that had stunned him with its potency, Rafe said easily, "I should get you home."

Karyn sighed, reluctant to leave even though she knew he was right. A romantic sunset, a beautiful beach, a man whose body entranced her: they'd all worked their spell. But now the spell was broken, and home was where she belonged. Back to reality, she thought ruefully, loosing the clasp of his hands and stepping away from him. "The water was like ice," she remarked, trying to mask how suddenly and inexplicably bereft she felt.

"Have you ever swum in the Bahamas? Or the Mediterranean?"

Steve had taken her to St. Lucia once; it had been a disaster from beginning to end, his obsessive jealousy poisoning every breath she took. She said evasively, "It must be lovely."

You're going to experience it very soon, thought Rafe. With me. What had started here, on an island beach, could only be continued. He took her by the hand and side by side they walked back to the car.

There were four vehicles left in the lot. A family was just getting into a red SUV, parents and a little boy.

Karyn's eyes widened in horror. She tried to duck behind

Rafe, but she was too late. The boy was waving at her. "Hey, Mum," he yelled, "there's Karyn!"

The woman's head swiveled around. "Karyn," she called, and after the smallest of hesitations walked over to them, followed by her husband and the little boy. "How nice to see you. Wasn't the sunset beautiful?"

Passionately wishing they'd met anyone else at the beach but this particular family, Karyn quickly made the introductions. "Sheila and Duncan Harvey, and their son, Donny. This is Rafe Holden, who's visiting from England."

If Duncan recognized the name, he was discreet enough not to mention it. He made some commonplace remark to Rafe as Donny ran over to Karyn, grabbing her by the skirt. She ruffled his tangled red curls; he smelled of salt water and seaweed. They all chatted for a few minutes, then Duncan said heartily, "We'd better get this fella back home, it's past his bedtime. Nice to have met you, Rafe. Karyn, we'll see you around."

Sheila gave Karyn a brief, hard hug. Then Karyn got into Rafe's car as fast as she could and busied herself fastening her seat belt. Rafe got in, too. His intuition operating in high gear, he said casually, "The little guy, Donny—he's got a crush on you?"

She bit her lip. "You could say so."

He put his hand on her wrist. "What's up, Karyn? There was something off-key about all that."

Dark hair feathered his forearm; she felt that inner shiver he could arouse in her simply by existing. If he'd had her investigated, he could do the same for Steve; she wouldn't put it past him. She said tonelessly, "My husband, Steve, saved Donny's life when the boy fell through the ice on the river near their house. Steve saw what was happening through the window—we were neighbors of the Harveys.

But after he'd lifted Donny onto the thicker ice, the current got hold of Steve and pulled him under the ice. They found his body two days later.''

Whatever Rafe had expected, it hadn't been this. "I'm so sorry,'' he said. "No wonder Sheila hugged you—and no wonder it's difficult to see them. They must feel so incredibly grateful, yet horribly guilty at the same time. I understand perfectly why you sold the house you and Steve were living in.''

Karyn made an indeterminate noise. She was sure it hadn't occurred to Steve that he might drown should he try and rescue a small boy from the river; Steve had never believed in his own mortality. However, the fact that he'd died in the act of saving a little boy's life still filled her with complex and conflicting emotions. She'd been freed from the terrible prison her marriage had become, no question of that; yet his last action couldn't help but redeem him in her eyes. It also made her feel unutterably sad.

How could she possibly explain all this to Rafe? She scarcely understood it herself.

Karyn was very quiet all the way back; and Rafe was busy with his own thoughts. So Steve had been a hero, who'd lost his life saving a small boy from drowning. How could Rafe possibly fault that? Yet he was jealous of a dead man.

Despicable, he thought. What kind of lowlife are you?

Doing his best to concentrate on the road, Rafe found himself for the second time wondering whether Karyn had directed him to take an unnecessary detour near Heddingley; he had an excellent sense of direction. He said nothing. After he'd parked in her driveway, he got out of the car and lifted the hamper from the trunk. "Have the leftovers for lunch tomorrow, Karyn.''

She took the hamper from him, holding it like a shield in front of her. "Good night," she said awkwardly.

"I'll pick you up tomorrow at six, does that give you enough time?"

She should say no. End this now. Everything rational within her told her to do just that. "Plenty of time," she said, turned on her heel and hurried into the house.

Rafe waited until she was indoors before driving back to his hotel in the city. He hadn't actually lied this evening about his reasons for seeking Karyn out; just prevaricated. His father, Reginald, was a demon bridge player who early on had taught Rafe one rule: play your cards close to your chest. It was a rule that had often stood Rafe in good stead.

With Karyn, was he playing the game of his life, with passion as the wild card? Would he win or lose?

Did his happiness depend on the answer?

As soon as she got in the house, Karyn phoned her best friend, Liz Gaudet, who managed to combine being a wife, a nurse and a mother without losing either her sanity or her warmth. "Liz? This is an emergency. I've been invited for dinner somewhere really fancy tomorrow night. What will I wear?"

"Wow. Where? Who with?"

Karyn swallowed. "I don't know where. I'll be with Rafe Holden—I told you about him. My sister Fiona's friend."

"The filthy rich Rafe Holden?"

"Who's used to sophisticated jet-setters in designer labels and makeup by Elizabeth Arden."

"He hasn't asked them out for dinner. He's asked you. Okay, let's think."

"I had lots of evening clothes when I was married because Steve and I used to go to insurance bashes. But I got rid of them all and I haven't needed any since.''

''Smart of you to turf them,'' said Liz; she'd made no secret of her dislike for Karyn's husband. ''How long's your lunch hour tomorrow?''

''Forty-five minutes max.''

''So that's out. I've got that wonderful sea-green dress I bought before Jared was born and that I've never been able to get into. It'd fit you.'' Liz sighed histrionically. ''You're so slim, just like I used to be.''

''It's not too dressy?''

''For Rafe Holden? No way. Can you come over now? And, Karyn, I can't tell you how happy I am that you're going out on a real date. The guy's a hunk—I've seen pictures of him. Just about made me salivate and I love my darling Pierre with all my heart.''

Panic flickering in her chest, Karyn rang off. An hour and a half later, she was home again. She hung the dress in her closet, taking a moment to admire it first. Liz had put the hem up an inch, but otherwise it had fit Karyn perfectly. She could wear the stiletto heels she'd bought on sale in town a couple of months ago because they made her ankles look so impossibly slim. Her mother had left her a pair of delicate crystal earrings that would be perfect with the dress; and in her precious forty-five-minute lunchbreak tomorrow she'd go to the drugstore for new eyeshadow and mascara.

And a new toothbrush?

She fingered the thin straps of Liz's dress. What was she doing, getting all dolled up to go out for dinner with a man wealthy beyond her imagining and so sexy he made her melt?

Playing with fire, for sure.

But hadn't Steve, in two years of marriage, crushed her

spirit of adventure? Dammit, she was going somewhere very special with an escort most women would die for, and she was going to have a good time. So what if she didn't have a clue exactly where they were going? So what if the next day she was back to eating macaroni and wearing work boots?

It'd be worth it, she thought, and went to have a shower.

Rafe was up early the next day. After breakfast he contacted his head office, swiftly delegating a job he'd planned to look after himself. He spent the rest of the morning working on his laptop. That afternoon, he drove through Heddingley and took the most direct route to Stanhope. Searching from side to side, he soon saw what he'd suspected he'd find: the Harveys' red SUV parked outside a split-level house. Their name was printed on the mail box. He drew up beside an elderly woman determinedly speed-walking along the shoulder of the road. "Excuse me? Can you tell me if Steven Patterson used to live around here?"

If she thought it odd that he was inquiring about a dead man, she was puffing too hard to question him. "In the Cape Cod next to the Harveys," she gasped. "His widow—such a sweet girl—sold it very soon after he died and moved into Heddingley."

"Thanks," Rafe said with his best smile. "You're setting a great pace."

"Why are calories so easy to put on and so hard to get off? If you can explain that to me, young man, you'll go far."

Saluting her, Rafe pulled a U-turn and drove back toward Heddingley. Yesterday evening, Karyn had twice avoided passing Steve's house. Plus, he thought with a catch at his heart, the river that wound so placidly behind it.

He then drove past the veterinary clinic. He could have

gone in; in a place this size, Karyn's boss would undoubtedly have known Karyn's husband. Or he could have in-
dulged in gossip at the local supermarket.

He didn't want to do either one. He wanted Karyn to tell
him about her marriage, and the grief that had followed
Steve's tragic death.

He'd phone the clinic, though, when he got back to his
hotel, and ask to speak to Karyn's boss. Planning ahead
was a strategy that had never done him any harm.

Even if Karyn did tell him about Steve tonight, he still
had to bide his time, building a relationship step by step.
No sudden moves. His passionate need of her leashed.

She was worth waiting for. With every moment he spent
in her company, Rafe was more and more convinced that
in some way that still eluded him, she was important to
him.

Wasn't that why he was here?

CHAPTER SEVEN

KARYN was ready at quarter to six. As ready as she'd ever be. She started pacing up and down her bedroom, growing more and more nervous by the second. More and more convinced that what she'd called playing with fire was nothing but insanity.

Rafe Holden wasn't for her. In bed or out.

In all likelihood she was risking a repeat of the terrible mistake she'd made with Steve, by getting in over her head with a man she knew virtually nothing about. Was she out of her mind?

At three minutes to six, the doorbell rang. She jumped as though someone had shot off a gun in her ear, made an unnecessary adjustment to the neckline of her dress and walked carefully downstairs in her high heels.

But two steps from the bottom, Karyn stopped. She wasn't walking toward a firing squad. She was going out to dinner with Rafe Holden. Any number of women would vaccinate a thousand sheep for the privilege. So was she going to behave like a terrified ewe?

No way.

She straightened her shoulders, pasted a brilliant smile on her lips and opened the door.

"My God," said Rafe.

Her dress was a brief shimmer of sea-green over impossibly long legs. Her shoulders and arms were bare, her cleavage...don't go there, Rafe. At her lobes, tiny earrings shot flashes of colored fire; her lips were luscious curves of iridescent pink.

Uncertainty flickered across her face. "Too much eye-shadow? Lipstick on my teeth?"

"You're perfect," he said unsteadily. "The most beautiful woman I've ever seen."

Her smile was more natural. "Oh, sure."

"I'm telling you the truth," Rafe said in a raw voice.

He meant it. Karyn's jaw dropped. "It's only my friend Liz's dress and makeup from the Heddingley drugstore."

"I don't care what it is, you take my breath away—and that's the truth, too."

Hadn't he done the same to her? Her cheeks flushing a bright pink that had nothing to do with makeup, Karyn said, "You don't look too bad yourself. Heck, who am I kidding? You're gorgeous, you're sexy, you look good enough to eat."

"Any time," Rafe said.

Her flush deepened. His light gray suit was impeccably tailored; his blue shirt was teamed with an elegant silk tie. He could have graced the pages of any glossy magazine. Yet beneath his highly civilized garments, she was all too aware of his sheer physicality: his muscular body, broad-shouldered and narrow-hipped; his every move with a predator's grace and sleek economy.

Danger, her brain screamed.

Shut up, she thought in an intoxicating surge of rebellion. I've earned a night out. The last three years have been hell on wheels and why shouldn't I have a few hours of fun? She fluttered her mascaraed lashes at him. "Is the restaurant—wherever it is—ready for us?"

"It might be. I'm not sure I am."

"I'm a small town girl, Rafe. Nothing fancy. Certainly not what you're used to."

Not like Celine, he thought. "Besides being so beautiful you knock my socks off, you're real, Karyn," he said forcefully. "You've got integrity and courage. If you made a promise, you'd do your best to keep it. Don't ask me how I know that, I just do."

"Well, of course I would," she said, slightly offended that he could even question that.

His voice deepened. "If I kiss you, will I wreck that shiny lipstick?"

"According to the label, it's kissproof."

"Why don't we put it to the test?"

Her breath caught in her throat. She closed her eyes, feeling his breath warm on her cheek, then the first tantalizing sweep of his mouth over hers. As her lips parted to the dart of his tongue, nothing could have stopped her low purr of pleasure. She locked her arms around his neck, lipstick and their destination dropping from her mind as he tasted and sought and explored.

He was clasping her by the hips, pressing her to his body; she could be in no doubt that he wanted her. In a thrill of pride, she allowed her own needs to surface, hot and urgent. Was this the adventure she craved? All her doubts and fears eclipsed in Rafe's arms?

It was Rafe who pulled back. With a hand whose tremor he couldn't quite disguise, he brushed a gleaming tendril of hair back from her cheek; then, briefly, buried his face in the sweet-scented curve of her shoulder. Bide your time, Rafe. Take it slow.

Easy enough to say, not so easy to do after a kiss that had made nonsense of his own counsel. "We'd better go," he muttered, "or we won't be going anywhere."

"I have to relay every detail of the menu to Liz," Karyn said faintly. "She'd never forgive me if I only took this dress up to bed with you."

"A terrible waste," he said with a wry grin. "Is that your shawl? It could turn cool later on."

As she nodded, he picked up a white shawl woven from the finest of wool and threaded with silver. He draped it around her shoulders, his fingers brushing the smooth ivory of her skin. Bide your time, don't rush and keep your cards close to your chest, he thought crazily. All he had to do was follow his own advice.

All? It sounded like one hell of a lot.

Outside her house a shiny black limousine was parked, a uniformed chauffeur at the wheel. Karyn blinked. "Are you trying to impress me? Because if you are, it's working."

"We only go this way once."

Rafe helped her into the back seat, trying not to stare at her slim legs in their glistening hose. Then he got in the other side. On the seat between them was a great sheaf of pink roses. Karyn lifted them, breathing deep of their fragrance. "Are those for me?"

Her face was rapt, the voluptuous softness of her lips almost more than he could bear. He said clumsily, "If you want them."

"How could I not? They're gorgeous!"

She gave him a radiant smile, her eyes sparkling like the crystals at her lobes. Any sensible thoughts fled from Rafe's brain. "How was your day?" he asked with a singular lack of originality.

She began describing the various cats, dogs and pigs that she'd seen since eight o'clock that morning, and gradually he relaxed. When the limo came to a halt, Karyn looked out. "We're at the airport," she said, puzzled.

"That's my private jet over there."

A shadow crossed her face. "Where are we going, Rafe?"

"An hour's flight, to a resort I own in Maine. I'll have you home in time for work tomorrow."

Trust me. That was the message. Perhaps she could trust him; it was herself she was worried about. Rafe added, "You'll like it there, I promise."

She said with a frown that charmed him, "You're really very rich, aren't you?"

"Very."

"How many resorts do you own?"

"A couple of hundred."

"And how many houses?"

She looked as suspicious as though owning foreign property was a criminal activity. He said meekly, "The stone house in Droverton, a penthouse in London and the cottage in the Hebrides. A ski chalet in St. Moritz. And a lovely open bungalow in the Caicos Islands. But I spend as much time as I can at Stoneriggs, and I often loan the others out to friends."

"We've got nothing in common!"

"Karyn," Rafe said with sudden authority, "we're not getting into any heavy-duty discussions before dinner. If you leave money out of the equation, we've got a whole lot in common. The pilot's waiting for us—let's go."

The sleek Learjet delighted Karyn with its deep leather seats, kitchenette and fully appointed bathroom. Laying her roses carefully on an empty seat, she put her small overnight bag in the overhead bin and settled down to enjoy herself.

The resort was on an emerald-green island off the coast of Maine, private yachts and cabin cruisers dotting a sea smooth as glass. As the jet descended, Rafe said, "I've designed this place as a conference centre for executives. So there's a helicopter pad, meeting rooms with state-of-the-art technology and a sportsclub. You can see the marina from the air. There's also an Olympic-size pool in the solarium."

Karyn grinned. "I'd find it awfully difficult to concentrate on business."

"It's been a good investment," Rafe said casually, as the jet touched down and taxied along the runway, coming to a halt near a manicured golf course. Another limo was waiting for them on the tarmac. They drove along a winding road edged with fir trees and silver birch, past chalets tucked among the trees, and gleaming sand beaches interspersed with great chunks of granite. The main lodge, built Adirondack-style out of stone and cedar, took Karyn's breath away. But the limo kept going, until they reached a secluded cedar bungalow surrounded on three sides by magnificent copper beeches, dense shrubbery and gardens scented with lilies, honeysuckle and roses. The other side was open to the ocean and a curve of pale sand.

As they got out, Rafe said easily, "There are three bedrooms, choose whichever one you want. Then we'll go for dinner at the lodge."

Each bedroom had its own balcony, a fireplace, and a marble bathroom with a whirlpool tub and piles of luxuriously thick towels. In the living room, paneled in bleached pine, hand-woven rugs were scattered over the hardwood floor; modernistic glass sculptures framed a stone hearth. Karyn had run out of superlatives; she had no idea how she was going to describe all this to Liz. Perhaps it would be easier to tell Fiona, who was used to this kind of luxury.

Feeling as though she was in a dream, she walked with Rafe to the lodge under a sky blazoned with gold-flecked clouds. As they were greeted in the vaulted foyer with its expanse of windows overlooking the surf, Rafe glanced sideways at his companion. She looked as composed as though she visited resorts like this every day of the week, he thought with a quiver of amusement. After they'd been seated at their table and left with the menus, Rafe said softly, "You're not to even look at the prices, Karyn, have you got that?"

Trying not to gape at the high timbered ceiling, priceless carpets and even more priceless view, Karyn picked up the menu and opened the embossed leather cover. "I'm hungry enough to reduce you to penury," she smiled. Then, in spite of herself, her eyes widened in shock. "Rafe—it'll be bankruptcy."

"I own the place, remember? Order whatever you want."

This time her smile was pure mischief. "We won't end up washing dishes?"

"Not tonight."

She gave a sigh of pleasure. "How am I ever going to decide?"

Celine, he remembered, had taken for granted everything he'd given her. But Karyn wouldn't. Any woman capable of medicating a sick bull wasn't going to be blasé about the finest gourmet cuisine.

Was he falling in love with her?

He began discussing the appetizers, steering away from a question he wasn't ready to answer. When their wine was poured, he raised his glass. "Shall we toast Fiona and John?"

"To their happiness," Karyn said, sudden tears shimmering in her eyes. "I really miss her…and I'm dying to meet John."

"You can stay at Stoneriggs any time you like. Use it as a base."

Her lashes flickered. It was on the tip of her tongue to say he was taking a lot for granted; but hadn't he warned her against heavy-duty discussions? Savoring the chardonnay on her tongue, she exclaimed, "I've never tasted anything so wonderful—who else can we toast?"

He laughed. "Your friend Liz?"

"Absolutely. To Liz and Pierre."

He clinked his glass with hers. "I'm so happy to be here with you, Karyn."

The words had come out before he could censor them. Her blue eyes, deep and unreadable, flicked to his and then away. "I'll take that as a compliment to my borrowed dress."

It was, very subtly, a brush-off. Rafe felt the stirrings of anger, and stamped them down. A confrontation was no doubt in the offing. But he had no intention of it taking place here. "So you should," he said easily. "Why don't we toast my parents next? To Joan and Reginald—who are as madly in love now as they were when they got married."

She echoed him, the wine sliding down her throat. She didn't want to discuss the institution of marriage as embodied in his parents. "They run the castle, don't they?"

"In their eccentric way, yes." He began describing Holden Castle as it was many years ago and now, moving to his mother's pack of irresponsible dogs and his father's obsession with contract bridge. His face was lit with an affection that touched her in spite of herself. How could she not be drawn to a man who so unselfconsciously loved his wacky-sounding parents?

As the wine sank in the bottle, she began to talk about her own parents, her father's long battle with heart disease and the hardships that had brought to the family; her mother's steadfast support of husband and daughter. "I buried myself in my books at university—how could I not when she'd given up so much to send me there?" she said, taking her first mouthful of a leafy green salad lightly tossed with a cranberry vinaigrette. "Mmm…luscious."

"They use local ingredients as much as possible." Rafe asked another question, drawing her out about her childhood and adolescence. A shrimp terrine, scallops from the bay with julienned garden vegetables, and a maple syrup mousse followed, each accompanied by the appropriate wine. But even then, Karyn's tongue didn't loosen in one particular area: when he mentioned Steve's name once or twice, she swiftly changed the subject.

His hope that she'd share some of the details of her marriage wasn't panning out. He could have been more direct, insisting on answers to specific questions. But he wasn't ready to be quite so unsubtle.

As she drained her espresso, Karyn gave a sigh of repletion. ''That was the best meal I've eaten in my entire life,'' she said. ''Thank you, Rafe.''

''My pleasure,'' he said, the simple words invested with new meaning. ''Want to wander around the grounds for a while before we head back? Or dance on the patio?''

''I used to love to dance,'' she said wistfully. Steve had been a technically perfect dancer; but the music had never entered his soul, and she'd soon learned not to take other partners. Briefly a memory of his savage temper rippled along her nerves; she shivered, her eyes downcast.

''Are you cold?''

''Too much wine,'' she said with a smile that didn't quite reach her eyes.

''Let's go dance,'' Rafe said. All evening he'd had the sense that someone else was sitting at the table with them: a man called Steve, who'd died a hero. It was a feeling he could do without, he thought, getting to his feet and offering her his arm.

The canopied patio was entwined with wisteria, the blooms like ghostly blue lanterns in the moonlight. Several other couples were circling the floor to music that was dreamy and romantic; Karyn gave herself over to it, moving into Rafe's arms as naturally as if she'd been dancing with him all her life. He said, smiling down at her, "You're taller than you were in your steel-toed boots."

She chuckled. "Actually, my feet are killing me. How do women ever walk in these shoes?"

"Take 'em off."

Scandalized, she said, "Here?"

"Darling Karyn, we can make our own rules."

Darling...and was it true? Could she make her own rules? If so, she wanted the evening to end with Rafe in her bed. Once he'd taken her home tomorrow, he'd be leaving for Toronto, so what could be the harm? He'd told her back in England that he'd sworn off passionate relationships; so he wouldn't want commitment any more than she did. They could go to bed together and then go their separate ways.

The perfect ending to a perfect evening.

She leaned into Rafe's body, intuitively following his lead, feeling fluid in his arms, slumberous with desire. Lifting her lips to his throat, she whispered, "We could go back to the bungalow."

He said huskily, "I think that's a fine idea."

Even his voice was perfect, she thought with a frisson down her spine. As deep and smooth as the amber-colored brandy he'd ordered after dinner. Her whole body a single ache of longing, she let him take her by the hand and lead her from the dance floor. Hand in hand, they walked back to the bungalow. As he unlocked the door and they went inside, Karyn said casually, "When are you flying to Toronto?"

"I'm in no hurry."

"I thought you had a sale to look after."

"I delegated it. Got the report late this afternoon, it doesn't look like the site suits our criteria."

A little edge to her voice, she said, "But you're going home soon."

"In a hurry to get rid of me?"

All her senses alert, she said with careful truth, "If we go to bed together tonight, it's not the start of an affair. Or of any kind of commitment."

Rafe said sharply, "You mean you'll spend the night with me providing I head across the Atlantic tomorrow morning?"

"You told me when you arrived that you were dropping in—not staying long, in other words."

"Maybe I've changed my mind."

"Maybe you should have communicated that to me." She gave a sigh of frustration. "Rafe, I don't want to end a magical evening by arguing with you. You said to me once that you'd sworn off passion for life...*she ripped the heart from my body* was how you put it. That's why you were thinking of marrying Fiona, who, to put it mildly, didn't turn your crank. But what's between you and me— if that's not passion, I don't know what to call it. So I've been going on the assumption that the last thing you'd want from me is any kind of commitment."

She'd found, unerringly, the weak point in his armor. "It's too soon to talk about the future," he said forcefully. "I just want to get to know you. To see if there's anything between us to build on."

"Build what?"

"You don't let up, do you?"

"Most people don't travel four thousand miles for a picnic!"

His eyes like gimlets, he said, "I don't like talking about this—why for years even the thought of passion made me run a country mile. But it's time I did."

She said mutinously, "I don't need to hear your life story."

His voice dangerously soft, Rafe said, "Just listen to me for five minutes, will you?"

All Karyn's euphoria on the dance floor had vanished, eaten up by a pervading anxiety. "All right, I'll listen. But don't expect me to change my mind—I'm not into commitment."

"We'll get to the reasons for that later," Rafe said curtly, by sheer willpower forcing her to hold his gaze. "But this is about me. Why I was just fine until you came along." He paused, trying to calm down. When had he ever let a woman get to him as easily as Karyn did?

So much for his famous defences.

"I met Celine when I was twenty-five," he said, ironing any emotion from his tone. He was asking for understanding; not sympathy. "I was on the way up, living in high gear twenty-four hours a day. Working my guts out, traveling all over the world, dealing with men who had ten times my experience. Celine was from Paris, she was a model and so beautiful she stole my heart the first time I saw her." He moved his shoulders restlessly. "I figured she was unattainable. But to my intense gratification she wasn't. We fell into bed and for the next eighteen months I was head over heels in love with her."

Karyn stood still; through the open windows she could hear the shush of the breeze through the beech trees. She hated every word he was telling her. She was jealous, she thought incredulously, jealous of a woman Rafe had loved years ago.

Perhaps he still did.

"Celine traveled a lot with her job, as did I. But whenever we could meet, we did." Rafe grimaced. "Now I can see that the long-distance aspect was what made our affair last as long as it did, yet simultaneously destroyed it. The ending was predictable. I got home early from Bangkok and found her in bed with another man. Not the only man she'd been seeing, so I discovered when I confronted her. She'd been systematically betraying me from the beginning, all the while swearing her fidelity."

In the dim glow of light from the hall, his face was bleak. Karyn said gently, "I'm sorry."

"We all have to grow up sometime...but I'd trusted her. Completely. She laughed in my face, that was the worst of it. As though I'd been an utter fool to take her at her word. *But, Rafe, no one stays just with one man...how bourgeois.*"

"That was hateful of her," Karyn said hotly.

"After that night, I never saw her again. But from then on I only dated women who knew the score, and I kept all my defences in place. Like you," he finished sardonically, "I wasn't into commitment."

What was she supposed to say to that? "Lots of women are capable of fidelity."

"Fiona would have been, certainly. I knew her. I trusted her. I loved her in a way that didn't scare the hell out of me."

The words were out before Karyn could stop them. "Do you still love Celine?"

"No. It took a while, but eventually my feelings for her died."

"You don't love me."

Rafe winced inwardly. "I don't know what I feel. Other than straightforward lust."

"Do I scare the hell out of you?"

"Yes."

His monosyllable hung in the air between them. Karyn

said evenly, "One more reason for you to fly straight home tomorrow."

"And live like a coward for the rest of my life? I don't think so." He hesitated. "I'm being as honest as I can when I say that marrying Fiona would have suited me in other ways. You see, I was ready to settle down. Spend more time at Stoneriggs, and raise a family. Fiona's always liked the idea of having children. It all fit together." He hesitated again. "I still want to settle down and have a couple of kids. Just not with Fiona."

A cold fist was squeezing Karyn's heart. She said quietly, "There must be lots of women who'd be very happy to be your wife and the mother of your children. Go home and find one, Rafe."

"I can't do that. Not when I'm beginning to think you're the one I want."

"That's ridiculous! We've scarcely spent any time together, and the circumstances have been so complicated—you don't know anything about me."

Some things you know from the beginning? She sure didn't want to hear that. "You're forgetting something. I know Fiona. So in a way I know you."

"My life's been completely different from Fiona's!"

"Why don't you tell me how? Not the money, not your career—the rest of it."

She bent to undo the straps of her shoes, her dress glimmering softly, her cleavage shadowed; her shawl was a ghostly white. "Let's cut to the chase. You're asking for intimacy. I don't do intimacy. I don't do long-term. Get that through your head."

"Why don't you?"

"Because it hurts too much." She was telling the truth, she told herself fiercely. Well, sort of. It had just hurt in a different way than anyone else realized.

Rafe gazed at her in silence, his nerves stretched tight. She was talking about Steve. About a pain so deep that a year later she wouldn't even consider getting involved with another man. "You're the one who suggested we cut to the chase, Karyn," he said evenly. "Talk to me about Steve…how you met and what he meant to you. I don't have any idea what he was like."

"I want to go to bed with you. Not wallow in reminiscences."

"You're a widow, for Pete's sake! Why wouldn't I ask about your husband?"

She tilted her chin stubbornly. "I don't want to—there's no point. Rafe, we both know what happens when you and I get within ten feet of each other—and there's nothing wrong with lust. But I'm not going to dress it up as something it isn't. We can go to bed together and you can leave for England in the morning. Or we'll sleep in separate rooms."

"You want us to make love and then act as though it never happened."

"That's right." Suddenly she reached out, laying her hand on his sleeve and speaking with passionate intensity. "I want to be naked in my bed with you naked beside me. I want to taste every inch of you, I want to be held, I want you inside me." Her voice broke. "But that's all I want— I can't be any more honest than that."

His whole body felt as though it had been streaked with fire. He looked down at her slender fingers, feeling the pressure of her nails and imagining them digging into his bare back, the softness of her breasts against his chest, her long legs wrapped around his thighs. His heart was thudding against his rib cage. Wasn't that what he wanted, too? Karyn, naked and willing in his arms? The whole night before them…

With an effort that felt monumental, he pulled back. "But tomorrow you want me to get in my jet, fly back to England and stay there."

She nodded. "I'm on the pill, so I won't get pregnant. There'll be nothing to tie us together—and that's just the way I want it."

He said flatly, "I've been insulted a few times in my life, but you take the cake."

"You'd rather we didn't use protection?"

"I'd rather you didn't treat me like a one-night stand!"

Her nostrils flared. "Sex without commitment—men have been doing it for years. But I'm not allowed to because I'm a woman?"

"Clever, Karyn. This isn't about equal rights—it's about caring and intimacy."

"It's about relationship. We don't have one. I don't want one."

"Then I'm not going near your bed. Now or ever."

"Fine!" she snapped, clutching her shoes to her chest. "Sleep well and don't bother dropping in on me again." Then she stalked across the room to the farthest bedroom and slammed the door. The lock turned with an aggressive *click*.

Feeling as though he'd just done ten rounds with a champion heavyweight, Rafe left the bungalow and marched back to the lodge.

A woman he lusted after had offered him a night in her bed and he'd turned her down flat.

He was a fool. An idiot.

Be damned if he'd make love with her all night and then fly home in the morning as though nothing had happened. He wasn't going to be treated that way—discounted as though he could offer nothing but physical release. If that's all she thought of him, to hell with her.

Systematically Rafe went through the highly colorful stock of swearwords he'd learned in the many corners of the world. He didn't feel one bit better afterward. He told himself Karyn was just a woman: pretty, sure; sexy undeniably; but replaceable. How long was it since he'd gone to bed with anyone? Too long, obviously.

He'd be a fool to fall in love with her.

So he wouldn't.

First thing tomorrow he'd tell the pilot to prepare for a transatlantic flight. There'd be no hanging around in Charlottetown.

He'd soon find someone to settle down with, to be the mother of his children. He could advertise, Rafe thought cynically. They'd be flocking after him. Him and his fortune.

Karyn didn't care one whit about his money.

Karyn didn't care about him. Period. All she wanted to do was use him for her own ends and then cast him aside.

She was honest about it, though, a little voice insinuated in his ear. After all, isn't that how you've been living your life for the last six years? Ever since Celine took your pride and trampled it on a Paris street?

It wasn't the same thing at all.

No? Think about it, Rafe.

Scowling, he crossed the lobby, heading straight for the bar. He sat down, got the bartender's attention and ordered a brandy.

When it came, he stared at it moodily. He didn't want anything more to drink. Cupping the glass in his palm, he swirled the liquid around and around. Wasn't that what he was doing—going around in circles?

He was through with Karyn and her little games. He'd see her at Fiona's wedding, and no doubt at the christenings that in due time would follow. But he could handle that. By then, he'd be married himself.

"Buy me a drink?"

His head swiveled around. A very pretty young woman in a black dress had slithered onto the stool next to his. Daughter of a CEO, he thought. No harm in her, out for a good time and she'd picked on him. So, he thought ironically, he'd been presented with Karyn's replacement sooner than he'd expected.

"Sorry," he said, feeling old enough to be her father, "I'm not available. You should be careful who you come onto—not everyone's harmless like me."

"You don't look harmless."

He nodded at the bartender, tossed a bill on the counter and said crisply, "Serve the lady the drink of her choice and keep the change." He gave her a cool smile. "Good night," he said and strode out of the bar.

I'm not available. That's what he'd said.

As he approached the bungalow, he stopped for a few minutes under the shadows of the beech trees. To be unavailable was to be committed. He was committed to Karyn, a woman of undoubted passion who'd freed his own deep needs.

He didn't understand what that commitment meant. But it wasn't to be taken lightly.

He'd bet Holden Castle and his beloved Stoneriggs that Karyn was afraid to fall in love again. She'd done so once, and lost the man she'd loved. Who could blame her if she didn't want commitment? He himself had avoided it for years after Celine had dumped him.

Why should Karyn be any different?

Loosening his tie and shrugging off his jacket, Rafe headed toward the bungalow. He knew exactly what he was going to do.

CHAPTER EIGHT

A HALF-MOON silvered the trees and shrubbery, the lawns like a black carpet; except for a light in the hallway, the bungalow was in darkness. The soft plash of surf was the only sound. Rafe took a deep breath, inhaling the scents of newly mown grass and honeysuckle, laced with the tang of the sea.

What he was about to do would have long-lasting repercussions, he thought soberly. He was more than ready to allow passion back into his life, he'd proved that to himself the last few days. But he wasn't standing here in the dead of night just because he wanted to make love to Karyn. No, it was far more complex than that.

He wanted more from Karyn, a lot more; and he was willing to give more. To let down his defences and allow her in. To hope that eventually, if he were patient, she'd surmount her grief and do the same for him. Where that would all lead, he had no idea. Trying to ease the tension in his shoulders, he walked up the path toward the front door.

Somewhere inside the bungalow, Karyn screamed.

For a split second Rafe stood like a man transfixed, a chill racing the length of his spine. Then she screamed again, a choked sound wild with terror.

She'd locked her bedroom door. He couldn't get in that way.

He raced around the corner of the bungalow and in a great surge of relief saw that she'd left her bathroom window open. Leaping over the flowerbed, Rafe punched in the screen and levered himself over the sill. If someone was hurting her, he'd kill the bastard. Landing on his feet, he crossed the ceramic floor, not caring how much noise he made. The door to her bedroom was closed. He burst in, his fists at the ready.

Karyn was alone in the room. Sprawled facedown on the bed, she was whimpering in her sleep, breathing hard as though she were running. Even as he watched, she flipped over on her back, her eyes tight shut, her face contorted in an agony of fear.

Swiftly Rafe crossed the room and sat down on the bed. "Karyn, wake up—you're having a bad dream," he said, taking her by the shoulders and gently shaking her.

Her eyes flew open, stark with terror. "Don't come near me—go away!" She struck out at Rafe, frantically twisting her body as she tried to pull free.

He said urgently, "It's Rafe—you're safe with me, Karyn...I won't let anyone hurt you."

He was still clasping her by the shoulders. She went very still in his hold. "Rafe?" she whispered.

He pulled her to his chest. "It's all right," he murmured. "You were having a nightmare, that's all."

She was trembling now, tiny shudders that lanced him to the heart. Stroking her back with all the tenderness at his command, he said, "Tell me about it, what was happening."

She burrowed her head into his sweater, her arms fastening around his ribs with desperate strength. She had to tell him; she could feel the words beating at her skull, desperate for release. "It's always the same dream," she faltered. "But this time it went further than it ever has. I was so frightened and—hold on to me, Rafe, please don't let go."

"I won't," he said; and at a deep level knew the words for a vow. Binding and inevitable.

"The dream's about Steve. It's always about Steve."

"About him drowning?"

She shivered. "If only it were that simple…"

"Tell me. It'll help if you share it with me."

Would it? Karyn had no way of knowing. But she couldn't bear to carry this load on her own any longer. "I— I'm running away from Steve, that's how it always starts," she gulped. "I've left him and I know I have to get away and hide somewhere or he'll find me. Track me down like a hunted animal. It's in a city, I don't know where and it doesn't matter. I'm running down these dark alley-ways…there are men sleeping on the sidewalk, all bundled up in newspapers like so much garbage, and I jump over them and run for the next alley. The whole time I'm ter-rified out of my wits—I keep hearing footsteps behind me but when I look, there's no one there. My lungs hurt and I can hardly breathe and I don't know how much longer I can keep going. Then, finally, I come out into the open and see the river, the water smooth as oil."

Her breath hitched in her throat. "Steve's standing there. His clothes are wet, still muddy from the river, and I realize he didn't drown after all. He has a gun in his hand and he's pointing it at my heart. Just as he's squeezing the trigger— that's when I usually wake up."

Rafe sat very still, listening with growing horror. A mar-riage was being revealed to him, a marriage the very op-posite of the idyllic love match he'd pictured. He said neu-trally, "What was different about the dream tonight?"

"I couldn't wake up. I was frozen, paralyzed, praying for release. Still holding the gun, he started walking toward me, taking his time, not saying a word because there was nothing he needed to say. We both knew I was powerless to stop him no matter what he did—that's when you woke me up.''

''Thank God I did wake you,'' Rafe said harshly.

Her arms tightened around him. ''I—I don't understand why you're here.''

''I went back to the lodge, cooled down and figured you were right—I *was* using a double standard about commitment, one for you and one for me. So I came to tell you so.''

Her brain still flashing with nightmare images, Karyn could scarcely take in what he was saying. ''Whatever the reason, thank heavens you came back.''

She was holding him so hard he could scarcely breathe. Her nightgown was made of some slithery material that bared rather more than it covered; to his nostrils drifted the same sensually layered scent he remembered from their first kiss. He still wanted her. That was a given. But when had he last comforted a woman, held her with a tenderness that sought to make her burdens his own? Or listened to an outpouring of terror that had appalled him?

Never, he thought. ''Tell me about Steve, Karyn. What he was really like.''

Wasn't it time for her to break her vow of self-imposed silence? And who better to do that with than Rafe? ''How did you get in my room?'' she asked, trying to steady her breathing. ''I locked the door.''

''Through the screen in the bathroom window. It now has a big hole in it—I'll have fun explaining that to the staff.''

Her giggle had a slight edge of hysteria. ''He-man stuff.''

''I heard you scream,'' Rafe said tersely. ''I wasn't going to hang around waiting for you to unlock the bedroom door.''

"What if it'd been a burglar?"

"I'd have flattened him first and asked questions afterward."

A little kernel of warmth curled around her heart. "I bet you would have…my throat feels kind of weird, I need a drink of water."

She was no longer trembling. Rafe eased back from her, smiling down at her in the semidarkness. "There are glasses in the kitchen, I'll only be a minute."

Karyn nodded, watching as he got up from the bed and left her room: a tall, rangy man with black hair and a body that entranced her. She got up and went into the bathroom, her gaze riveted to the ripped screen. After closing and latching the window, she walked over to the sink. She looked like a ghost, she thought dispassionately, all big eyes and pale cheeks. Turning on the cold tap, she scrubbed at her face, wishing she could as easily scrub away the past.

When she went back to the bedroom, Rafe was sitting on the bed, propped up against the pillows, looking very much at home. She took a long drink from the glass he held out to her and perched a couple of feet away from him on the mattress.

He said easily, looping an arm around her, "Come closer."

It was so easy to yield to him, to let her head fall to his shoulder, to burrow into it and feel her overstretched nerves relax. For now, she was safe.

Knowing she'd lose courage if she planned what she was about to say, Karyn plunged right in. "I should never have married Steve. We scarcely knew each other—it was a classic case of love at first sight. Only trouble is, no one told me that kind of love can be blind as a bat…well, that's not strictly true. My mother tried to warn me, and so did Liz. But I ignored them both."

Rafe's shirt was smooth under her cheek; the slow rhythm of his breathing was very comforting. "Steve was handsome. He was sexy and charming. Polished, sophisticated and ambitious—he was an accountant with an international firm. So he represented a wider world than the island where I'd grown up and gone to university and gotten my first job. Yet he was in love with me, ordinary Karyn Marshall from Heddingley, Prince Edward Island. I knew I was the luckiest woman in the world. We got a special licence, got married, had a honeymoon in Hawaii and then came home and broke the news."

She sighed. "Once we were settled, we threw a big party to celebrate our marriage. An old boyfriend—he was there with his wife—asked me to dance. We hadn't taken ten steps before Steve cut in and whirled me away. I remember thinking at the time how strong Steve was and how much he loved me—so much so, that he wouldn't want me dancing with anyone else…naive, wasn't I? You can probably guess the rest. I gradually realized that Steve was enormously possessive and pathologically jealous. I work mostly with men. I visit a lot of farms, where there are more men. And yes, I'd dated at university, why wouldn't I? He questioned me obsessively, he didn't want to let me out of his sight in my off-duty hours, and he soon let it be known he didn't approve of my friendship with Liz."

"So you had no one to confide in?"

Grateful that Rafe had so quickly understood her isolation, Karyn nodded. "I suppose Steve did love me, in his way. That's what's so frightening—how many guises love can take, not all of them pleasant."

"Did he hurt you? Physically, I mean?" Rafe asked, taking care to keep any emotion out of his voice.

"Very rarely—he didn't need to." She frowned. "It was so insidious, Rafe. At first I thought he was joking. *If you ever dance with Dave again, I'll break your neck.* But then I realized that it was no joke. He meant it. He was bigger than me, much stronger...and yes, I was afraid of him. Outwardly—to my mother, at the clinic—I kept up this huge front that we were a loving and happily married couple. But all the while I was trying desperately to figure out how to leave him."

"Living a lie's one of the hardest things you can do."

"Just ask me," she said unhappily. "A foolproof way to leave Steve—that's all I wanted. I couldn't just disappear from the face of the earth, and he'd told me if I left him he'd track me down no matter where I went. Was I going to spend the rest of my life looking over my shoulder?"

"You'd have left him," Rafe said. "Eventually."

"Maybe," she said, unconvinced.

"There's no question of your courage."

"But that's just it! You know why I still don't talk about him? Not even to Liz, who's my best friend. Or to Fiona, my very own sister. It's because I'm so ashamed. He turned me into someone I scarcely knew. A coward, who jumped if a shadow moved. A woman who kept trying to placate her husband, please him, keep everything smooth on the surface. It would have been funny if it hadn't been so awful. I couldn't make him happy, no matter what I did, or how much I circumscribed my life and my friendships. My self-esteem plummeted. I despised myself because I didn't dare tell him to go to hell, because I was too afraid to walk out my own front door and never come back."

She let out her breath in a long sigh. "Well, you got an earful there."

"Karyn, you had good reason to be afraid. There's nothing to be ashamed of."

"I hated the woman I'd become," she said in a low voice.

She was picking at the fringe on her bedspread, her head downbent. Rafe lifted her chin, looking straight into her eyes. "Your dream is prophetic—you knew all along that Steve was capable of violence. So you were wise to be afraid of him, and sooner or later you'd have figured out a way to get clear of him. I know you would."

Tears caught on her lashes, she mumbled, "I wish I could believe you."

"You have nothing to be ashamed of," he repeated forcibly.

She ducked her head still lower. "Yes, I do. I haven't told you the worst. When the police came to the clinic and told me Steve had drowned in the river, do you know what I felt? Relief. As though a huge weight had been lifted from my shoulders. That's a terrible epitaph for a marriage." She gave an unsteady laugh. "And then, of course, he was hailed as a hero in the community, and I had to go along with it. It was true—he did save Donny's life at the cost of his own. I've tried so hard to believe that he redeemed himself at the end."

Rafe kept to himself his own conclusions: that Steve's ego had been so immense he couldn't have conceived he might drown in the river that ran behind his house. "You've never told anyone any of this?"

"I couldn't bear to. It was so tawdry, so unconvincing— sure, he gave me a few bruises every now and then, but otherwise I had no evidence. Outwardly, Steve adored me. People used to tell me how lucky I was to have such a handsome husband who doted on me." She grimaced. "I sold the house we'd lived in, I sold his car, and I changed my name back to Marshall. The whole village looked at me askance, but there was no way I could explain."

"Maybe you should try telling Fiona, who loves you. Or your friend Liz. Now that you've told me."

Karyn sat up, turning to face him. "I'm glad I've told you, Rafe," she said slowly. "Thank you for listening."

She looked heartbreakingly fragile in her pale gown, her skin with the sheen of ivory. He could see the jut of her breasts under the silky fabric, and felt his mouth go dry. But how could he possibly suggest they make love after everything she'd told him? "If you're okay, I'll go to my room now."

"Stay here with me."

"Karyn, I—"

"I don't want to be alone, Rafe."

"All right," he said slowly, "I'll stay. I can sleep in the armchair."

She grabbed him instinctively. "No! Here in bed with me. I need you close."

A test, Rafe thought wryly. Of restraint, self-control and willpower. Could he lie beside Karyn in the velvet darkness, hold her in his arms and only offer comfort?

Sure he could. If that's what she needed.

Besides, how could he even be thinking of making love to her now that he knew what a wasteland of fear and loneliness her marriage had been?

Karyn sank down on the bed and tugged at his sleeve. "Hold on to me, Rafe…please."

He pulled off his shoes and socks, and tossed his tie and belt on the chair. Lying beside her, he drew her into his arms, gently pressing her face into his shoulder. She felt as tense as a cornered animal. "You're safe," he murmured. "No one will ever hurt you while I'm around."

For a space of time that felt like forever to him, she lay still; he had no idea what she was thinking. Then she pulled away, gazing up at him in the darkness. "Rafe," she said unevenly, "I want you to make love to me."

He reared up on one elbow. He'd outfaced tycoons and

bluffed his way through cutthroat negotiations on which his whole future had depended; but a handful of words from Karyn and he was speechless.

Ducking her head, she blurted, "I shouldn't have asked you—I'm sorry."

"Karyn, I'm not hesitating because I don't want you," Rafe said forcibly. "But are you sure this is the right time? You've just had a horrible nightmare and you're upset..."

"I want you, Rafe," she said in a low voice. "Now."

His heart overflowed with an emotion he couldn't even name. He said huskily, "You're sure?"

"Yes."

She looked as high-strung as a racehorse, by no means as certain as she was striving to sound. So it was up to him to bridge the gap between the terror that was Steve's legacy and the joy that could be his own gift.

Rafe reached out and drew her into his arms again, her soft curls tickling his chin as he began stroking the length of her spine, smoothly and rhythmically. "We've got all the time in the world," he whispered, closing his eyes and allowing his senses to be saturated with her: her scent, her warmth, her beauty. He moved to her shoulders, rubbing the tension from them, feeling her gradually begin to relax.

She gave a tiny sigh of pleasure and lifted her face to be kissed. "I feel as though I've never done this before," she said with a shaky laugh.

"We haven't. Not with each other." He bent to find her lips, their waiting softness sending a shaft of heat the length of his body. He stamped it down. This wasn't about him. With exquisite control he laved her lips with his tongue, nibbling them, teasing them open, then kissing her in a surge of tenderness. A kiss he wanted to go on forever, he thought dimly.

The first flick of her tongue sent another of those heated

flashes through every nerve. He ran his hands along the yielding curve of her back, let his palms span her ribs and drift to the ripe swell of hip. The satin of her gown tantalized him with its smooth flow; frustrated him because it hid from him her nudity. Need slammed through him. But he couldn't rush her. He mustn't.

Then she undid three buttons on his shirt, sliding her hand beneath it. He gasped involuntarily as she tugged at his chest hair, exploring the arc of rib and the hardness of his belly. Releasing her briefly, Rafe hauled his shirt off, and in a firestorm of desire felt her press her breasts to his bare skin. He took their firm ripeness in his palms and lowered his head; pushing her gown aside, he suckled her, tasting, lingering, caressing, all the while inflamed by her small moans of pleasure. Her head was thrown back. He trailed his mouth the length of her throat, skimming the shells of her ears, nipping her lobes. Then, fighting for restraint, he kissed her again.

She said jaggedly, "Take off my gown, Rafe."

Her eyes were like deep pools of darkness; as she rose to her knees, he slipped the gown over her head and let it fall to the bed. Her body was illumined in the pale glow of the moon, all flow and surrender. He said, scarcely trusting his voice, "You're so beautiful, Karyn."

Drawing her closer, he buried his face between her breasts, the rapid staccato of her heartbeat echoing in his ear. He held the whole world. All he had ever wanted or desired.

As her fingers ran through his hair, he shifted his head, tonguing the sweet rise of her flesh and flicking its tip to hardness. She was whispering his name, over and over, her eyes closed in ecstasy, her body arching backward. He slid his mouth down the tautness of her belly, grasping her by the hips and then touching her between the thighs. She was hot and wet; he almost lost control.

With his fingertips he found her center, watched her shudder in response, her face a blur of desire. Using all the skill at his command, he played with her until she was writhing and sobbing. Beneath his fingers, the throbbing gathered and spun out of control and with the harsh cry of a falcon as it plummets from the sky, she collapsed into his arms.

Her heart was thrumming against his rib cage. Her tiny puffs of breath warmed his bare skin. Then she muttered, "Thank you, Rafe...oh, thank you."

"You don't have to thank me," he said, and knew, instinctively, that for Steve her pleasure would never have been paramount. He, Rafe, was more than making love to her; he was exorcising a ghost. Hadn't he known that all along?

He held her, his heart pounding, his whole body craving its own release. Very slowly she raised her head, her breath still as rapid as if she'd been running. Then she kissed him, her teeth scraping his lips in deliberate seduction.

He couldn't take much more. "Don't you think we should go easy, you must be worn-out—"

She was sinking down on the bed, fumbling for the catch on his trousers. "It's not fair," she whispered, "I haven't got a stitch on, and look at you." She gave a tiny, incredulous laugh. "Just look at you," she repeated, her eyes wandering over his body like licks of fire. "You're beautiful, too."

A simple compliment, yet it speared him to the heart. "Karyn," he said helplessly, "all I want is for you to be happy..."

She was edging his zipper down, her tongue caught between her teeth in concentration; suddenly impatient, he twisted off his trousers and his boxers. Since he'd first started massaging her shoulders, he'd been hard and ready for her; and had kept his distance, not wanting to frighten her.

She smiled at him, a smile of such sweetness that his breath caught in his throat. "I want you to be happy, too."

"I am," said Rafe, his laugh exultant. "How could I not be? I'm in bed with the most beautiful woman in the world."

"Come off it! What about Celine?"

He didn't want to talk about Celine; her many infidelities and the aftermath of her betrayal were past history. Over and done with. In a way, hadn't she done him a good turn over the years by keeping him single until Karyn erupted into his life? "Her beauty was on the surface," he said. "Yours goes all the way to your soul."

Karyn said unsteadily, "That's the loveliest thing anyone's ever said to me."

"Hang around," he teased.

Something flickered across her face. Then she said with an assertiveness that charmed him, "Kiss me, Rafe."

"Anything to oblige."

He eased her down to lie beside him, face to face, kissing her with an intensity that battered at his control. As he fought to hold fast to it, she caught his lower lip in her teeth, gently nibbling, each tiny sensual bite driving him closer to the brink. When she wrapped her arms around his waist and rubbed the whole length of her body against his, he couldn't hold on any longer. Imploding with desire, careless of his own strength, Rafe flipped her on her back and covered her, plunging to find her mouth.

And saw, briefly but unmistakably, the flick of remembered fear on her face.

It was gone before he could say anything; before he

could even draw back. Her eyes fathoms deep, Karyn took his face in her hands and kissed him with a kind of passionate desperation.

How could she ever have doubted her own courage, he wondered. Overwhelmed by sensations utterly new to him, Rafe kissed her back, his one desire to give her a depth of pleasure that would make nonsense of the past. Their tongues danced. Their hands roamed and caressed and explored; thigh was intertwined with thigh, hip held to hip. Their breath, ever more and more heated, mingled. Yet still he held back.

It was she who drew his hand to the damp heat between her thighs, who begged him, her head thrown back, "Rafe, I need you inside me...I can't wait any longer. Oh God, Rafe, now..."

With exquisite care he parted the wet petals of her flesh and eased inside her. His face convulsed as she tightened around him, need coursing like a jolt of electricity through his frame. "I can't—" he began, and heard her cry out his name as the inner throbbing caught her and tossed her as though she was boneless, weightless.

It was all Rafe needed. He allowed himself to rise to the crest, heat and urgency lifting him until he could bear it no longer. His release was fast and tumultuous; his own cry hoarse in his ears.

His breath sobbing in his chest, he rolled over so she was lying on top of him, and held her tightly, his face buried in her neck. Beyond words. Beyond thought. Beyond anything but a storm of gratitude that he had found her: his mate, his beloved.

Beloved, he thought blankly, the truth hitting him between the eyes: a truth he'd been fighting for weeks. He loved Karyn, of course he did. Hadn't every second he'd spent with her since that first incendiary kiss in the woods been leading inevitably to this moment?

He was bound to her with a love as deep as the ocean, as wild as the fells. His soul in her keeping.

But he couldn't tell her so. Not yet.

Then, from a long way away, he became aware of the cool slide of tears on his shoulder. "Karyn?" he said hoarsely. "Did I hurt you?"

She was crying in earnest now, her slender body shuddering in his arms. Helpless to do anything but hold her, Rafe waited until her storm of weeping subsided. He reached with one hand for a tissue from the bedside table, pressing it into her palm. "What's wrong? If I hurt you, I'm more sorry than I can say."

Her breath caught in a hiccup. "You didn't hurt me— you were wonderful. More than I'd ever dreamed. I'm just so—Steve was the only man I'd ever gone to bed with, so I didn't know—"

"You mean you were a virgin when you married him?" Rafe asked with careful restraint.

"I was brought up with strict standards, and in university I was too busy studying to fall in love. So Steve was the first and only one until tonight…it somehow never worked with him, I never felt—I don't even know how to say it." She scrubbed at her eyes. "He used to blame me, saying I was too uptight, and of course the more he blamed me the more uptight I got. I—I just never realized what it could be like."

Her eyes downcast, she plucked at the hairs on Rafe's chest. "You must think I'm an awful—"

"I think you're the bravest woman I've ever met, as well as the most beautiful."

She lifted her head, tears still streaking her cheeks. "You mean it, don't you?"

"Yes. Every word." He longed to tell her how much he loved her; and with every vestige of his self-control, held back. It was too soon. She wasn't ready.

"I really want to believe you. I can't tell you how much I want to."

"You will. Soon."

Again her cheek fell to his chest. Her eyes drooped shut. "I'll work on it," she said, and within moments her breathing slowed and deepened.

Rafe lay still, staring at the shadows on the ceiling. The small hesitancies in her love-making, the dazzled smile when he'd teased her nipples to hardness, the shocked gasp when he'd first brought her to climax: they all made sense now.

He couldn't think of a word harsh enough for the man she had, in all innocence, married.

He was going to get her away from Heddingley for more than one night, he thought. Away from the river and the Cape Cod house. Away from Donny and Donny's parents and all her memories. To a place where he could tell her how much he loved her.

How was he going to do it, and where would he take her?

Within two minutes, a plan fell neatly into his mind.

CHAPTER NINE

"I'VE NEVER seen anything this beautiful in my life, Rafe. The blue—it's so intense, so dazzling."

"The color of your eyes," Rafe said.

Karyn smiled at him uncertainly. "How did I end up here? Yesterday morning I was in Maine, and today I'm in this utterly gorgeous place—when you pull strings, you pull them hard."

"Gets results," he said. He'd pulled them hard because he'd been afraid that, given time to think, Karyn might not fall in with his plan. "Your boss told me he was happy to give you the time off, and I bet you'd rather be here than at the clinic."

"I'm not that addicted to my job. But I'm still not quite sure why I agreed to this."

"Because you wanted to. Because you haven't traveled much. Because I was very persuasive."

"Right on all counts...especially the last."

She turned back to the breathtaking azure of the Saronic Gulf, Cape Sounio a gray-green blur on the horizon. Waves lapped the shore; the sky was another shade of blue, cloudless and hot. A foreign sky, she thought with a tremor of excitement. A Greek sky. Hadn't she always wanted to come to Greece?

"You own this hotel just like you own the resort in Maine," she said, remembering the deference with which she'd been treated half an hour ago when she'd walked through the blindingly white archway of the Attica Resort. The whole place was luxurious beyond anything she could

have dreamed. She and Rafe were staying in his personal
suite, with its private outdoor swimming pool, its hedge of
pines and olive trees that gave them an unassailable privacy. It boasted a patio trellised with grapevines, which
overlooked the pool and the bay. All the rooms had tall
windows, each opening onto a view more stupendous than
the previous one, while the furnishings were modern, their
hues complementing the outdoors, beckoning it within.

She had, quite simply, never seen anything like it.

She was going to enjoy every minute of her stay, she
decided. No matter that Rafe had overridden all her objections to spending four days with him in a place of his
choice. No matter that she'd been too excited to sleep on
the overnight flight; or that her wardrobe—even including
Liz's borrowed dress—seemed hopelessly inadequate. Her
clothes, inadequate or otherwise, were already hanging in
the walk-in closet in the spacious, cream-painted bedroom
that she was, apparently, to share with Rafe.

She would make love with him again. Her nerves tingling, she wondered if their second love-making could possibly match their first, in a moonlit bedroom thousands of
miles away.

Maybe it wouldn't. Maybe that had been a fluke.

"You look very serious," Rafe teased. "What are you
thinking about?"

She blushed fierily. He looked very much at home in his
white shirt and trousers, his feet bare, his black hair gleaming in the brilliant sun. Why not make love with him now
and find out?

No one, other than Rafe, knew her here. The woman
who'd gone underground in the months of her marriage
could be allowed to surface here. To take all the risks and
have all the fun that had been denied her for too long.
Karyn gave a sudden ripple of laughter, kicked off her san-

dals and walked over to him, the boards hot under her soles. His eyes, a darker blue than any ocean, smiled down at her. She looped her arms around his neck, pulled his head down and kissed him very explicitly.

Lifting her off her feet, Rafe kissed her back, stunned by the hard, hot thrusts of her tongue. God, how he wanted her. The last twenty-four hours, until he could get her here, had felt like the longest in his whole life.

She whispered, pausing to nip at his lips, "Take me to bed, Rafe."

His answer was to sweep one arm under her knees and pick her up as though she weighed nothing. "I thought you'd never ask."

Her cheek against the crisp cotton of his shirt, she was carried across the dining room, through the elegant ease of the living room to the bedroom. The spread was a soft yellow; one window was shaded by a thicket of trees, the other open to the gulf and the Mediterranean sunshine. When he put her down by the bed, then stripped back the covers, she began, very slowly, to undo the row of tiny buttons that fastened the bodice of her green sundress.

Rafe stood still, watching her. Her face was flushed a delicate pink, her lips were parted and her hair was like spun gold. The dress slid from her shoulders, slipped to lie in a green pool on the floor. She was wearing nothing but silken panties, also green. Lifting one knee with a grace that cut him to the heart, she eased them down her legs. Then she leaned over and started to undo his shirt, her tongue caught between her teeth in concentration.

He reached for his belt, and within moments they were both naked. She closed the distance between them, her breasts brushing his chest, and went with her intuition. "You held back last time, didn't you?" As he nodded, she said with gathering conviction and a boldness that startled her, "I'm glad you did. I was frightened and you were so good to me, so gentle. But now I want more. Remember our first kiss, in the woods near Willowbend? I want that again. I want you to drive me out of my mind."

With brutal truth he said, "Just looking at you drives me out of my mind."

So she had that power…her blood pounding in her ears, Karyn lifted her face for a kiss that swept aside any lingering doubts she might have had. He was her lover, the man who'd reawoken her to passion. This time she wouldn't be afraid.

He pushed her back on the bed and straddled her, his body hovering over her as his mouth plummeted to find hers. Their lips fused, feverish and demanding, his teeth scraping her tongue. She locked her arms around his nape, devouring him, tasting him, savoring him. "I need to touch every inch of you," she gasped, her body arching to meet his; his chest hair abraded her breasts, inflaming every nerve she possessed. He fell on top of her, then rolled over so she was riding him; lifting both hands, he cupped her breasts, playing with their tips until she threw her head back in ecstasy, the light molten on her skin.

Then his fingers, those wondrously sensitive fingers, were tracing the curves of her waist, the rise of her hips, drifting, always drifting, closer and closer to the juncture of her thighs. She was almost sobbing with need by the time he touched her there; sensation after sensation ripped through her body until she couldn't hold back any longer. Shuddering, she fell into the tumult, her hands gripping his wrists as though she were drowning and they were all she could clasp.

Gradually she came back to herself; she wasn't drowning, she was achingly and brilliantly alive, at one with the blue of the sea and the sunshine streaming in the window.

Her breasts rising and falling with the pounding of her heart, she said softly, "You're the most generous of lovers. But now it's your turn...lie still."

She lowered herself to the mattress beside him, and gave herself over to a sensual haze of taste and touch. Exploring him. Learning him. Hearing, with that thrill of power, his gasps of pleasure, watching his features blur with desire. Her hands roamed lower, down the tautly muscled belly until she was circling the silken heat and hardness of that desire.

His face convulsed. With a suddenness that sent a fast jolt of excitement through her, he lifted her so that she was, again, riding him. Then he drove into her, into the wetness and slick warmth, into the welcome that was Karyn. The woman he loved.

The words, those three little words *I love you* that were so all-important, were on the very tip of his tongue. Rafe forced them back. Not yet. Not yet.

She was sliding up and down, gripping him, sharp cries of mingled pleasure and need rising in her throat. Deep within her, the drumbeat of her climax was rising, too, toward its inevitable crescendo; overwhelmed, Rafe let his own pounding rhythms meet hers and meld in simultaneous and explosive release.

Slowly Rafe came back to himself. Karyn was lying on top of him, her body damp with sweat. Against his chest he heard her say raggedly, "I've never in my life felt like that—I didn't know I could. Oh, Rafe, I don't think I can breathe. Let alone sit up."

Holding her close, he kissed her ear; her soft, sweetly scented curls were tickling his cheek. "You don't have to sit up. Breathing would be good, though."

How else, other than with humor, was he to defuse a lovemaking that had taken him to a place he'd never visited before? Every instinct was warning him against speaking his love. It was too soon; he risked frightening her off.

He had time. The next few days, to start with.

Minute by minute the days passed, each one convincing Karyn that she would never forget even a single second of this magical interlude. She and Rafe swam in the pool, lazed in the sun and ate delicious meals that appeared from nowhere and whose flavors were often new to her: *tsipoura, tzatziki, gemista*. Every day they agreed they should drive north into Athens, and see—at the very least—the Parthenon; and every day they delayed this outing once again.

On the second day, Karyn phoned Fiona. "Guess where I am," she said.

"Somewhere with Rafe, I hope—he told me he was going to see you."

"I'm lying by the pool at a gorgeous resort south of Athens."

"I want all the details."

Karyn laughed. "Not quite all—I'd be arrested."

"Are you trying to tell me you and Rafe are an item?"

"For now," Karyn said hastily.

"We all have to start somewhere. Karyn, I'm so glad—ever since I met you, I thought you and Rafe were made for each other."

"You *did*? You never said so."

"Thought it might scare you off. You're what you might call gun-shy."

"Fiona, I'm ready to tell you about Steve now. Not on the phone—but the next time I see you."

"You and Rafe should get together more often." Fiona's voice sobered. "I'm always happy to listen to whatever you want to tell me."

Rafe had just emerged from his office, where he spent

part of every morning working. Karyn watched him peel off his shirt and shorts and dive into the pool, as naked and beautiful as a Greek god. A thread of panic in her voice, she said, "This isn't permanent. Rafe and me, I mean."

"Nothing's permanent," Fiona said grandly. "Well, that's not true. My wedding plans are. Did I tell you..."

Ten minutes later, Karyn said, "I've got to go—Rafe wants me to join him in the pool. This is such a heavenly place, Fiona, I don't know how I'll go back to ordinary living."

"Perhaps you won't. Give my love to Rafe. And Karyn, I'm so glad you're happy."

"I am happy," Karyn said blankly. "You're right."

"Good," said Fiona. "Love you. Bye."

Suddenly frightened by just how happy she was, Karyn plunged into the pool and gave chase to Rafe. She spent that afternoon browsing in the hotel boutiques, driving her credit card to the limit with her purchase of a flowing pink silk nightgown; it very satisfactorily caused Rafe to abandon his computer the next morning to ravish her, once again, in their big bed.

Because, of course, that was the other thing they did. Make love. Day and night, she thought, with a secret smile of delight. The whole four days one long haze of sensuality.

Rafe said lazily, "You look like the kitchen cat when he finds fish in his bowl."

He was stretched out beside her under the trellis, where the grapes were ripening; sun and shadow dappled his body. "Fish? No way. Caviar," she said, letting her eyes run suggestively from his tanned shoulders to his narrow swim trunks.

"We're going dancing tonight in the ballroom—we should save some energy for that."

"Can't take the pace, Rafe?"

"Try me."

This time they made love under a screen of green leaves and blue sky; once again Rafe drove Karyn out of her mind with a desire so hot and sharp she wondered if she would survive it. When, finally, she lay back on the soft pillows, she muttered, "Dancing? Did you say dancing?"

"I did." In a lithe movement he got up from the lounger. "Come with me—I bought you something this morning. If it doesn't fit, it can be altered this afternoon."

She took his hand, following him into the bedroom. He opened the cupboard and took out a long evening gown, strapless, made of delphinium-blue raw silk.

"I saw that yesterday in one of the boutiques," she stammered. "I didn't dare try it on because I knew I couldn't afford it. Oh, Rafe, I adore it."

"It's yours."

Her instinctive protest died on her tongue. "To wear tonight?"

"With this," he said.

The rectangular box he was holding out was made of black leather embossed with gold. She said breathlessly, "You've given me so much already. These last four days…"

"Karyn, I make a lot of money. Let me enjoy spending a little of it on you."

"If I refuse, I'll sound ungracious."

"That's right…say, *Thank you, Rafe,* and try it on."

She pried the box open. A single teardrop diamond on a delicate gold chain was nestled into the white velvet lining. "Thank you, Rafe," she whispered and lifted it from the box with fingers that were trembling. "No one's ever given me anything so beautiful."

He took the chain from her, looped it around her neck and fastened it at her nape. Then he drew her over to the mirror, where she saw a naked woman still glowing from the act of love, the diamond sparkling like fire in the valley between her breasts.

Was that woman herself? She said faintly, ''I'll be proud to be your partner tonight,'' and knew she'd said just the right thing.

In the glorious ballroom, open on two sides to the gulf and a sky glittering with stars, Karyn danced until her feet hurt. At midnight the buffet was spread with a dazzling array of dishes, each like a work of art, the table decorated with pale pink orchids and ice sculptures that caught the light from the chandeliers. Rafe was punctilious about introducing her to the other guests and to some of his business associates; Karyn tried out her newly learned Greek and danced some more.

The whole evening she was aware of Rafe's body held to hers, of the electricity that lay just below the surface, waiting until they were alone to be ignited. His body language said, more clearly than words, that she was his. Yet when she danced with other men and Rafe with other women, she sensed he was comfortable with this in a way Steve had never been. She also knew he was only waiting for her to return to his arms.

Where she longed to be.

At two-thirty in the morning, they made a round of good-byes and left the ballroom. As Rafe locked the door of their suite behind them, Karyn kicked off her high-heeled sandals. ''I hate to take the dress off,'' she said wistfully, ''I feel like a flower in it.''

''A very lovely flower,'' he said, and kissed her long and hard. The result was predictable; Rafe took off the dress for her, and they made languorous and overwhelmingly sensual love: one more of the many moods of passion. Afterward, Karyn stretched as gracefully as a cat. ''How many times was that today?''

Rafe laughed. "We both need to go home for a rest."

"Tomorrow," she pouted. "Back to reality. Yuk."

"We'll come again. Or go somewhere else. There are Holden Hotels all around the globe."

She didn't want to think about the future. Just the present. "I've had a wonderful time," she said impulsively. "I'm so grateful you brought me here."

"Gratitude goes both ways, Karyn."

He? Grateful to her? What for? "You own everything you could possibly need," she exclaimed. "Just look at what you've given me—how can I ever thank you?"

"By being yourself...that's all I ask."

She shifted restlessly. "How will it work tomorrow? Will I fly commercially from England to get back home?"

"No need for that—we'll use the jet. I'll go with you."

Her eyes widened, a shadow in their depths. "Why would you go with me?"

"Because I want to."

She lay still in the circle of his arms. In the last four days Karyn had learned considerably more about Rafe than the overpowering fascination his body held for her. There were the ordinary things: that he was an expert swimmer, he danced like a dream and his tennis backhand was a killer. He was well-versed in matters political, artistic and literary; their conversations entranced her, expanding her horizons. He treated the staff with an innate courtesy that she could only respect.

She'd learned something else: when he retreated to his office every day, his voice on the phone had a forceful edge, a decisiveness all the more powerful for being understated, that made her ill at ease for a reason she wasn't quite ready to examine.

Her eyes lingered on his hands, with their long, lean

fingers and strong wrists. She would miss him. Desperately. She'd have to get used to sleeping alone again; in the privacy of her own thoughts, she could admit how much she loved waking in the night and finding Rafe's arm lying heavy over her shoulders, or drawing her snug to his hips in sleep. But hadn't she known from the start that this was an interlude, beguiling and impermanent?

She didn't want him to come back with her to Heddingley. Far better that she make any adjustments on her own, in her own time. "I'll have to go back to work as soon as I get home," she said crisply.

"Then I'll cook supper for you," he drawled; because her head was bent, she didn't notice how sharply he was watching her. He reached over to the bedside table, where there was a tray of exquisitely prepared fruit, and passed her a sliver of mango. "It'll be a comedown from the meals here, I warn you."

The mango was ripe and slippery. Licking her fingers, Karyn said, "I'm not sure I like this conversation. All good things have to come to an end."

"Do they, Karyn?"

"Yes, they do," she announced. Suddenly exhausted, she kissed him in the vicinity of the chin and closed her eyes. While it might be perfectly clear to her that she didn't want Rafe coming to Heddingley, it was, after all, his personal jetplane; she could hardly kick him off it. Not when he'd been so overwhelmingly generous to her, and she owed him so much.

Once they got back to Heddingley, she'd insist that he leave right away, so that her life could settle back to normal. By no stretch of the imagination could normal include Rafe Holden.

He'd understand her point of view.

*   *   *

It was in London, as they waited for the jet to be refueled, that Karyn discovered Rafe wasn't interested in understanding her point of view. In fact, he didn't see eye to eye with her at all. He was sitting in the private lounge reading a Greek newspaper, its script incomprehensible to her. He was frowning. She said lightly, "Is the news that bad?"

He scarcely heard her. The headlines on the second page concerned an Italian businessman who had traveled to Athens and murdered his estranged wife there. The story sickened him; it could so easily have been Karyn.

She said patiently, "Rafe? Hello? Is anybody home?"

His lashes flickered. "Sorry. We won't be much longer. You can sleep all the way home if you want to."

Filled with confusion, she burst out, "I still don't understand why you're coming with me!"

"What did you expect me to do? Dump you at my earliest convenience?"

"Of course not," she said shortly. "But there's no point in you crossing the Atlantic when I have to go right back to work. This has been absolutely wonderful, and I can't thank you enough. But it's over now. There's no point in dragging it out."

"Is that how you see spending more time with me?" he said with menacing softness.

She bit her lip. "I have to pick up my normal life. I have a job, a house, friends and responsibilities—and so do you." Attempting to lighten the atmosphere, she added, "Several houses, in your case, and megaresponsibilities."

"And when—in this busy life of yours—will you find time to see me again?"

Her temper flared, driven more by nerves than actual anger. "Cut the sarcasm. I'll be in England for Fiona's wedding, I'll see you then."

"What if I want more than that?"

"You don't. So why are we fighting like this? The last thing I want to do is ruin a perfectly marvelous four days."

"How, all of a sudden, do you know what I want?"

His voice was tight with controlled anger. In an ugly uprush of emotion, all Karyn's old fears resurfaced. Steve had never been ready to let go of her: the more she'd given him, the more he'd demanded. Was Rafe the same?

Surely not. Not Rafe.

But no matter how hard she tried, she couldn't force her anxiety back where it belonged. Her own anger flared to match his. "Okay, so I don't know what you want. How about enlightening me?"

Rafe tossed the newspaper on the marble table and said in exasperation, "This is all wrong, Karyn. Trading cheap shots with each other like this."

She said flatly, "Tell me what you want. We'll go from there."

He gazed at her in silence. She was wearing simply cut linen pants and an embroidered vest she'd bought at the Athens airport. She didn't look conciliatory. Neither did she look at all like a woman in love. For a moment fear ripped through him, as imperative in its own way as desire. Thrusting it down, he said, "I want to keep on seeing you."

"Why?"

"We fit together. And I don't just mean sexually."

"We're great in bed. But other than that, we couldn't be more different. Look where we just stayed, Rafe! On my own, I couldn't afford that suite for four minutes, let alone four days."

"There's a lot more to me than my money."

"You're enormously rich. I'm a country vet. You travel the world while I drive from the pigsty at LeBlanc's Farm to the local stables. You're cultured and sophisticated. I've barely been off Prince Edward Island and half the time I'm covered in mud. Your lifestyle and mine, they're as different as—''

As she fumbled for an analogy, Rafe rapped, ''As I am from Steve. Because that's what this is really about, isn't it? It's not about money, it's about Steve.''

She stood up, jamming her hands in her pockets, determined not to cry. ''Of course it's about Steve. You're the only person in the world who knows what he did to me. How he changed me. And yet you expect me to keep on seeing you? To start some kind of relationship with you? You, of all people, should understand why I can't do that.''

She now sounded despairing rather than angry; again a deep unease spread through his body. ''Yes, you can,'' he said forcibly. ''You did tell me about him, that was a huge step—and I know you're going to tell Liz and Fiona. Since then, you've spent the better part of four days in bed with me. I'm going to sound arrogant as hell, but you liked making love with me—nobody can fake the way we were together. Wasn't that another giant step? In bed with me, you let yourself be the woman you really are.''

The force of his willpower battered at her defences; his eyes were a hard steel-blue. ''I can't risk getting close to you.''

''Dammit, you've been as close to me as you can get. In bed, in my arms.''

''That's not what I mean. That's just sex. Astounding and incredible sex. But still sex. I mean intimacy, real intimacy. The kind that hurts too much when it goes wrong.''

''You're assuming it's going to go wrong.''

''You say you're different from Steve. But you're also like him. Handsome, charismatic, sexy, from a wider world than my own, with more money. I fell for Steve lock, stock and barrel—and I've paid for that mistake ever since. I can't afford to get involved with you.'' Her voice rose. ''Why don't you understand?''

''Outwardly, maybe I am like Steve. But did you yell at him like you just yelled at me?''

She flinched. ''Initially, yes.''

''Are you afraid of me, Karyn?''

Her shoulders sagged. As usual, he'd gone to the heart of the matter. Choosing her words, she said, ''I'm afraid of what might happen if we continue seeing each other. You're a very powerful man—you wouldn't have risen to the top if you weren't. You're used to getting your own way. In business, and with women, I'm sure.'' Her smile was twisted. ''I don't imagine you get turned down very often.''

This time some of his anger escaped in his voice. ''You think I'm after you just because you're unwilling? That's how I get my kicks?''

''I didn't say that! All I'm saying is no. Two letters, one syllable, not a complicated word. No, I don't want you to come to Heddingley with me. No, I'm not interested in a relationship with you.''

''Because of Steve.''

''Because I lived in fear of my husband for months—a man I'd married for love.''

''We all have our nightmares.''

In deliberate challenge she said, ''What are yours, Rafe?''

''Realizing at age seven that my parents, for all their fine lineage, were dirt poor, and that I might be stuck in a moldering old castle for the rest of my days.''

''From which Douglas rescued you…is that all?''

''Going to boarding school and having the tar beaten out of me because word had gotten out that I didn't have two pennies to rub together. After that, I learned to fight dirty.''

"You still do," she said caustically.

"No, I don't—I don't need to." Briefly his jaw hardened. "Celine was the one who fought dirty. Telling me she adored me and neglecting to mention she adored three other men at the same time. Now that's dirty."

"Then for the next six years you avoided passion and intimacy—six years, Rafe! Steve drowned a year ago. Yet you want me to pretend it didn't happen?"

He said with fierce conviction, "If I'd met you a year after I dumped Celine, I'd still be acting the way I'm acting right now."

"I'm supposed to believe that?"

"Yes," he grated, "you are. Look, I understand that my nightmares, bad as they were at the time, can't possibly compare with yours. I'll give you all the time you need. But in the meantime I have to be able to see you."

"Rafe, I hate this! I can't do it. I won't."

"Then Steve wins—is that what you want?"

"Of course he wins," she said wearily. "His kind always does."

"That doesn't have to be true—get to know me and see that I'm not like him at all."

Rafe was gripping the back of the nearest chair, his knuckles bone-white with strain. Compassion ripped through her; but even that didn't—couldn't—change her mind. "The only way you get to know someone is by living with him," she said in a low voice. "I trusted the world until Steve came along. He destroyed every vestige of my innocence. My trust in men, of course. But even worse, my trust in myself, in my own judgment."

"So are you going to stay alone for the rest of your life?"

She shivered. "How can I answer that?"

Ruthlessly he drove his advantage. "Don't you want children? You'd make a wonderful mother."

Her face pinched, she whispered, "Yes, I'd like to have children. But not so much that I'll marry to get them."

He played his last card…what did he have to lose? "I want to marry you—you must have figured that out by now."

"You *what?*"

He glanced around the elegant, impersonal lounge with its aura of impermanence, of travelers passing through on their way to other destinations. "I'd hoped to tell you this in a more romantic setting," he said harshly. "I've fallen in love with you, you're the woman I want to spend the rest of my life with. Wife. Lover. Mother of my children. The whole deal."

She said the first thing that came to mind. "But you scarcely know me."

"I know you. Going to bed with you, spending the last four days with you, how could I not know you? Anyway, you're forgetting I've known Fiona all my life. Your identical twin, who had the courage to fall in love and fight for a new life. You've got that same courage, Karyn. You just have to find it and trust in it."

"I was married for twenty-three months to a man who made every day a living nightmare," Karyn said bitterly. "That's the difference between Fiona and me."

He was losing her, Rafe thought. Right in front of his eyes, Karyn was moving away from him. He'd never begged for anything in his life; but if ever he needed to, it was now. He said roughly, "Forget I said I want to marry you. Or that I've fallen in love with you. Dammit, we'll even stay away from the bedroom if that's what it takes. But just let me keep on seeing you—that's all I ask."

Tears stung her eyes. For a man of Rafe's pride to hum-ble himself for her sake…how could she bear it? "I'm not the woman for you, Rafe. I can't give you what you want— I'm so sorry. We should never have gone away together. I swear I wasn't using you, it just didn't occur to me that you might fall in love with me. If I'd thought there was any chance of that, I'd never have agreed to going to Greece with you."

Naked honesty shone from the shimmering blue of her irises. She wasn't playing games with him, Rafe thought. She wasn't like that. "Give me time," he said in a voice he scarcely recognized as his own. "Let me prove I can give you all the freedom you need, and that I trust you utterly. But don't send me away."

"I have to." Her voice wavered. "I'm sorry, Rafe, I hate hurting you like this. But I can't love you the way you want me to. Far better to end this now than drag it out and cause you more pain. Please—don't come to Heddingley with me. Go back to England and forget about me. Please."

He had his answer, and it was no. Finally and irrefutably no. His one need to get out of the lounge and away from her without revealing the raw agony clamped around his heart, Rafe pushed himself upright and said with formal politeness, "I'll speak to the pilot. He'll take you to the Charlottetown airport. I'll stay in London, I have some business I can do there."

She'd won. Exhaustion settling on her shoulders like a dead weight, Karyn said with answering formality, "Thank you. Goodbye, Rafe." She didn't hold out her hand or try to kiss him; to touch him would have undercut the last remnants of her control.

He said, "Wait here, the pilot will come for you shortly." Looking around like a man unsure of his bearings, he picked up his leather briefcase from the marble table and marched out of the lounge. The door swished shut behind him.

Karyn sat down hard on the nearest chair. She couldn't cry now, not when an employee of Rafe's could walk in at any moment. She concentrated fiercely on her breathing, trying to loosen the tight bands of tension around her chest.

She was going home. Home was where she needed to be. Until then, all she had to do was concentrate on holding herself together.

Her little house, the birch trees, the weed-ridden garden…that was where she belonged.

CHAPTER TEN

HOME had subtly shifted while Karyn was in Greece with Rafe. It echoed with silence and with her self-imposed solitude. Rafe wasn't there with her to share her jokes, to argue about a political situation, to describe a painting he'd seen in Moscow or a sculpture in Florence. To offset this, she put the TV on for white noise, played a lot of raucous rock music and did her best to root out the weeds in her mother's garden.

He wasn't there in bed with her, either. Not when she lay down, or when she woke in the night reaching for him, or when her body tormented her with hungers only he could feed.

He didn't contact her, by e-mail, phone or letter. It was as though he'd dropped off the planet.

She'd told him, more or less, to do just that. She had no cause to complain.

At the clinic she worked like a woman possessed, taking on extra shifts and staying after office hours, ostensibly to bring her records up to date, in actuality because she didn't want to go home. At least there were other people at the clinic; and when they got too much, there were dogs and cats who didn't require intelligent conversation of her.

Her second evening home, Liz phoned. "You got back yesterday, didn't you? Tell me all about your holiday—was it wonderful?"

"I'm not seeing Rafe again," Karyn blurted. "Except at Fiona's wedding." Which now loomed as ominous as a herd of sick elephants.

155

"Whatever happened?"

Her tongue falling over the words, Karyn found herself pouring out an abbreviated version of her marriage. "We can talk more about it some other time," she finished, her voice jagged. "But you do understand why I can't keep on seeing Rafe."

Liz said carefully, "So you didn't enjoy yourself in Greece?"

"Of course I did, it was fantastic. But it was totally divorced from reality…Rafe and I are worlds apart and that's the way I'm going to keep it. I'll bring back your dress tomorrow, Liz. Just don't ask any questions, okay?"

Liz would have had to be stone-deaf not to hear the misery in her friend's voice; she changed the subject, invited Karyn for dinner and didn't mention Greece, Rafe or the pretty sea-green dress. That same day, Karyn boxed up the diamond pendant Rafe had given her and sent it by registered mail to Stoneriggs.

Lacking the courage to talk to Fiona by telephone, Karyn e-mailed her. It was a brief and chirpy note, saying she'd had an incredible holiday but she was back to her real life now.

Three days passed without a reply, Karyn each morning searching in vain among her new messages for one from her sister. On the fourth day she fired off another e-mail, chatting about the dogs and cats she'd been tending, and asking about John. Again, there was no response.

Surely, Karyn thought in despair, focusing on the screen as though she could conjure up the reply she sought, her breakup with Rafe wouldn't cause her to lose Fiona's love. Life couldn't be that cruel.

The next day was Saturday, Karyn's day off. She slept in, had a luxurious soak in the tub and made a fruit salad and pancakes for breakfast. The sun was shining; she could work in the garden all day. She should have been happy.

She wasn't.

She was upstairs cleaning her teeth when the doorbell rang. She glanced out of the window; a taxi was reversing from the driveway. Her heart gave a great lurch in her chest. Rafe, she thought. Who else would arrive by taxi other than him?

Oh, God, what would she say to him?

She looked down at herself: denim cutoffs, an old tank top and bare feet. She sure wasn't dressed for the Attica Resort. Taking a deep breath, she walked downstairs and pulled open the door.

Fiona was standing on the step, a small overnight bag in her hand.

Karyn's jaw dropped. "Fiona," she cried, "I—come in, I wasn't expecting to see you."

Then, in a jolt of pure terror, she realized Fiona didn't look at all happy to be here. Her sister looked—grim was the only word that came to mind. "Rafe," Karyn said faintly, the color draining from her face, "something's happened to Rafe." She grabbed Fiona by the wrist. "What's wrong? Is he okay?"

Fiona said coldly, "What do you care?"

"Don't, Fiona! Just tell me if he's all right—you've got to tell me!"

"Except for a broken heart, he's fine."

Karyn leaned back against the nearest wall, her breath escaping in a big whoosh. "You just took ten years off my life."

Fiona said slowly, "So you do love him…"

"I do not!"

"We'll see about that. In the meantime, lead me to your

kitchen and make me a very strong cup of tea along with two fried eggs and a mountain of toast.''

Fiona looked, minimally, less unfriendly. Karyn said crisply, ''You'd think England was just down the road the way you and Rafe zip back and forth. Without even bothering to phone. You don't get the tea unless I get a hug first.''

''Huh,'' said Fiona. But she opened her arms, and Karyn fell into them.

Burying her nose in Fiona's shoulder, Karyn gulped, ''You didn't answer my e-mails.''

''I had no intention of answering them. You look awful—shadows under your eyes and you've lost five pounds.''

''Six, actually. You look great…you've had your hair cut.''

Fiona's hair now fell in soft waves to her shoulders. ''I did. Mother's in a perpetual snit anyway, so what does one more thing matter?''

''It suits you. You look different somehow.''

''More grown up, you mean.''

There was indeed a new maturity in Fiona's bearing. ''Here, sit down at the table,'' Karyn said, ''and I'll put the kettle on. Did you sleep on the plane?''

''Like a baby.'' Fiona gave a smug smile. ''I only have to think of John, and I forget all about being five miles high over a very large ocean.''

Karyn took out the tea pot and the frying pan. As she cracked two eggs into the pan, she said, ''I'm so happy to see you. But I don't understand why you're here.''

''Breakfast first,'' Fiona said with impressive authority, and leaned over to undo her bag. ''I brought swatches of the bridesmaid's fabrics with me, you can choose which color you'd prefer.''

So as Fiona ate her way steadily through eggs, toast and jam, washed down with liberal quantities of inky tea, they talked fabrics, flowers, cake and the etiquette of a wedding where one set of parents was far from delighted with their child's choice. Finally, replete, Fiona sat back. "That's better," she said. "Now we'll get down to business. Rafe arrived back at Stoneriggs looking worse than my father the day his investments went belly-up. I poured some brandy into Rafe—well, the best part of a bottle, actually—and got the whole story out of him. He told me about kissing you in the woods, and spending four days in bed with you and—"

"Fiona..."

Fiona gave another of those smug smiles. "I'm not nearly as easily shocked as I used to be. Rafe's in love with you, Karyn. Madly in love. A total goner. Ever since you sent him packing—for reasons best known to yourself—he looks as though someone bashed him on the head with one of Father's concrete statues. I haven't seen him like that since that bitch Celine ran circles around him and no, I'm not quite ready to use that word in front of my mother yet."

"I didn't do anything to encourage Rafe."

"In the woods at Willowbend you kissed him back. You went to Maine with him and to Greece. Where you had, by all accounts, torrid sex on the floor, on the patio, in the pool and even, occasionally, in bed." As a hot blush surged up Karyn's cheeks, Fiona added, "It was very good brandy. It loosened his tongue big time. At least you're not indifferent to him."

"Maybe not. But that doesn't mean I have to keep on seeing him."

"You're a coward."

"When I married Steve, I made a horrendous mistake. I'm trying to learn from it, that's all."

Fiona shoved back her chair, leaning both hands on the table. "How dare you compare Rafe to Steve!"

Karen stood up too, glaring right back. "How can I not? Two handsome, sexy men who swept me off my feet—I'm damned if I'll marry Rafe."

"Let me tell you something. I've known Rafe all my life. We're neighbors, we're best friends, I know him through and through. I've seen him with his parents, his servants, his crofters, and his horses. He taught me how to climb trees and ride bareback and steal ripe raspberries from under the gardener's nose. He rescued kittens from being drowned, he set false trails in the fox hunts, he stood up for kids who were being bullied. Yet you dare compare him with a man who by all accounts was a thoroughly nasty piece of work?"

"I didn't—"

"You were smart to be afraid of Steve. God knows what he might have done had you tried to leave him. But to equate him with Rafe—don't you see how *stupid* that is? Rafe's solid, he's decent, I'd trust him with my life. Let me ask you something. Do you think Rafe's capable of murdering you?"

"Of course not!"

"Of hitting you?"

"No."

"Threatening you?"

Karyn said furiously, "He doesn't let up. He's relentless, he rides over me like a ten-ton truck."

"Answer the question."

"He's never threatened me," Karyn said sullenly.

"Then would you mind explaining to me how he's like Steve—who did hit you and threaten you? Who kept you in line because underneath it all you were terrified for your life?"

Put like that, it did sound ludicrous to have compared the two men. Karen bit her lip, her face strained and unhappy. "I don't trust my own judgment any more. Especially with men."

"Then rely on mine for a while. I adore Rafe. Do you think I'd adore him if he abused his power? He definitely has power, don't get me wrong. Huge power. But his staff adore him, too, and that's because he treats each and every one of them like a human being." She paused, her head tilted in thought. "Maybe it's because he grew up poorer than most of the local boys. Blue blood's all very well, but it doesn't put food on the table or fix the roof."

Karyn said grudgingly, "I guess you're right, Rafe hasn't let his power go to his head."

"Of course I'm right. Here's another question. How did your husband treat the waitresses when you went out for dinner?"

"Badly," Karyn said in a small voice.

"There you go."

"Rafe was lovely with the staff at the Attica. I noticed."

Fiona said more gently, "Look, I'm not belittling what happened to you in your marriage, Karyn. It must have been terrible, and of course you're afraid to trust your judgment. So I'm asking you to trust mine instead. Rafe's a good man, I'd take that to the bank—and as for you and me, we're identical twins. If I trust Rafe—and I'd trust him with my life—then so can you."

"I don't know how! I don't know where to begin."

"Then I'll tell you something else. I've had to fight for my relationship with John, tooth and nail. Now that I'm in love with him, I'm freeing myself from my parents, from a lifetime of being—oh, ever so lovingly—crushed and controlled. I've been frightened sometimes, but I knew I couldn't back down or I'd be lost."

Forgetting her own problems for a moment, Karyn ventured, "You were like a sleeping princess, and then John woke you up?"

Fiona nodded. "And I'm staying awake. If I can defy my parents, you can flush that rotter Steve Patterson straight down the toilet."

Gentle, sweet-natured Fiona was scowling so fiercely that quite suddenly Karyn began to laugh. Fiona's scowl deepened. "Don't you laugh at me, Karyn Marshall—this has gone beyond a joke! Rafe's in pain, he's horribly unhappy. I can't stand seeing him so lost and all because you've locked yourself in the past and you're afraid of the future...I've got one more question, then I'll shut up."

Karyn knew what Fiona was going to ask. Did she, Karyn, love Rafe? How was she going to answer?

"Do you like Rafe, Karyn?"

"Like him?" Karyn said, surprised. "Yes...yes, of course I do."

"How can you like someone you're afraid of? You can't. It's impossible. I rest my case."

"You're wasted in the animal shelter," Karyn said vigorously. "You should be a high-powered lawyer—you could talk circles around any judge in the land."

"I like the animal shelter. I'm its new director and that's why I'm going home tomorrow, so I can be at work first thing on Monday morning."

Karyn bit her lip. "You left John behind on a weekend and came all this way to see me."

"To talk some sense into you."

Tears sparkling on her lashes, Karyn walked around the table and threw her arms around her sister. "Thank you, Fiona."

"Don't thank me," Fiona muttered, blinking back her own tears. "Go and see Rafe instead."

Karyn stepped back and straightened her spine. "Okay," she said, "I'll go and see him."

"You *will?*"

"I promise."

Fiona grabbed her twin and waltzed her around the tiny kitchen. "That's wonderful, that's terrific, I'm so glad."

"Rafe means an awful lot to you, doesn't he?"

Fiona raised expressive eyebrows. "Do horses have four legs?"

"Does he know you're here?"

"No, he took off to Thailand and won't be back until the end of next week. Late Friday night."

"Then I'll arrive on Saturday."

"I'll meet you at the Droverton station."

"Don't tell him, will you, Fiona?" Karyn said shakily. "I have to do this my way."

"I wouldn't think of telling him. Everyone in the village, including my parents, thinks I'm in London this weekend shopping for a wedding dress. Except for John, of course."

Karyn felt as though a whirlwind had picked her up, swirled her around and dropped her, disconcertingly, in a very different place. One where she wasn't sure she had her bearings. Fiona's wedding dress, she thought, surely that's a safe topic. "What sort of dress are you looking for?"

"I've got pictures."

The rest of the day, Fiona talked about John and about some of her youthful escapades with Rafe. Once the clinic had closed for the weekend, Karyn took her sister on a tour of the building, noticing how at ease Fiona was with all the animals. She ended the visit at the kennel of a mongrel called Toby; because Toby had been abused, he was reluctant to leave the safety of the kennel.

Kneeling beside Karyn, Fiona accepted a dog biscuit and

pushed it between the bars. "Come on, boy, you can do it," she coaxed, then smiled at Karyn. "Don't you think a nice tasty biscuit's worth the risk of leaving the cage?"

"Very funny."

"I don't mean to be funny—it takes a lot of guts to change things that went deep." She clucked at Toby as he sidled forward. The dog grabbed at the biscuit and retreated to chew on it. Then he came forward more confidently for another one. Within five minutes Toby was standing outside the kennel, with Fiona very gently massaging his shoulders. Karyn said softly, "He trusts you."

"Of course he does," Fiona said with a gamine grin. "Why wouldn't he?"

Why indeed? Fifteen minutes later, the mongrel was outdoors in the little field behind the clinic, sniffing at the grass and wagging his tail. Rafe would like to hear about Toby, Karyn thought.

She could tell him. On Saturday.

Had she really committed herself to visiting Droverton for the second time?

On Saturday afternoon Karyn landed at Heathrow. The plane was twenty minutes early; even so, she didn't have a lot of time to catch her train north. After going through customs in an agony of impatience, she hurried through the exit doors, tugging her wheeled suitcase.

An elderly couple stepped out of the crowd and approached her. The man was tall with a thatch of salt-and-pepper hair and bright blue eyes; his suit was unexceptional, although the trouser legs were tucked into blindingly red socks. The woman, short, rail-thin, was wearing an Indian cotton skirt and an old T-shirt; her eyes were almost black in a face that blended character and beauty to startling effect.

The man said bluffly, "You're not Fiona, so you must be Karyn. Reginald Holden, m'dear, pleased to meet you."

As he almost crushed her hand in his, the woman said, narrow-eyed, "Are you here to see Rafe?"

"I'm on my way to Stoneriggs, yes—I'm in a hurry, I have to catch the train. Are you his mother?"

"He's not at Stoneriggs. He's here in London. Are you going to marry him?"

"Now, Joanie," said Reginald, "that's not your question to ask."

"Yes, it is, Reg. She's making our son miserable."

"Irascible, I'd have said."

"Same thing. Answer the question, girl."

Karyn said coolly, "My name's Karyn. I'm not a girl, I'm a woman. I don't know if I'm going to marry Rafe."

Reginald gave a bark of laughter. "She'll do," he said to his wife. "That's what Rafe needs, someone to stand up to him."

"He needs someone who loves him."

"Can't expect him to be as lucky as you and me, m'dear."

Reginald enveloped his wife in a bear hug; when she smiled up at him, Karyn's breath caught in her throat. She exclaimed, "You're so lucky to love each other like that!"

"We're Rafe's parents, so we're scarcely objective," Joan announced. "But we couldn't have a better son. If I'm not falling all over you, it's because you've hurt him deeply, and it makes me crazy not to be able to fix it."

"My husband wasn't a nice man," Karyn said with careful understatement.

"We're all entitled to the occasional mistake," Reginald said breezily. "Jolly good thing the chap's out of the way."

Karyn raised her brows. "That's one way of looking at it."

Joan said fiercely, "You're breaking Rafe's heart. You've got to choose one thing or the other—waste your life in fear and regret, or get on with it."

"Wallow in the mud," Reginald said cheerfully, "or climb back on the horse that threw you."

"I packed my jodphurs," Karyn said.

"Then you're all set," Reginald replied. "After all, she's here, isn't she, Joanie? That's got to count for something. She doesn't live in the next county, you know."

"Do you love my son?" Joan asked in a voice like a steel blade. A voice that reminded Karyn strongly of Rafe.

"I don't know," she replied, refusing to drop her eyes. "But I'm willing to try and find out. Providing you'll tell where in London I can find him."

Joan passed her a crumpled invitation. "He's got a gala opening of a new hotel tonight—here's the address. You could attend. If you wanted to."

"I'll do that," Karyn said. "You could wish me luck. If you wanted to."

Joan nodded, as though Karyn's answers had pleased her. "Something dies inside us when we don't take risks," she remarked. "You probably know that, or you wouldn't be here."

"Are you going to the gala?" Karyn asked.

"We've got a sick dog at home, so we have to get back—we commandeered Rafe's helicopter so we could meet you."

Karyn said, smiling for the first time, "I'm honored you left the dog just to see me."

Then a blur of movement caught her eye; Fiona, wearing a pretty blue suit, was pushing through the crowd toward her. Karyn said in happy surprise, "Fiona, how lovely to see you."

Fiona stopped dead, gaping at Rafe's parents. "What are

you doing here?" she said tactlessly. Her eyes widened. "You were asking about Karyn last night—picking my brains. I just hope you haven't been giving her a hard time."

"Came to check her out," Reginald said.

"She's not a prize filly," Fiona said crossly and gave Karyn a distracted kiss on the cheek. "So you know Rafe's in London? I only found out this morning. I was so afraid I'd miss you and you'd be on your way to Droverton... although I wouldn't have worried if I'd known Reg and Joan were planning to be here," she finished, frowning at them.

"We knew you wouldn't want us interfering," Joan said briskly. "So we didn't tell you."

"This is getting much too complicated," Fiona complained. "Karyn, I didn't bring John with me because I thought you'd be in a tizzy. You can meet him when you come home with Rafe after the gala."

"It's not a tizzy, it's a funk," Karyn said, "and you're making one heck of a big assumption about Rafe and me." She hugged her sister fiercely. "No matter what happens, I'm so glad to see you, and thanks so much for coming all this way—it's getting to be a habit, rescuing me like this."

"I won't have to do it any more, because once you see Rafe you won't need rescuing," Fiona said triumphantly.

"How is he, Fiona?" Karyn burst out.

"I talked to him this morning at the hotel—he didn't sound in a very gala mood. But he'll feel a million percent better when he sees you," Fiona said. "How's Toby?"

"He has new owners—a wonderful couple who live in the country and love him to bits. He's a different dog."

"He's a walking metaphor, that dog," Fiona said with a sideways grin.

Karyn hoped so. But even if she herself had changed

enough to come in search of Rafe, what if he didn't want to see her? What if he was so angry with her that he turned his back on her? Wouldn't that serve her right?

Worse, what if he'd changed his mind? It was fine for Fiona and Joan to insist Rafe was still in love with her. But what did they know? Maybe all those feelings he'd talked about had been brought on by too much Greek sunshine and an overdose of sex.

Then there were her own feelings. Was she in love with him? Or would she have to rebuild trust before she'd know?

All her doubts and fears must have shown in her face. "Karyn, it'll be fine. With Rafe, I mean," Fiona said forcefully.

"Maybe," said Karyn, "and maybe not. But I have to see him, no matter what. I couldn't live with myself if I didn't." She hesitated. "Fiona, I don't want to send you away. But I've got to do this on my own...do you understand?"

"Of course I do! You don't need the whole darn family tagging along...by the way, I booked a room for you at Rafe's hotel. It's next door to some incredible boutiques, in case you didn't bring anything to wear."

Tears on her lashes, Karyn said, "You've thought of everything."

"The rest is up to you," Fiona said. "You can do it."

Reginald interjected, "Fiona, you could come back with us in the 'copter. You'll be home in no time." He gave Karyn a courtly bow. "Best of luck, m'dear. Drop by the castle for tea, why don't you?"

Joan kissed Karyn on the cheek, a gesture that felt like an accolade. "That way you can meet the dogs."

"I'd like that," Karyn said.

She hugged Fiona again, then watched as the three of them disappeared through the jostle of other passengers.

Her first step was to get a taxi to the hotel, where she was going to gate-crash a very fancy gala.

Hosted by Rafe.

CHAPTER ELEVEN

As THE cab wound through the London streets in a series of jerky stops and starts, Karyn could hear, far in the distance and overriding the sound of traffic, the grumble of thunder. The sky between the tall buildings was heaped with purple-edged clouds; the trees were whipped by a wind that whirled dust from the gutters and tossed scraps of paper into the air. If she were back home, she'd say they were in for a storm. She was trying very hard not to see this as a bad omen.

She was wearing her expensive linen slacks with a blue linen blazer and an ivory silk blouse; as the taxi lurched forward, she did her best to repair her makeup. In her case, carefully packed in tissue, was the delphinium-blue dress Rafe had given her in Greece. She'd brought it hoping that he'd strip it from her body and make love to her, just as he had once before in their big bedroom that overlooked Cape Sounio. But instead she'd be wearing it to the most momentous confrontation of her life.

The crumpled piece of paper Joan had given her said the gala began with cocktails at seven. Karyn was already praying she wouldn't bump into Rafe before it began; she wanted him to see her first in the midst of the invited guests. That way he'd have more time to cool down. Less time to consider homicide, she thought wryly. He couldn't very well send her packing in front of everyone. Could he?

He could try. It didn't mean she had to obey him.

Lightning flickered between two office towers. The cabbie slipped through an opening in the traffic, the meter clicking with monotonous regularity. Her eyes scratchy from lack of sleep, because she'd been up since four that morning, Karyn gazed out at crowded pavements and red double-decker buses, at stone and brick architecture rooted in history. She might be scared to death of meeting Rafe; but she was also unable to quell a tremor of excitement that she was finally in London, a city that for her had always been wreathed in romance.

Briefly her overstretched nerves loosened. Perhaps she'd come home, she thought. Maybe England was where she belonged, with a man as civilized as this great city, as unyielding as the granite crags of his estate, as wild and powerful as the windtorn sky. Were he to love her, were she to allow that love to permeate her, and were she to return it, strength for strength...was that why she was here? To find out what that would be like?

With one final jolt, the cab drew up in front of an elegant Edwardian stone building, lights gleaming from its myriad windows. Quickly Karyn paid the fare, added a generous tip and got out. Trundling her bag behind her, she walked toward the huge arched entranceway, where a uniformed doorman greeted her as though she was royalty, took her bag and indicated the front desk.

For a moment, awestruck, her steps faltered. She was standing under a domed ceiling centred with a magnificent gold chandelier; the ivory walls were outlined in gilt, the ceiling a baroque marvel of swirled gold and exquisite murals. A bouquet of tropical lilies rested on a marble pedestal; the floors were pale marble, the carpets handloomed. With all the dignity at her command, she approached the desk and within moments was being whisked in the elevator to her room on the fifth floor.

She hadn't seen Rafe.

She had two hours to get ready.

Staying even one night in this room was going to wreck her budget for the next twelve months; all the more reason to enjoy it while she was here. Recklessly Karyn ordered afternoon tea to be brought to her room, even though according to her it was only lunchtime. When it came on a mahogany trolley with immaculate linens, she tucked into tiny sandwiches and luscious little cakes, pouring Prince of Wales tea from an antique silver pot.

Perched on her bed, she looked around her. Silk-damask upholstery and drapes, a deeply piled carpet in forest-green, dark cherry furnishings, two delicate prints of dancers: every detail was perfect. She'd already checked out the marble bathroom with its fleecy robe and lavish toiletries.

Having consumed every scrap of food, she soaked in fragrant bubbles in the whirlpool tub, painted her nails, and took her time making up her face. When she was finally ready, at quarter past seven, she took one last look at herself in the mirror.

A glamorous stranger looked back at her, a woman with delicately flushed cheeks and brilliant blue eyes, her hair in soft tendrils around her face. Crystal earrings twinkled at her lobes; the blue dress encased her like the petals of a slender flower.

The only thing missing was the gold chain with the teardrop diamond that she'd sent back to Rafe.

She tilted her chin. She was going downstairs, she was going to find Rafe, and she was going to fight for him. In fighting for him, she'd be fighting for her own life. Defeating Steve, once and for all.

Freeing herself to be with Rafe. If he'd have her.

She tucked her door card in her silver clutch purse, and left the room. Five minutes later, she was standing at the entrance to the lobby bar. A group of guests was ahead of her, giving her a moment to get her bearings.

Small gold lamps cast a warm glow on the deep red walls, giving the polished walnut trim a lovely sheen. Intricately woven carpets were scattered on an expanse of gleaming parquet. The room was already crowded with men in tuxedos, the women's gowns a mingling of hues like a midsummer garden. White-jacketed waiters moved smoothly among the guests.

Rafe was standing with his back to her, talking to several men and one woman, a brunette whose beauty and sophistication Karyn couldn't hope to emulate. Even from here she could see diamonds in a sparkling cascade around the woman's throat. For a moment Karyn quailed. What if Rafe had indeed put her behind him? A regrettable interlude, the sooner forgotten the better.

What if this woman was his new partner? Or even his partner for the evening?

She'd been a fool to come.

You're breaking his heart...so Joan had said and so Fiona had suggested. As he laughed, bending his head to hear what the woman was saying, he didn't look as though his heart was broken.

"Your name, madam?"

The doorman, in a scarlet jacket and a high starched collar, was addressing her. "Dr. Karyn Marshall," Karyn said clearly. She rarely used her title; but this seemed an occasion that called for it.

He ran his eyes down the list in his hand. "I don't believe your name is here," he said delicately. "Could there have been some mistake?"

Gate-crashers. Jewel thieves. Unwanted interlopers. Of course there'd be security for an event of this size. "I flew in at the last minute from Canada," she said. "If you mention my name to Mr. Holden, I'm sure he'll be delighted to welcome me."

"Certainly, madam."

The doorman made an unobtrusive gesture to one of the waiters and whispered instructions in his ear. The waiter walked across the parquet toward Rafe, discreetly got his attention and spoke to him very briefly. For a split second Rafe's body went utterly still. Then he said something to the waiter and turned back to his guests.

Not once did he look Karyn's way.

All right, Rafe, she thought in a wave of fury. If that's your game, I can play it, too.

The waiter returned and the doorman said with impeccable courtesy, gesturing her into the room, "Enjoy your evening, madam."

She planned to. Her blood up, Karyn helped herself to a chilled martini from one of the waiters and took the first sip, its bite almost making her choke. A man standing nearby said, with amusement, "They're extremely good martinis."

He was handsome and gray-haired, with that indescribable polish that generations of wealth can confer. Karyn introduced herself, and soon discovered he was laird of a vast estate in Scotland and had a keen interest in sheep-breeding. As they talked animatedly, he said, "Let me introduce you to those three gentlemen over there…they'd like to hear your views on Cheviots."

The three men were standing close to Rafe. Sipping her martini with caution, for she needed all her wits about her, Karyn crossed the room and joined the three men. Even then Rafe paid her no attention whatsoever. We'll see about that, she thought, waited for a gap in the conversation and said pleasantly to her companions, "Would you excuse me, please? I want to speak to Mr. Holden."

Holding herself very tall, she closed the gap until she

stood at Rafe's elbow, then said clearly, "Good evening, Rafe."

He turned, his glance flicking over her face. "Dr. Marshall," he said. "What an unexpected pleasure."

"They're the best kind, don't you think?" she said, and smiled at the other guests. She was damned if she was going to show that his use of her last name had flicked her like a lash.

Rafe said imperturbably, "May I introduce Dr. Karyn Marshall." He reeled off the others' names, not one of which Karyn could have repeated, although she did catch that the brunette was the wife of the handsome aristocrat standing across from Rafe.

Calling on every ounce of her poise, she talked and laughed and smiled until she thought her jaw would crack. Then Rafe said, "Ah, the ambassador's party has arrived...please excuse me. Karyn, I'll see you later."

Briefly his eyes rested on her with a such a blaze of emotion that she almost dropped her glass. So he wasn't indifferent to her. Far from it. She said coolly, "Perhaps."

"It's not a suggestion, it's an order." His smile impartially included the whole group. "Karyn and I have some unfinished business," he remarked, took her hand, kissed her palm with lingering pleasure and walked away from her.

Scorched by the contact, her cheeks flaming, Karyn said, "He's exaggerating and he's much too used to having his own way. I need another martini."

The brunette, whose name was Lydia, signaled the waiter. "Rafe is never indiscreet," she said, "how interesting. Where did you meet him, Karyn?"

Karyn had no intention of sharing a convoluted story about separated twins and a picnic on a faraway beach. "By chance,'' she said, and to her great relief heard the doorman announce that dinner was ready to be served.

Now was her opportunity to leave with some degree of dignity. But nadn't Steve destroyed every vestige of her fighting spirit? Was she going to run away from Rafe and that blaze of emotion he'd banked as swiftly as if it had never occurred; or was she going to match him, thrust for thrust, parry for parry? His opponent and his equal.

Steadily she walked with Lydia and her husband toward the dining room. Its gold-framed mirrors reflected the dazzle of chandeliers and gold-leaf tracery on walls of a soft moss green. An array of crystal glasses shot little rainbows on the circular tables with their bouquets of roses and tall gold candelabra. At the door, the maitre d' took her name and said politely, ''Ah yes, Dr. Marshall...you're on Mr. Holden's right at the head table.''

She said with the utmost composure, ''Thank you,'' winked at Lydia and crossed the room toward the long table flanked by twin marble fireplaces. Her heart was fluttering in her breast; so this was Rafe's next move. He'd out-guessed her; she'd expected to be seated in a corner as far from him as possible.

On her other side was a charming French count whose passion, she soon found out, was horse racing. From the corner of her eye she saw Rafe approach. ''Mr. Holden,'' she said with edgy mockery, ''what an unexpected pleasure.''

''I thought I could keep an eye on you here,'' he said.

''Do you like my dress?'' she asked provocatively.

''A pity you don't have a gold chain to go with it.''

''Flinging down the gauntlet—what a romantic gesture that is.''

''I'm not sure what I'm feeling right now, but romantic doesn't cut it.''

She widened her eyes, aware that she was thoroughly enjoying herself. "So I shouldn't pin my hopes on having had my hand kissed?"

His gaze lingered on the soft curve of her mouth. "It depends what your hopes are. We'll discuss them later—when we're alone." Turning to the woman on his left, he said, "Countess, may I introduce Dr. Karyn Marshall?"

Valiantly Karyn held up her end of the conversation, working her way through Beluga caviar, delicately flavored bouillon, flame-roasted quail, and pastries shaped like swans surrounded by plump raspberries. Rafe made a speech notable for wit and brevity, then everyone moved to the baroque splendor of the ballroom, where the orchestra was tuning their instruments.

Karyn, by now, was light-headed with fatigue, wine, repressed sexuality and suspense. Rafe led off the dancing, taking her into his arms and sweeping her around the floor in an old-fashioned waltz. His arm around her waist, his fingers clasping her own to his shoulder, the closeness of his determined jaw and unfathomable dark eyes all worked their magic. Her body yielded in his arms in a way that spoke volumes. He said harshly, "So that hasn't changed."

"Did you expect it to?"

"I've given up knowing what to expect from you."

His fingers were now splayed over her hip in overt possessiveness. How important was Steve likened to the elemental simplicity of Rafe's embrace? It was Rafe who matched her, body and soul. Rafe who from the beginning had shown her that passion could be coupled with integrity, willpower with trust.

What a fool she'd been to compare him to Steve. In all the ways that mattered, there was no comparison. How could she have forgotten the first time Rafe had made love to her, in the bungalow in Maine? He'd put his own needs on hold in order to soothe her fears and bring her to fulfillment. He'd been breathtakingly generous.

Yet she'd run from him like a terrified sheep.

Not paying attention, she stepped on his toe. "Sorry," she muttered.

"Only another three hours," he said heartlessly. "I have to circulate…I'll pass you over to the count."

Soon Karyn was whirling around the dance floor with a succession of partners young and old. Normally she would have enjoyed this immensely. But as the minutes and hours passed, the knot in her belly tightened. Rafe hadn't danced with her again. Nor did she have any idea what she was going to say to him when, as he'd promised, they found themselves alone.

Promised or threatened, she wondered with a shiver along her spine.

For the second time she watched him lead a frail, white-haired dowager onto the floor, dancing with her with such care for her pleasure that sudden tears shimmered on Karyn's lashes. As she rubbed them away, it was as though she rubbed scales from her eyes.

She loved Rafe. Of course she did.

She had for weeks.

Her new knowledge didn't arrive in a blinding flash, like the lightning flickering over the city streets. It held none of the threat of a stormy sky. Rather, it had the integrity of Rafe's beloved Stoneriggs, and the deep roots of her connection to Fiona. It was as dependable as stone, she thought; as beautiful as the sea. She could feel her heart expanding to encompass him, to hold him there forever. Happiness welled up within her.

She loved him. Now she must tell him so.

The orchestra announced the last waltz. With a sense of inevitability, Karyn watched Rafe return the dowager to her equally aged husband and then swiftly search the crowd. For herself. Talking and laughing as he went, he eased his way toward her and took her in his arms.

I love Rafe, she thought. That's all I need to remember. The rest will look after itself.

I hope.

But she couldn't recapture the delight of being in his arms. Twice she tripped over her own feet; her body felt clumsy, her brain empty of any kind of strategy. Finally the waltz ended; as the guests started to depart and Rafe began a round of goodbyes, she slipped into the ladies room and repaired her makeup. Lipstick for courage, she thought ruefully, running a comb through her tangled curls. She didn't look like a woman who'd been up for twenty-one hours. She looked fully and invigoratingly alive.

When she went back out, the great ballroom was nearly empty, the musicians putting away their instruments as the staff cleared the tables of used glasses. The party's over, she thought, and slowly walked over to Rafe, who was shaking hands with the last of the guests.

As though he sensed her presence, he turned. His face inscrutable, he said, "Let's go."

Deliberately she laced her arm with his, feeling the muscles rigid as steel beneath the sleeve of his tuxedo. They crossed the lobby to the elevators. The attendant pressed the button for the penthouse suite, and in silence they were whooshed upward. Rafe unlocked tall double doors and stood aside for her to enter.

In one quick glance, she took in her surroundings. Space and simplicity, she thought with a sigh of relief. "Is this your own suite?"

"Yes. We won't be disturbed here. Why did you come to London?"

So there was to be no social chitchat. Karyn sat down

on the arm of the nearest chair and eased her stiletto sandals off her feet. "I came to see you."

"Why?"

I've all of a sudden realized I love you? It didn't sound very convincing. "You don't look too happy that I'm here."

"The jury's out on that one. How did you know where to find me?"

"Your mother told me." With a flick of satisfaction she saw she had surprised him. "If I can get past your mother, you should be congratulating me."

"Just how did you meet her?"

"She was at the airport, waiting for me. She gave me the third degree. I like your father's socks."

"Stick to the point, Karyn."

"You're not making this very easy!"

"Give me one good reason why I should. I've just had the worst two weeks of my whole life. When Celine fouled me up, that was kidstuff compared to you. So I don't feel particularly friendly toward you, and if you try to compare me to Steve one more time, we're through—have you got that?"

Her visions of a romantic late-night tryst in ruins at her feet, Karyn let her own temper rise to meet his. "You're not the least bit like Steve."

"Then why did you send me away?" he snarled.

"Isn't it obvious? Because I hadn't figured that out yet."

"So you sent me packing along with the necklace I'd given you—you wouldn't even keep that."

"I'm sorry!" she cried, then modulated her tone. "I really am sorry, Rafe. I did the best I could at the time—and it wasn't good enough. I see that now. But hindsight's always twenty-twenty and I came here to make amends. Well, that's sort of why I came."

"I laid my cards on the table at Heathrow," Rafe said in a harsh voice. "I love you, I want to marry you—that's what I said. Causing you to bolt like a frightened pony. Good move, Rafe. I might be a dab hand at building a business empire but when it comes to one five-foot-seven blue-eyed blonde, I'm—"

"Oh, stop!" she yelped. "You know what I really want to ask? Do you still love me? Do you still want to marry me? But I'm not going to. I'm going to say my piece first. I love you, Rafe Holden. I want to marry you. That's why I'm here, and if I could get past your redoubtable mother, you ought to be down on your knees kissing my feet."

"I'm damned if I'm getting down on my knees—I did that at Heathrow. What changed your mind? Why all of a sudden aren't I the reincarnation of Steve?"

"It's a long story."

"I've got all night."

Panic-stricken, because her declaration of love might as well have been spoken to the four corners of the room, Karyn began by describing how Fiona had turned up on her doorstep last Saturday morning in a rage. "You should have seen her—maybe she's been taking lessons from your mother. Anyway, I promised I'd come here as soon as I could, and...well, see you. I guess that's what I promised."

"You're seeing me. Right now."

"Did I ruin everything by sending you away?" Karyn croaked. "Oh, please, tell me I didn't..."

"You answer me first. Am I dreaming this whole scene? This whole evening? Any minute am I going to wake up in a bed that feels like a desert because you're not in it?"

"I'm real." She reached out and touched him, snatching her hand back before he could react.

"So you are. You love me," he said, advancing one step

toward her, "and you want to marry me. You did say that?"

His eyes were gleaming with something other than anger; the first tiny quiver of hope rippled through her body. "Yes," she said primly, "and it's not even a leap year."

"I accept."

"Huh?"

"I accept your proposal of marriage," he repeated, "and I'll make damn sure our grandchildren know it was you who asked me and not the other way around."

"You asked first."

"Don't remind me. When are we going to get married? It had better be soon."

"Whoa," she said, "you're leaving something out. Something basic. If you don't love me any more, the proposal's off."

"Oh, I love you," Rafe said softly, taking one more step. He was now so close she could feel the heat of his body and see the tiny flames deep in his eyes. "Do you think I'd change that quickly? That's the whole point, Karyn. I'm in this for life. Forever. For better and for worse, and since Heathrow I've had more than enough of the worse, thank you very much."

A smile lighting her eyes, she said severely, "You're playing very hard to get."

"You're darn right I am. Although if you got past my mother, maybe, just maybe, I should forgive you."

She laughed, a delightful cascade of sound. "You're darn right you should."

Still without touching her, his voice deepening, Rafe said, "I love you, Karyn. Love you more deeply than I knew it was possible to love. I want you to be my wife, to be the mother of our children, to live with me day by day, to sleep in my bed." The little flames kindled to points of fire. "To make love with me again and again, because I'll never have enough of you.''

Her face radiant, Karyn whispered, ''That's what I want, too. More than I can say.'' Then, very naturally, she moved into the circle of his arms, linked her hands behind his head and kissed him.

It was a kiss that seemed to last forever, an avowal of love, an ache of desire, a pledge of belonging. When Karyn finally raised her head, her cheeks were bright pink. She said the first thing that came into her mind. ''Rafe, I'm so sorry I sent you away.''

''You're forgiven,'' he said and kissed her again.

Through the windows that opened onto the balcony, Karyn heard the faraway growl of thunder. ''We're in for a storm.''

Rafe laughed, his white teeth gleaming. ''We are the storm, sweetheart.'' When he ran his eyes down her body, it felt as intimate as a caress. ''Let's go to bed.''

''Yes,'' she whispered, ''oh, yes.''

''When you look at me like that—'' He pulled her hard into his body, smothering her face and throat with hot, urgent kisses. ''I want you, I need you, I love you.''

Karyn rested her palm on Rafe's cheek, smiling into his eyes. ''I love you, too,'' she said. ''Oh, Rafe, I love you so much.''

''That's all you have to do—keep telling me that for the rest of my days.''

''That's easy,'' Karyn said contentedly, reaching up to unhook his tie. He swung her off her feet, carrying her through the sitting room into the bedroom with its panorama of city lights. Laying her on her back, he covered her with his big body.

She was home. In Rafe's bed, in his heart. Where she belonged.

*   *   *

A month later, on a Friday evening, Karyn was maid of honor and Rafe best man at Fiona and John's wedding in the thick-walled Norman church in Droverton. On Saturday afternoon, Karyn was standing at the end of the same aisle, her hand tucked into John's sleeve as the organ pealed the wedding march. Her gown was an elegant flow of white crepe, her bouquet exquisite lilies from Joan's conservatory at Castle Holden. The diamond pendant Rafe had given her in Greece hung on its delicate gold chain around her neck.

Fiona, wearing apple-green crepe, turned to smile at her. "Your turn," she said. "May you be as happy as I am, Karyn."

"It's because of you that I'm standing here."

"It's because of Rafe."

Karyn could see him at the far end of the aisle, his black hair uncharacteristically tidy, his morning suit molded to his broad shoulders. Joy spilled over in her heart. She leaned forward and kissed her sister on the cheek. Then she smiled at John, whom she already liked enormously. "Ready?" she asked.

"Be happy, Karyn," he said.

"I will be. I am."

She paced slowly up the aisle, the stained glass throwing a mosaic of brilliant colors on the guests. Clarissa and Douglas, valiantly smiling; Rafe's mother, severely elegant in bottle-green silk; Reginald enlivening his formal clothes with an orange bowtie.

Her new family.

Also among the guests were Liz, Pierre and their children, whom Rafe had brought here to surprise her: a gift that had, predictably, made her weep.

Then Rafe himself turned to find her, his dark blue eyes meeting hers with such an immensity of tenderness that her heart overflowed. She took her place at his side. In a few moments Rafe would be her husband and she his wife.

She'd freed herself from the past. Freed herself to a life-long commitment with Rafe and, she hoped, to bearing his children. She could ask for nothing more.

Resting her hand on Rafe's, she smiled up at him, and as the music swelled around her, the future began.

VACANCY: WIFE OF CONVENIENCE

BY
JESSICA STEELE

Jessica Steele lives in the county of Worcestershire, with her super husband, Peter, and their gorgeous Staffordshire bull terrier, Florence. Any spare time is spent enjoying her three main hobbies: reading espionage novels, gardening (she has a great love of flowers) and playing golf. Any time left over is celebrated with her fourth hobby: shopping. Jessica has a sister and two brothers and they all, with their spouses, often go on golfing holidays together. Having travelled to various places on the globe, researching backgrounds for her stories, there are many countries that she would like to revisit. Her most recent trip abroad was to Portugal, where she stayed in a lovely hotel, close to her all-time favourite golf course. Jessica had no idea of being a writer until one day Peter suggested she write a book. So she did. She has now written over eighty novels.

CHAPTER ONE

SHE had first seen him at her father's funeral, and had not expected to see him again. But here he was standing in front of her, tall, as she remembered, dark-haired and somewhere in his middle thirties.

Colly had not had the chance then to learn who he was; her stepmother of two years, only five years older than her, had monopolised him as they stood at the crematorium after the service. 'Do come back to the house for some refreshment', Colly had clearly heard Nanette urge.

He had suavely declined, looked as if he might come over to Colly to offer his condolences, but she had been buttonholed by someone else and had turned away. He spoke to her now, though, apologising that Mr Blake—the man she was at the Livingstone building to see—was unfortunately incapacitated that day.

'Silas Livingstone,' he introduced himself. She had not known his name; he obviously knew hers. 'If you could hang on here for ten minutes, I'll be free to interview you in his stead.'

'Would you rather I made another appointment?' She would prefer not to do that. She was nervous enough about this interview as it was, and was unsure if she would ever have the nerve to come back.

'Not at all,' he replied pleasantly. 'I'll see you in a short while,' he added, and was already on his way to the adjoining office.

'Would you like me to wait elsewhere?' Colly asked the smart, somewhere in her late thirties PA, who appeared to be handling at least three tasks at one and the same time.

5

'Better not,' Ellen Rothwell replied with a kind smile. 'Mr Livingstone has a busy day. Now that he's found a slot for you, he'll want you to be where he expects you to be.'

Colly smiled in return but decided to say nothing more. She found it embarrassing enough as it was that apparently, so Ellen Rothwell had explained, Vernon Blake's present secretary had phoned around all the other applicants to cancel today's appointments. But, on phoning Colly's home at the start of business that day, had been informed that she was out and that there was no way of contacting her.

She had known that her stepmother had a spiteful streak. To deliberately refuse to call her to the phone when she had been in all the time only endorsed that fact.

Colly held back a sigh and tried to direct her thoughts to the forthcoming interview. Vernon Blake was the European Director at Livingstone Developments, and was looking for a replacement multilingual senior secretary. The salary advertised was phenomenal and, since Nanette wanted her to move out, would, if Colly were lucky enough to get the job, enable her to rent somewhere to live and be independent.

That had been her thinking at the time of spotting the advert. Never again would she be dependent on anyone. She had read the advert again. 'Multilingual senior secretary.' What was so difficult about that? She could, after all, type. And, though a little rusty with her languages, she had at one time excelled in French and Italian, and had scraped through with a pass mark in Spanish and German. So what else did a multilingual secretary need?

Watching Ellen Rothwell expertly deal with telephone calls, take notes in rapid shorthand and then calmly and charmingly sort out what seemed to be some sort of a problem, Colly realised that there was a lot else to being a secretary. And what experience of being a secretary did she have? Absolutely none!

She almost got up then, made her excuses, and bolted. Then

she remembered why she wanted this job that paid so much. Very soon she would be homeless. And she, who had never had paid work in her life, desperately needed some kind of well-paid employment.

It hurt that her father had left his will the way that he had. His twenty-eight-year-old widow had inherited everything; his daughter nothing. He had a perfect right to leave his money and property to whoever he cared to, of course. But she, his only child, his housekeeper since the last one had walked out seven years ago, was now about to lose the only home she had ever known. Not that it felt like home any more.

Colly had been little short of staggered when, just over two years ago now, her dour, often grumpy parent had gone all boyish over the new receptionist at his club.

The first Colly had got to suspect that he was seeing someone was when he'd suddenly started to take an interest in his appearance. She'd been glad for him. Her mother had died when Colly was eight—he had been unhappy for far too long.

Her pleasure for him had been tinged with dismay, though, when a short while later he had brought the blonde Nanette home—Nanette was about forty years his junior! 'I've been so longing to meet you!' the blonde twenty-six-year-old had trilled. 'Joey has told me such a lot about you.'

Joey! Her staid father, Joseph, was *Joey*! For his sake, Colly smiled and made her welcome and tried not to see the way Nanette's eyes swept round the room taking inventory of anything valuable.

Had Colly secretly hoped that her father would still be as happy when Nanette backed away from whatever sort of relationship they had, then she was again staggered when, far from the relationship ending, Nanette showed her the magnificent emerald ring Joseph Gillingham had bought her, and declared, 'We're getting married!'

For the moment speechless, Colly managed to find the words to congratulate them. But when, adjusting to the idea that Nanette was to be mistress of her home, Colly mentioned that she would find a place of her own, neither her father nor Nanette would hear of it.

'I'd be absolutely hopeless at housekeeping,' Nanette twittered. 'Oh, you must stay on to be housekeeper,' she cooed. 'Mustn't she, darling?'

'Of course you must,' Joseph Gillingham agreed, the most jovial Colly had ever seen him. 'Naturally I'll continue to pay you your allowance,' he added, with a sly look to his intended, making it obvious to Colly that her allowance—not huge by any means and which, with increasing prices, went to supplement the housekeeping—had been discussed by them.

The whole of it left her feeling most uncomfortable. So much so that she did go so far as to make enquiries about renting accommodation somewhere. She was left reeling at the rent demanded for even the most poky of places.

So she stayed home. And her father and Nanette married. And over the next few months her father's new 'kitten' showed—when her husband was not around—that she had some vicious claws when things were not going quite her way. But she otherwise remained sweet and adoring to her husband.

Living in the same house, Colly could not help but be aware that Nanette had a very sneaky way with her. And within a very short space of time Colly was beginning to suspect that her new stepmother was not being true to her Joey. That Nanette plainly preferred male company to female company was not a problem to Colly. What was a problem, however, was that too often she would answer the phone to have some male voice enquire, 'Nanette?' or even, 'Hello, darling.'

'It isn't Nanette,' she would answer.

Silence, then either, 'I'll call back,' or, 'Wrong number.'

Colly could not avoid knowing that Nanette was having an affair when some months later she answered the phone to hear an oversexed voice intimately begin, 'Who was the wicked creature who left me with just her earrings beneath my pillow to remind me of heaven?'

Colly slammed down the phone. This was just too much. Nanette, who was presently out shopping, had, so she had said, been out consoling a grief-stricken girlfriend until late last night.

When a half-hour later Nanette returned from her shopping trip Colly was in no mind to keep that phone call to herself. 'The earrings you wore last night are beneath his pillow!' she informed her shortly.

'Oh, good,' Nanette replied, not in the slightest taken aback to have been found out.

'Don't you care?' Colly felt angry enough to enquire.

Nanette placed her carriers down. 'What about?'

'My father...'

'What about him?'

Colly opened her mouth; Nanette beat her to it.

'You won't tell him,' she jibed confidently.

'Why won't I?'

'Is he unhappy?'

He wasn't. Never a very cheerful man, he seemed, since knowing and marrying this woman, to have had a personality transplant. 'He's in cloud-cukoo-land!' Colly replied.

Nanette picked up her clothes carriers. 'Tell him if you wish,' she challenged, entirely uncaring. 'I've already—tearfully—told him that I don't think you like me. Guess which one of us he's going to believe?'

Colly very much wanted to tell her father what was going on, but found that she could not. Not for herself and the probability that, as Nanette so confidently predicted, he would not believe her, but because he was, in essence, a much happier man.

So, awash with guilt for not telling him, but hoping that he would not blame her too much when, as he surely must, he discovered more of the true character of the woman he had married, Colly stayed quiet.

A year passed and her father still adored his wife. So clearly Nanette was playing a very clever game and he had no idea that his wife had a penchant for flitting from affair to affair.

That was until—about six months before his sudden totally unexpected and fatal heart attack—Colly first saw him looking at Nanette with a little less than an utter doting look in his eyes.

He appeared only marginally less happy than he had been, though, but did during his last months spend more time in his study than he had since his marriage.

Her father had been a design engineer of some note and, though in the main largely retired, she knew from the top executives and first-class engineers who occasionally called at the house to 'pick his brains' that he was highly thought of by others in his specialised field.

And then, completely without warning, he died. Colly, in tremendous shock, could not believe it. She questioned the doctor, and he gravely told her that her father had suffered massive heart failure and that nothing would have saved him.

She was still in shock the next day, when Nanette sought her out to show her the will she had found when sorting through Joseph Gillingham's papers. It was dated a month after his marriage, and Colly soon realised that Nanette had been more looking for his will than sorting through, especially when, triumphantly, Nanette declared, 'What a little pet! He's left me everything!' And, without any attempt to look sorry, 'Oh, poor you,' she added. 'He's left you nothing.'

That was another shock. Not that she had expected to be left anything in particular. Naturally Nanette, as his wife, if she were still his wife by then, would be his main heir. Colly realised she must have assumed her father would go on for ever; he was only sixty-eight, after all. And while he was not enormously wealthy, his income from some wise investing many years before was quite considerable.

It was two days after her father's death that Colly received a fresh shock when Nanette barged into her bedroom to coldly inform her, 'Naturally you'll be finding somewhere else to live.'

Somehow, and Colly hardly knew how she managed it, she hid the fresh assault of shock that hit her to proudly retort, 'Naturally—I wouldn't dream of staying on here.'

'Good!' Nanette sniffed. 'You can stay until after the funeral, then I want you out.' And, having delivered that ultimatum, she turned about and went from whence she came.

Feeling stunned, Colly couldn't think straight for quite some minutes. She had no idea what she would do, but heartily wished her uncle Henry were there to advise her.

Henry Warren was not a blood relative, but her father's friend, the 'uncle' being a courtesy title. She had known him all her life. He was the same age as her father but, newly retired from his law firm, he had only last week embarked on an extended holiday. He did not even know that his friend Joseph had died.

Not that the two had seen very much of each other since Joseph's remarriage. Her father's trips to his club had become less and less frequent. And Henry Warren seldom came to the house any more. It was because of their friendship that her father had always dealt with a different firm of solicitors, believing, as he did, that business and friendship did not mix. But Colly's first instinct was to want to turn to Uncle Henry.

But he was out of the country, and as her initial shock began to subside she realised that there was no one she could turn to for help and advice. She had to handle this on her own. She had no father, and no Uncle Henry—and Nanette wanted her out.

Hot on the heels of that realisation came the knowledge that she barely had any money—certainly not enough to pay rent for more than a week or two on any accommodation she might be lucky enough to find. That was if prices had stayed the same in the two years since she had last looked at the rented accommodation market.

She was still trying to get her head together on the day of her father's funeral.

She clearly recalled seeing Silas Livingstone there—his name now known to her. How Nanette managed to look the grieving widow while at the same time trying to get her hooks into Silas Livingstone was a total and embarrassing mystery to Colly. He and another tall but older man had gone to his car and had left straight after paying their respects at the crematorium anyhow, so Nanette's invitation to 'come back to the house' had not been taken up.

Having applied for a job with Livingstone Developments, Colly had done a little research into the company. And, on thinking about it, she saw that it was not surprising that the firm should be represented at her father's funeral that day. Livingstones were not the only big engineering concern to be represented.

She came out of her reverie to watch Ellen Rothwell handle whatever came her way. Secretarial work, it was fast being borne in on Colly, was more than just being able to type!

She had known that, of course. But supposed she must still be suffering shock mixed in with stress, strain and grief for her father, as well as a helping of panic thrown in, that, on seeing the advertisement for a multilingual senior secretary, and believing she could fulfil the multilingual part without too much trouble, she had applied.

She watched Ellen Rothwell for another thirty seconds, and realised more and more that she must have been crazy to apply. Colly got to her feet, ready to leave, but just then the door to Silas Livingstone's office opened and there he was, a couple of yards away—so close, in fact, that she could see that his eyes were an unusual shade of dark blue.

'Come through,' he invited, standing back to allow her to precede him into his large and thickly carpeted office. She was five feet nine—and had to look up to him. She had been about to leave, but found she was going into his office. He followed her into a large room that housed not only office furniture but had one part of the room—no doubt where he conducted more relaxed business—given over to a coffee-table and several padded easy chairs. He closed the door behind them and indicated she should take a seat to the side of his desk. 'I was sorry about your father,' he opened.

So he knew who she was? 'Thank you,' she murmured.

'Columbine, isn't it?' he asked, she guessed, since he had her application form in front of him, more to get her to feel at ease before they started the interview.

'I'm called Colly,' she replied, and felt a fool when she did, because it caused her to want to explain. 'I thought, since I was applying—formally applying—for the position with Mr Blake that I should use my full name—er—formal name.' She was starting to feel hot, but did not seem able to shut up. Nerves, she suspected. 'But Columbine Gillingham is a bit of a mouthful.' She clamped her lips tight shut.

Silas Livingstone stared at her and seemed glad that she had at last run out of breath. But, when she was getting ready to quite dislike him, he gave her a pleasant look and agreed, 'It is, isn't it?' going on, 'I stopped by Vernon Blake's office earlier. His present secretary said everything was running smoothly in his absence with the exception of an interviewee, Columbine Gillingham, who could not be contacted. Your father's obituary mentioned he had a daughter Columbine—I didn't think there would be two of you.'

It was her turn to stare at him. Was that why he had decided to interview her himself—because of her connection with her father? But there was no time to ask, and she supposed it was irrelevant anyway, because, obviously a man with little time to spare, Silas Livingstone was already in interview mode.

'What secretarial experience have you?' he enquired, glancing down at her application form as if trying to read where, in invisible ink, it was stated she had any office experience at all.

She felt hot again. 'I'm a bit short of actual secretarial experience,' she felt obliged to reply, wondering anew at her temerity in actually applying for the senior secretarial post. 'But my languages are good. And—and I type quite fast.'

He leaned back in his chair, his expression telling her nothing. 'How fast?' he enquired politely.

'How fast?' she echoed.

'Words per minute.' He elucidated that which any secretary worthy of the name would know. And, clearly already having formed a picture of her secretarial expertise—or lack of it, 'Any idea?' he asked.

She had no idea. Could not even give him a hint. She sat up straighter. 'Shall I leave?' she offered proudly.

He shook his head slightly, but she was unsure whether it was at her non-statement of work experience there before him or whether he was telling her that *he* would decide when the interview was over.

'Have you ever had a job?' He looked straight into her wide green eyes and asked directly.

'Er—no,' she had to admit. But quickly added, 'I kept house for my father. When I left school I took over the housekeeping duties until…'

'Until he remarried?' Again that direct look.

'I… My father's new wife preferred I should continue to look after everything.' Heavens, how lame that sounded!

'So you have never had an actual job outside of the home?'

Keeping house had kept her pretty busy. Though there was her interest in art. 'I usually help out at an art gallery on a Tuesday,' was the best she could come up with. She had visited that particular gallery often enough over the years to get to know the owner, Rupert Thomas, who at one time had asked her to 'hold the fort' for him when he'd had to dash out. From there it had grown and, today being Tuesday, she would normally be doing a bit of picture-dusting, a bit of invoicing, a bit of dealing with customers, not to mention making Rupert countless cups of coffee were he around.

'Is this paid employment?' Silas Livingstone wanted to know.

She was feeling uncomfortable again, and knew for sure that she should never have come. 'No,' she admitted.

'Have you ever worked in paid employment?'

'My father gave me an allowance,' she mumbled. She was unused to talking about money; it embarrassed her.

'But you've never earned—outside of the home?' he documented. Then abruptly asked, 'Tell me, Columbine, why did you apply for this job?'

He annoyed her. He clearly could not see why, with her lack of experience, she had bothered to put pen to paper. She couldn't see either—now. But his formal use of Columbine niggled her too. So much so that she was able to overcome her embarrassment about money to tell him shortly, 'I am not my father's heir.' She locked antlers with Silas Livingstone—and would not back down. But she did not miss the glint that came to his eyes.

'Your father left you something, though? Left you provided for?' he did not hesitate in asking.

Colly did not want to answer, but rather supposed she had invited the question. 'He did not,' she answered woodenly.

'I thought he had money?'

'You thought correctly.'

'But he left you—nothing?'

'Nothing.'

'The house?'

'I need to find somewhere else to live.'

There was a sharp, shrewd kind of look in those dark blue eyes as he looked at her. 'Presumably the new Mrs Gillingham did quite nicely,' he stated—and Colly knew then that, while her father had been blind to the taking ways of Nanette, Silas Livingstone, within the space of the few minutes he had been in conversation with her at the crematorium, had got her measure.

But Colly was embarrassed again, and prepared to get to her feet and get out of there. It went without saying that she had not got the job. He must think her an idiot to have ever applied for the post in the first place. All she could do now was to try to get out of there with some shred of dignity intact.

She raised her chin a proud fraction. 'Thank you for seeing me, Mr Livingstone. I applied for the job because I need to work, and not from some whim…'

'Your allowance is stopped?' He said it as if he knew it for a fact. 'You need to finance yourself?'

'I need a job that pays exceptionally well if I'm to live in a place of my own and be self-sufficient. But…'

'You're looking for somewhere to rent?'

'That's one of my first essentials,' she confirmed. 'That and to be independent. I intend to make a career for myself. To—'

She broke off when Silas Livingstone all at once seemed to be studying her anew. There was certainly a sudden kind of arrested look in his eyes, an alertness there, as if some thought had just come to him.

But even while she was scorning such a notion she could not deny he seemed interested in what she was saying. 'What about men-friends?' he asked slowly. 'You obviously have men-friends,' he went on, flicking a brief glance over her face and slender but curvy figure. 'Where do they come into your career-minded intention to be independent?'

She had thought the interview was over, and had no idea where it was going now. But since she had told this man so much, without ever having intended to—it spoke volumes for his interviewing technique—there seemed little point in holding back now. 'My father saw fit to leave everything to his new wife, and that was his prerogative. But it was a shock to me just the same, and it has made me determined to never be dependent on anyone ever again.' She went to get to her feet, but Silas Livingstone was there with another question.

'You have one man-friend in particular?' he enquired.

'Right now I have no interest in men or even dating,' she replied. 'I...'

'You're not engaged?'

'Marriage is the last thing on my mind.'

'You're not thinking of settling down, or living with some man?'

'Marriage, men or living with one of them just doesn't enter my plans,' she answered. 'I'm more career-minded than husband-minded. I want to be independent,' she reiterated. She had never been interviewed for a job before, so supposed being asked such detailed and personal questions must be all part and parcel of a job interview, but to her mind the interview was over. 'I apologise for taking up so much of your time,' she began, prior to departing. 'I thought when I applied for the job that I would be able to do it. It was never my intention to waste Mr Blake's time—or yours. But, since I obviously haven't got the job, I won't waste any more of it.'

She got up from her chair—but, oddly, Silas Livingstone motioned that she should sit down again. She was so surprised by that—she'd have thought he could not wait for her to be gone—that she did in fact sit down.

'I'm afraid you haven't the level of experience necessary to work for Vernon Blake,' Silas Livingstone stated. 'But,' he went on, before she could again start to wonder why, in that case, she had sat down again, 'there is the possibility of something else that might be of interest.'

Colly's deflated spirits took an upturn. While it was fairly certain that this other job would not pay as well as the one advertised, there was hope here that she might find a job that would lead to better things. Why, a company of Livingstone Developments' size must employ hundreds of office staff. Why hadn't she thought of that? She had a brain, there must be quite a few other jobs she could do!

'I'd be interested in anything,' she answered, trying not to sound too eager, but ruining it by adding, 'Absolutely anything.'

He silently studied her for what seemed an age. Studied her long and hard, before finally replying, 'Good.'

'What sort of work is it? I'm fairly good with computers. Or perhaps it's something to do with translating? I'd—'

'It's a—newly created post,' he cut in. 'The details haven't been fully thought through yet.' Again he seemed to study her, his eyes seeming to take in everything about her. 'Perhaps you'd be free to join me for lunch—say, Thursday?'

'Lunch?' she repeated. Was this the way of interviews?

He did not answer, but opened a drawer and withdrew what appeared to be a desk diary and began scanning it. But even while she was getting her head around the notion of lunching with this man while he told her more fully the details of this new vacancy he was shaking his head.

'By the look of it lunch is out for the next couple of weeks.' That was a relief. Personable though the man was, not to say downright good-looking, she somehow felt oddly reluctant to have lunch with him. Her relief, however, was short-lived, because, rehousing his diary, Silas Livingstone looked across at her. 'It will have to be dinner,' he announced. And, as cool as you please, 'Are you free this Friday?' he enquired.

Colly wasn't sure her jaw did not drop. She closed her mouth and stared at him. While admittedly she did not have all that much experience of men—this was a new approach. She might also not have any experience with general job interview procedure either, but she did not feel she had to be a genius to work out that this was far from the norm.

'Forgive me, Mr Livingstone,' she replied, striving hard for some of his cool tone. 'But I believe I've already told you that my interest rests solely with finding a job that pays well.' And, in case he had forgotten, she repeated, 'Men and dating just do not figure in my plans for the foreseeable future.'

'I heard you,' he replied evenly, adding—totally obscurely as far as she was concerned— 'That is an excellent start. But,' he went on, 'my sole intention in requiring you to have dinner with me is so we may discuss, in informal detail, this newly arisen—vacancy.'

Colly eyed him warily. Two years ago she hadn't had a suspicious bone in her body. But two years of living under the same roof as the devious Nanette had taught her not to take everything at face value.

'This *is* business?' Colly stayed to probe.

'Strictly business,' he answered, with not a smile about him.

Colly studied him. It made a change. But, looking at him, she somehow felt she could believe him. Could believe that this was not some newfangled way of him getting a date. And, looking at him, sophisticated and virile, she suddenly saw it was laughable that this man, who probably had women falling over him, would need to use any kind of a ruse to get a woman to go out with him anyway. Indeed, Colly started to feel a trifle pink about the ears that she had for one moment hinted that he might be interested in her in more than a 'business' way.

'Friday, you said?' she questioned finally, when he had given her all the time she needed to sift through everything.

'If you're free,' he agreed.

'This job—' she gathered her embarrassed wits together '—you can't tell me more about it now?'

'The—situation is recent, as I mentioned. I need to do some research into all it entails.'

'You'll have done your research by Friday?'

'Oh, yes,' he replied evenly.

She wanted to ask if the job was working for him. But, since he was the head of the whole shoot, she thought it must be. 'Bearing in mind my lack of experience, you think I would be able to do the job?'

'I believe so,' he replied, his dark blue eyes steady on her.

Colly got to her feet. She felt not a little confused, and hoped it did not show. 'Where shall I meet you?' she asked.

Silas Livingstone was on his feet too. Tall, unsmiling that she had just agreed to have dinner with him on Friday. 'I'll call for you at eight,' he stated.

She opened her mouth to tell him her address. Then closed it again. It was on her application form, and at a rough guess she felt that this man would not have missed that. In fact, she had a feeling that this man, who was obviously going to research into this newly created job pretty thoroughly before he offered it to her—or otherwise—never missed a thing.

CHAPTER TWO

HER first interview with Silas Livingstone had been on Tuesday. By Thursday of that same week Colly's head was beginning to spin from the effort of trying to pinpoint exactly what kind of job was in the offing that would be better discussed in 'informal detail' over dinner.

She still inwardly cringed whenever she thought of how, without a pennyworth of secretarial experience, she had applied for that senior secretarial job. It just went to show, she realised, how desperate she was for a job that paid well enough to afford her somewhere to live.

And that she would have to find that somewhere to live, and quickly, had been endorsed for her again last night, when Nanette had entertained a few of her rowdy friends. It was her right, of course, but the gales of laughter, male and female, that had come from the drawing room had impinged on Colly's sensitivities. Her father had barely been dead a month.

His widow had obviously decided to be the merry sort. If that was her way of grieving, so be it, but Colly had seen little sign of genuine grief. And all she wanted to do now, she mused, as she began to clear up the debris from the previous night's entertainment, was find a place of her own and get started on being solely independent. She knew then that whatever this job was, that was being newly created by Silas Livingstone, she would take it.

While it might not pay as well as that multilingual secretary's job, Silas Livingstone was well aware of her circumstances, so surely he would not be considering her for this new vacancy unless the salary that went with it was an adequate living wage.

By early Friday evening Colly had reasoned that, because her only skills were in keeping a well-run house, some small knowledge of art and an ability with languages, this newly created vacancy must involve the use of her languages in some way—which, plainly, was not secretarial. But, again, why dinner? It was almost as though the job was not in his office at all! As if it were nothing to do with office life—and that was why he was interviewing her in 'informal detail' outside of the office.

She was getting fanciful. Colly went upstairs to shower and get dressed, ready for Silas Livingstone to call.

Because this was to all intents and purposes a business dinner, Colly opted to wear a black straight ankle-length skirt of fine wool and a heavy silk white shirt-blouse. She joined the two with a wide suede belt that emphasised her tiny waist. She brushed her long brown hair with its hint of red back from her face in an elegant knot, and when she took a slightly apprehensive glance in the full-length mirror she was rather pleased with her general appearance. It was only then that she accepted that, with no other likely-looking job being advertised in the paper this week, she was pinning a lot of hope on this interview. She did so hope she would not come home disappointed. It was just that afternoon that Nanette had bluntly asked when she was leaving.

It was her luck that when, at ten minutes to eight, with a black wool cloak over her arm, she went downstairs to wait, she should meet Nanette in the hall. 'Where are you off to?' Nanette asked nastily, her eyes looking her over.

'I'm going out to dinner.'

'What about *my* dinner?' Nanette asked shrewishly.

Only just did Colly refrain from telling her that she had been her father's housekeeper, not hers. 'I thought you might be going out yourself,' she replied quietly; the atmosphere in the house was hostile enough without her adding to it.

'A—friend will be joining me later,' Nanette snapped. And,

an anticipatory gleam coming to her eyes, 'Don't disturb us when you come in.'

Colly went into the breakfast room to wait. It was a dark January night and she would see the car's headlights as they swept up the drive. Now, don't hope for too much. She attempted to calm herself down. There was every chance she might not yet be offered this job which could mean independence and a new way of life.

A minute or so later car headlights lit up the drive. Colly donned her cloak and, hoping it was Silas Livingstone and not Nanette's 'friend', left the breakfast room and went out to meet him.

It was her hopefully prospective employer. He left the driver's seat and came to open up the passenger door. 'Hello, Colly,' he greeted her amicably.

Well, that sounded friendly enough. She preferred Colly to Columbine. 'Hello,' she murmured. In no time she was seated beside him and they were motoring back down the drive. 'You found the house all right?' she asked politely. It was a nice house, in a very well-to-do neighbourhood.

'Not a problem,' he returned pleasantly, and matched her for polite conversation as he drove them to the eating establishment he had chosen, which happened to be a hotel.

He waited in the foyer while she checked her cloak. After taking a deep breath, her insides churning, she went out to join him. She gave him a smile. He smiled back, his eyes taking in her smart appearance. She had been out on dates before—but never with someone like him.

But this was not a date, she reminded herself as he escorted her to a lounge area. 'You're over your disappointment of last Tuesday, I hope?' he enquired as he waited for her to be seated.

'I blush whenever I think of my nerve in even applying,' she answered as he took a seat facing her.

He seemed to approve of her honesty. But, when she

thought that he would now begin to interview her for this other job, the newly arisen job, to her surprise did not, but merely commented, 'You're having a rather desperate time of it at the moment,' and asked, 'What would you like to drink?'

He went on to be a most courteous and pleasant companion.

'Mr Livingstone—' she began at one point.

Only to lose her thread completely when, 'Silas,' he invited—and kept up a polite flow of conversation as they transferred to the dining room.

He asked her opinion on sundry matters as they ate their way through the first course, and in fact was everything she could wish for in a platonic dinner partner. So much so that they were midway through their main course before she recalled that they were not here as friends but as prospective employer and employee.

'This job,' she inserted during a break in the conversation, realising only then how thoroughly at ease with him she felt. If that had been his aim he could not have done better.

'We'll get to that in time,' he commented. 'Is the steak to your liking?'

They were back in the lounge drinking coffee before Colly found another chance to introduce the subject of work without appearing to be blunt.

'I've very much enjoyed this evening,' she began politely, 'but…'

'But now, naturally, you'd like to know more about the vacancy.' He favoured her with a pleasant look, and explained, rather intriguingly, she felt, 'I wanted to get to know you a little before we embarked on a—full discussion.'

'And—er—you feel you have?'

'Sufficiently, I believe,' he replied, going on, 'I also wanted privacy to outline what I have in mind.' His mouth quirked upwards briefly. 'I hesitated to ask you back to my home.'

Her lovely green eyes widened somewhat. 'You're—um—

making this sound just a little bit personal,' she answered warily.

He considered her answer, but did not scoff that it was nothing of the sort, as she had expected him to. Doing nothing for her suddenly apprehensive feelings, he said, 'I suppose, in an impersonal way, it could be termed personal.'

'Do I get up and leave now?' she enquired coldly.

'I'd prefer you stayed until you'd heard me out,' he replied, his dark eyes fixed on her apprehensive green ones. 'You're quite safe here,' he added, glancing round what was now a deserted lounge. 'And we have all the privacy we need in which to talk this vacancy through.'

So that was why he had not gone into detail over dinner! A few fellow diners had been within eavesdropping distance should they have cared to listen in. 'So, you having assured me I'm not required to sing for my supper, I'm listening,' Colly invited, relaxing again, because should this conversation go in a way she did not care for she could decline to allow him to drive her to her home, and could ask someone at Reception to get her a taxi.

To hear that she was ready for him to outline the job was all Silas Livingstone was waiting for. Though, instead of outlining the work, he first of all stated, 'I've learned a little of you this evening, Colly. Sufficient, at any rate, to know that I should like to offer you this—position.'

Her heart lightened. Oh, thank heaven. She was on her way! Silas Livingstone must believe she could do the job, or he would not be willing to offer it to her. 'Oh, that's wonderful!' She beamed, her overwhelming relief plain to see. She might soon be self-sufficient, have money of her own and be able to afford somewhere to rent, and not beholden to Nanette for a temporary roof over her head.

He looked at her shining green eyes. 'You don't know what the job is yet,' he cautioned.

'I don't care what it is,' she answered delightedly. 'As long as it's honest and pays well. You wouldn't offer if—'

'Are things really so bad for you?' he butted in softly.

Colly took a breath to deny that things were in any way bad for her. Though when she thought of the dire state of her present finances, and then of Nanette's daily barbs that she pack her bags and leave, Colly couldn't think that they could be much worse.

'What sort of work would I have to do?' she enquired, ready to turn her hand to anything.

Silas studied her for a moment, not commenting that she had not given him a detailed account of just how awful things were at the only home she had ever known. Instead, he asked, 'Tell me, Colly, if it were not so very essential for you to find somewhere to live and to find a job with a salary sufficient with which to pay rent, what would be an ideal scenario for you?'

Again Colly found herself wishing she knew more about the usual interviewing techniques. Though, looking into the steady dark blue eyes of Silas Livingstone, she had an idea that he would not always follow the path of what was usual anyhow.

She looked away from him. 'I want to be independent,' she replied. 'I thought, a couple of years ago, that I'd like to have a place of my own…'

'But your father wanted you to stay on as housekeeper?'

'Nanette, the woman he married, she preferred that I stayed on.'

'And now, now that she has inherited the house and every-thing else, she wants you gone.'

It was not a question but a statement. And one that Colly could not argue against. 'So that makes my first priority to find somewhere to live and, of course, a job too.' She shrugged, feeling more than a touch embarrassed, but, it not needing any thinking about, she went on to honestly answer his question about her ideal scenario. 'From choice, I would prefer to do some sort of training. Perhaps take a year's foundation course while I looked into possible careers—or even go on to university.' She felt awkward again as she looked Silas in the eyes and confessed, 'I probably shouldn't be telling you this, but apart from an interest in art—though no particular talent—I have no idea what, if anything, I'm especially good at.'

Silas smiled then. He did not do it too often, but when he did she momentarily forgot what they were talking about. 'You have a nice way with you,' he answered. 'You have integrity, and I have formed an opinion that I can trust you.'

Colly felt a touch pink. Was that what all that non-business chat over dinner had been about—Silas gauging from her answers, her questions, her general demeanour, what sort of a person she was? My, but he was clever. So clever she had not had a clue what he was about. 'Yes, well,' she mumbled, just a trifle embarrassed. 'You must—er—trust me to have offered me the job.' She got herself more of one piece. And, on thinking about it, considered it was more than high time that she found out more about this vacancy. 'May I know exactly what the job entails? What my duties will be?' she asked.

Then she discovered she would find out what she wanted to know, but only when he was good and ready—because he had not finished asking questions of his own yet. 'First of all,' he began, 'tell me what you know about the firm of Livingstone Developments?'

Realising that since he was paying the piper she would have to dance to his tune, she replied, 'That's fairly easy. When I knew I had an interview last Tuesday, I made it my business to find out all I could about the company. I'd never been for an interview before,' she explained, 'so I had no idea of what sort of questions I should know the answers to.'

He accepted that as fair comment. 'What did you discover?' he wanted to know.

'I discovered that Livingstone Developments—only it wasn't called that then—was founded years and years ago by one Silas Livingstone.'

'Sixty years ago, by my grandfather,' Silas filled in.

'It was only a small company then—dealing with industrial equipment, I think.' She waited for him to interrupt. He didn't, so she went on. 'The firm expanded when your grandfather's son took over.'

'The firm made quite a progressive leap forward when my father took over,' Silas stated. 'Under his leadership the firm went on to become a leading international firm of consulting engineers.'

'And when, five years ago, Borden Livingstone stepped down and you were voted to be chairman, you led the firm onwards to take in the design and manufacture of more advanced engineering products.'

'You *have* done your homework,' Silas commented when she had nothing more to add. Then, giving her a straight look, 'All of which perhaps makes you see what a tremendous amount of hard work has gone on over the past sixty years to make Livingstone Developments into the much-respected and thriving company it is today.' His eyes were still steady on her when quietly he added, 'And what a colossal waste of all those years of hard labour, of effort, it would be if I can't come up with some way to prevent the company from sinking into decline.'

Startled, Colly stared at him. 'Livingstone Developments is in trouble?' she gasped, forgetting about her own problems— the company employed thousands of people!

But he was shaking his head. 'No,' he denied. 'We're thriving.'

The firm was thriving, yet sixty years of effort might be

wasted? It didn't make sense. There had to be an 'if', and a very big 'if' at that. 'But...?' she questioned.

Silas gave her an approving look that she was keeping up with him. 'A massive but,' he agreed, and went on, 'I had a meeting with my father on Monday. My father, I should explain, is the most level-headed man I know. I have never seen him panicky and have seldom seen him anything but calm. But there was no denying that on Monday he was extremely agitated about something.'

'Oh, I'm sorry to hear that,' she murmured politely. She discovered she would like to know more, but knew Silas would not tell her, and felt it went beyond the bounds of good manners to ask.

'No more sorry than I was to hear just why he was so disturbed,' Silas commented.

Her curiosity was piqued, not to say her intelligence—she was suddenly realising that Silas would not have brought her here and begun to tell her what he was telling her were there not some purpose behind it.

'I don't want to pry,' she began, 'but—'

And was saved from having to pry any further when Silas interrupted to inform her, 'All this has been a bit of a jolt for me, but I've had time since Monday to adjust. By the time I saw you on Tuesday I was beginning to acknowledge what had to be done, and that if the company was not ultimately going to go to the wall that it was down to me to do it.'

'I'm trying to keep up,' she commented. Fog? The fog was getting thicker by the minute.

'I'm telling you this in the strictest confidence, of course.'

'Of course,' she answered—whatever 'this' was.

'I'm also telling it very badly. Perhaps I'd better go back to the beginning,' he decided.

'It might be a good idea,' she conceded. If this was the way all job interviews went, she had to confess herself intrigued!

'To start with, my grandfather had a simply wonderful marriage.'

'Ye-es,' Colly said slowly, with no idea what direction they were heading in now.

'Sadly, my grandmother died six months ago.'

'Oh, I'm sorry,' she murmured sensitively.

'As you can imagine, my grandfather was devastated. But he at last seems to be coming to terms with his grief. Naturally we've all rallied round to try and help him at this dreadful time. My parents and my aunt Daphne—my grandfather's daughter—particularly. In actual fact, my parents spent the weekend with him at his home in Dorset only last weekend.' He paused, then added, 'Which is why my father rang me the moment he got home on Sunday. I wasn't in. He left a message saying it was of some importance that we meet without delay. I should explain—' Silas broke off what he was saying to note '—that my father does not use such language unless something of very great import is going down.'

Colly's brain was racing. 'It was to do with Livingstone Developments having some kind of sword dangling over its head?' was the best she could come up with.

'Got it in one,' Silas approved. 'My father isn't one to panic, as I mentioned, but he knew something serious was afoot when my grandfather told him that he wanted to talk privately to him in his study. My father came out from the study shaken to the core, still taking in what my grandfather had told him.'

Colly was desperately trying to think what any of this could have to do with her and this vacancy that had been created.

'Your grandfather needs a housekeeper?' She took a disappointed guess. It would be a job, and with accommodation thrown in. But did she really want to be a housekeeper for some elderly gentleman?

'He already has a housekeeper,' Silas informed her.

She was lost again. 'Sorry. I'll keep quiet until you've finished. Er—you haven't finished yet?'

'I'm getting there. The thing is that since my parents and aunt can't be with Grandfather all the time he spends many hours alone reliving the past. And at this present time, and with the loss of my grandmother so recent, he spends a lot of time thinking of her and their long years of very happy marriage. Which,' Silas said, 'brings us up to Sunday, when, in his study, my grandfather spoke to my father in terms of altering his will. Instead of my cousin Kit and I inheriting his considerable holding of shares in the firm between us—as I've always been lead to believe will happen—he intends to leave the whole basket-load of shares to Kit—if I don't buck my ideas up and marry.'

Colly blinked—and didn't know which question to ask first. 'You're not married?' was the first one to pop out.

'Never have been.'

'But your cousin—Kit—is married?'

'Has been this last ten years.'

'You're not engaged or living with anyone?' she questioned, more or less in the same way he had asked her on Tuesday.

He shook his head. 'No, nor likely to be.'

'Nor do you want to marry?'

'Definitely not. And, much though I'm fond of the old chap, I resent him, just because he has this sublime respect for the institution of marriage, attempting to force me to take a wife.'

'But unless you do you stand to be disinherited,' she reasoned. 'Join the club.'

'It's not going to happen.'

'Your father thinks he'll change his mind?'

'Very doubtful. My father's anxiety stems from the certainty that it *will* happen, and that all that he and I have worked for over the years will be as nothing if Kit gets a controlling interest in the firm. Which, with those shares, he most definitely will.'

'He's—er—not up to the job?'

'Don't get me wrong. Kit and I had a lot to do with each other during our growing years. I'm fond of him, despite his faults. But, as well as being no powerhouse when it comes to work—and that's being kind—he is far too easily swayed by others. Although he's already parted with some of the shares his mother gave him, he, like me, already has enough shares to guarantee him a seat on the board. But while we have a duty to our shareholders we also have a duty to our workforce. And I'm afraid Kit feels a duty for neither. It's a foregone conclusion that the ship will sink if he has any hand in guiding it.'

Colly did not know much about big business, but if Silas Livingstone thought it was so, she was quite willing to believe him. 'So…' she brought out the best her brain could come up with '…either you marry and inherit a sufficient number of shares to deny your cousin control, or you ultimately have to stand by and watch him ruin all that three generations of Livingstones have worked for?'

'Exactly,' Silas agreed. 'And while God forbid that anything untoward happens to my grandfather for years and years yet, I have to face the reality that he's currently aged eighty-four. Which is why I have determined that when that awful day comes, and he's no longer with us, I am not left hearing that unless I have been married for a year and a day the shares that should be mine have been inherited by my cousin Kit.'

By then Colly had forgotten entirely that she had only dined with Silas Livingstone to hear about a job he was now offering her. She recalled how wounded she herself had felt at the way her father had left his will. By the look of it, the shares Silas Livingstone had always been led to believe were half his would be willed elsewhere.

On thinking over all he had just said, though, she could

only see one way out for him—if he was dead set on keeping the company safe. 'I'm sorry, Silas,' she said quietly, 'but it seems to me that unless you're prepared to let the company fail you're going to have to get over your aversion to marriage and take yourself a wife.'

For ageless moments after she had spoken Silas said not a word. Then, drawing a long breath, 'That is the only conclusion I was able to reach too,' he said. And then, looking at no one but her, 'Which,' he added, 'is where you come in.'

She stared at him. 'Me?' she questioned, startled.

'You,' he agreed.

Her brain wasn't taking this in. 'No,' she said on a strangled kind of note as what he might possibly be meaning started to filter through. Then, as common sense swiftly followed, 'I'm sorry,' she apologised. 'For one totally absurd moment I had this weird notion that you were asking me to marry you.'

She laughed awkwardly, feeling that she had made a fool of herself. She was on the brink of repeating her apology, only, daring to take a glance at him, certain that he must be laughing his head off, she could see not one glimmer of being highly amused about him!

Colly swallowed hard. 'You weren't doing that, were you?' she asked, her voice gone all husky in shock.

'I cannot fault the idea,' he answered, his look steady, his expression unsmiling.

Did that mean that he *was* suggesting that he marry her? No, don't be ridiculous. Good heavens, she... Colly got herself more together. Whether he was suggesting what it very much sounded as if he was suggesting or not, she thought it was time she let him know her feelings.

'I don't want a husband!' she told him bluntly.

'Good!' was his answer, doing nothing for her feeling that she had just made one enormous fool of herself. 'I don't want a wife.' She wondered if she should get up and leave right now. 'But…' he added—and she stayed to hear the rest of it, '…you and I both have a problem, wouldn't you agree?'

'I know what your problem is,' she agreed.

'And your problem is that you need somewhere to live and the wherewithal to finance your training.'

'I hope you're not thinking in terms of giving me money!' she erupted proudly—and, oddly, saw a hint of a smile cross his features. 'I shall work for any money I—'

'Look on this as work,' he cut in quickly.

'This is the job you're offering me?' This wasn't happening; she'd got something wrong somewhere.

He took a long breath, as if finding her uphill work. She did not care. The whole notion was absurd—that was if she had got all this right. 'Try and see this logically,' Silas said after some moments.

Colly looked at him levelly, took a deep breath of her own, and supposed her reaction *had* been more instinctive than logical. 'So?' she invited, as calmly as she could.

'So in my line of business I have to work not for today but for tomorrow. Use forward planning techniques to the full.'

'As in marrying someone before your grandfather's will gets read?'

'Which hopefully won't be for years yet. But, yes. Had anyone but my level-headed father told me what the stubborn old devil intends to do I'd have paid scant attention.'

'But your father isn't one to panic unnecessarily?'

Silas nodded. 'I'd twenty-four hours to take on board what he said when the daughter of a much-respected man in the engineering world was there in my office—telling me she had been disinherited…'

'And that rang a bell?'

'Too true it rang a bell. You then went on to say how you needed a job that paid well, and how you were going to have to find some place to live, and I find I'm suddenly going into forward planning mode.'

'You—um...' She couldn't say it. She did not want to make a fool of herself again. Though she could not help but recall how he had asked her about men-friends, and if she were engaged or anything of that sort.

'I had an idea,' he took up. 'An idea that I've had since Tuesday to look at from every angle.'

'That idea being...?' she questioned, and waited, barely breathing, to hear whether she had been foolhardy to think he might be meaning what she thought he was so amazingly suggesting, or whether her brain, her instincts, had got it right.

'That idea being,' he said, looking at no one but her, his gaze steady, unwavering, 'to marry you.'

A small sound escaped her. Even though she had thought that might be what he meant, she could not help that small gasp of shock. 'Thank you for dinner,' she said, and stood up.

He was, she discovered, not a man to give up easily. He had cynically, no emotion in it, decided he would marry, case closed.

But he was on his feet too. 'Hear me out, Colly?' he asked of her. 'Neither of us wants to marry, so that's all in our favour.'

'How on earth do you make that out?'

'Neither of us is emotionally involved. And it's not as if we have to live with each other.'

'We don't?' she found herself questioning, even when she was just not interested.

He put a hand under her elbow and guided her from the lounge, waited while she retrieved her cloak, then escorted her out to his car. But instead of driving off once they were in his car, he turned to her and stated, 'You too have a problem, Colly.'

She half turned to look at him. 'I'm fully aware of that,' she answered shortly.

'And I'm in a position to solve your problems,' he said.

And before she could give him a curt, No, thank you, he was informing her, 'My grandfather owns a small apartment here in London where he and my grandmother stayed whenever they came up to town. He hasn't used it since her death, and he's said he will never again use it. But, because of his very happy memories of times spent there, neither will he part with it. He's asked me to keep an eye on the place, and I've stayed the occasional night there. But you'd be doing me a favour if you'd take it on. The place needs living in.'

Good heavens! 'You're offering me the tenancy?' she exclaimed, guessing in advance that she would never be able to afford the rent.

'What I'm offering, in return for you giving me a half-hour of your time and standing up in front of some registrar and making the appropriate responses when asked, is somewhere to live. I think you'll be comfortable there. Further to that, I'll undertake to fund any training you desire, be it a foundation course followed by university, or whatever you may wish to do.'

This was jaw-dropping stuff! She had come out with him for a job interview and had never expected anything like this! She just had to recap. 'In return for an "I will" you're prepared to...'

'On the day you marry me,' he replied unhesitatingly, 'I shall arrange for ten thousand pounds to be paid into your bank, with subsequent top-ups as and when required.'

'No!' she said, point-blank, and, nothing to argue about, she turned to face the front.

'Think about it,' he returned.

'I'd like to go home,' she told him woodenly. She was aware of his hard scrutiny, but was relieved when after some seconds he too faced the front and started up his car.

Neither of them spoke on the way back to her home. What he was thinking about she had no idea, but her head was positively buzzing. 'Think about it,' he had said—how could she not?

When she was desperate for somewhere to live he was offering her free accommodation! When she had a need to train for a career—and by twenty-three most women had a toe-hold on several rungs of the career ladder—he was offering to finance her career training!

She should be snatching his hand off. But—marry him! Colly knew that to marry him was something that she could just not do.

Having been silent all the way home, it was as if Silas Livingstone had thought to give her all the space she needed to get used to the idea. Because no sooner had he driven up to her front door than he turned to her.

'What's it to be?' he enquired mildly.

'I thought I'd given you my answer.'

'That was instinctive, spur-of-the-moment, an unanalysed reaction.' He shrugged that away. 'Marry me,' he urged.

'I—don't even know you!' she protested.

'You don't need to know me,' he countered. 'Just a half-hour—we need never see each other again.'

'No,' she repeated. 'I can't. I'm sorry. I know how very important this is to you, but—'

'You're right there,' he cut in abruptly, causing her to stare at him. But, relenting suddenly, 'I've had since Tuesday to adjust to the notion. Four days in which to weigh everything up, to mull it over and over, to get used to the idea before reaching the decision I have. On reflection, perhaps I'm not being fair, dropping it on you like this and expecting you to come back with the answer I want.'

She was about to reiterate that her answer was no. And that had she had those same four days it would not have made any difference—her answer would still be no—that she just did not need to think about it, or need to get used to the idea either. But Silas was no longer beside her. He was out of the car and had come round to the passenger door.

She stepped out and he stood with her for a moment on the gravel by the front door. He glanced down to where, in the light of the security lamps, her dark hair glowed with red lights. 'Think about it,' he said. 'Think about it and I'll call you. I'll phone you Tuesday evening.'

Colly looked up. His expression was telling her nothing. She opened her mouth to again tell him no, that she had no need to think about it, then realised that he was not in any kind of mood to take 'no' from her.

'Goodnight,' she said, and went indoors.

Saturday and Sunday passed with Colly still trying to believe that the conversation that had taken place on Friday night had actually taken place and was not some figment of her imagination. Had Silas Livingstone really suggested they marry? Had he really told her to think about it and that he would call her for her answer?

Whatever—his astonishing proposal did achieve one thing: her head was so full of it there was small room for her to take much heed of Nanette's spiteful barbs whenever they were within speaking distance of each other.

Though on Monday morning Nanette was at her most vicious. 'You still here?' she snapped when she eventually came down the stairs.

'I'm making plans,' Colly returned, without a plan in her head.

'You'd better make them pretty quick, then,' Nanette retorted, going on to inform her nastily, 'If you're not out of this house by the end of the week I'm having all the locks changed!'

'You can't do that!' Colly gasped.

'Who's going to stop me? Joseph Gillingham left this house to me.' And, with a triumphant smirk, 'It's mine!'

Not for the first time Colly wished that her father's lawyer friend Henry Warren were there to advise her. Surely she could not be barred from her home of twenty-three years? Be put out in the street—just like that! But Uncle Henry was still holidaying abroad, and to seek help from some other legal representative would take money. And money was in rather short supply just then.

How short was again brought home to her when, a little while later, she went looking for a flat to rent. Prices were sky-high! She couldn't so much as pay the first month's rent in advance for even the lowliest bedsit!

Silas Livingstone's proposal that she stand with him in front of some registrar suddenly started to have a weakening effect on her. She stiffened her backbone. She couldn't do it. Marry him? Take money from him? No, it was out of the question.

She returned to her car, but had no wish to return home. It was not home any more. She began to feel all stewed up—what other options were open to her? There were none. She replayed again that morning's spat with Nanette and could not get it out of her head. That was when Colly realised that if she dwelt on it many more times she might yet weaken completely. And she could not weaken. She could not marry Silas Livingstone.

On impulse she took out her phone. She would tell him now. She would not wait until tomorrow for him to call her. She would tell him now—while she still had the strength of mind.

She supposed she should have realised it would not be as simple as that to get in touch with him. He was a busy man. He had not even had any free time in which to take her to lunch last week, had he?

Though she did get through to his PA, and it was almost as if Ellen Rothwell had been instructed to put her through to him were she to ring, because the PA was most affable and informative when she apologised and said, 'I'm sorry, Silas isn't in right now. All being well, he should be in the office at some time between three and four if that's any help?'

'Thank you very much. I—er—may call back,' Colly replied, and, unable to sit still, she left her car wishing that it was all over and done with.

As she walked aimlessly about so she started to blame him. It was all his fault that she was in this stew. If he had taken her at her word on Friday she would not now be wandering around fretting the pros and cons of his whole astonishing suggestion anyway.

Not that she had thought too deeply about his side of things. Though it was plain that Silas must be more than a little desperate to have put the preposterous proposal to her in the first place. He, with his forward planning, could see everything he and his father before him—and his grandfather too, come to that—had worked for going down the drain if his cousin got his hands on those controlling shares.

He knew his cousin better than she, who had never met him. But surely this Kit person was not so bad as all that? If he were, then would Grandfather Livingstone really change his will in the married Kit's favour? She could not see it.

But suddenly then Colly was shocked into reconsidering. It had never dawned on her that she would be made homeless when her father died—but he had changed *his* will, hadn't he? And, when she might have been forgiven for not expecting to be left destitute, he had left her not a penny.

Feeling a little stunned, Colly began to wish she had not started to think about this marriage proposal from Silas's angle. Because now that she had she began to think of all those employees who would lose their livelihood, the shareholders who might have invested perhaps more than they could afford in the prosperous company—all of whom stood to suffer financially should Silas's worst fears come to fruition. It was as weakening as knowing that she was about to be made homeless, and that come the weekend she could throw away her house keys for all the use they would be to her.

By half past two, while appearing outwardly calm, Colly had become so het-up from going over and over everything in her head that she just could not take any more. Neither could she marry him, and that was that, and the sooner she told him the better. She would phone again—oh, grief, with his tight schedule he would be too busy to take phone calls.

That was when she noticed that she was not all that far away from the Livingstone building. At five to three she was pushing through the plate glass doors.

While she knew where Silas Livingstone's office was, there was a way of doing these things. And, anyhow, he might have someone in his office with him, which meant that she could not just bowl in there unannounced.

She went over to the desk. 'I'm Columbine Gillingham,' she told the receptionist. 'Is it convenient to see...' she got cold feet '...Ellen Rothwell?'

Her insides started to act up, and that was before the receptionist came off the phone to pleasantly say that Mrs Rothwell was expecting her. 'You know the way?'

Colly hoped that by the time she reached Ellen Rothwell's door she might have calmed down somewhat. But not a bit of it; she felt even more hot and bothered and was fast wishing that she had not come. She was recalling those steady dark blue eyes that had looked into hers—almost as if he could see into her soul.

I'm being fanciful, she scoffed. But her insides were still rampaging when she found Ellen Rothwell's door and went in.

'Silas isn't back yet, but if you'd like to take a seat he won't be long,' Ellen informed her pleasantly.

Colly thanked her, but felt more like standing up and pacing up and down than sitting. But she went and took a seat, realising as she did so that, while it was highly unlikely Silas

would have confided in his PA any of this very private business, it looked very much as if—appointments with him being
like gold dust—he must have mentioned that he was prepared
to take calls from Columbine Gillingham, and that if she appeared personally he would fit her in with his busy schedule
somehow.

Then the outer door opened, and while her heart leapt into
her mouth it quieted down again when she saw it was not the
man she had come to see. This man was about the same age
as Silas, and about the same tall height. But that was where
any likeness ended. He was sandy-haired, and where Silas had
a strong, rather nice-shaped mouth, this man's mouth was
weak—and that was before he opened it.

'Ellen, lovely girl—is my cousin in?' he wanted to know,
his eyes skirting from her to make a meal of Colly.

'Not yet,' Ellen replied, but his attention was elsewhere as
he turned his smile full beam on Colly.

'Are you here to see Silas?' he queried—and, before she
could answer, 'Kit Summers,' he introduced himself, and held
out his right hand.

It would have been churlish to ignore it. Colly shook hands
with him—and wanted to pull her hand back when he held it
over-long.

'What's a nice girl like you doing in a place like this?' Kit
Summers asked flirtatiously.

Heaven help us! This man might be left to run the company! Colly caught Ellen doing an eye-roll to the ceiling, and
felt a hysterical kind of laugh wanting to break loose.

Kit Summers was not at all put off that Colly did not answer, but, continuing to beam at her, suggested, 'Look, Silas
might not be back for ages—why don't I take you for a cup
of tea?'

Colly stared at him. This chinless wonder was married, yet
by the look of it did not miss an opportunity to flirt. She was

about to give him a cool, No, thank you, when Ellen Rothwell interceded.

'Have you the figures Silas wanted?' she enquired evenly.

That shook him sufficiently for him to take his eyes off Colly for a moment. 'Hell, was it today he wanted them? Strewth, I'd better be going. Don't tell him I was here,' he said. 'And deny any rumour you may have heard that I was on the golf course this morning!' With that he was gone.

Colly sat there feeling stunned and with her insides churning. Silas's cousin was a lightweight, and it showed. And if first impressions were anything to go by he was not fit to run any development company, much less an international one.

Then suddenly her mouth went dry. She heard sounds coming from the next-door office. If she wasn't very much mistaken, Silas was back.

She was not mistaken—the intercom buzzed into life. 'Has Kit been in?' Silas asked.

'Been and gone, I'm afraid,' his PA answered, and quickly, before he could enquire about any figures, 'Miss Gillingham is here to see you.'

The announcement was met with total silence. And, quite desperately wishing that she had written, or phoned, but certainly that she had not come in person, Colly went from hot to cold and to hot again. All at once there was movement on the other side of the door, and a moment later the door was opened and Silas Livingstone, tall, commanding, and the very opposite of his cousin, stood there.

He did not smile, or remind her that he had been going to give her a call tomorrow evening, but, 'Hello, Colly,' he said mildly, with his eyes fixed on hers as if he would read there what she had come in person to tell him.

Colly stood up. The time had arrived to give him the answer that would not wait until he telephoned tomorrow. He took a step back, so she should go first into his office, and following her in closed the door behind them, giving them all the privacy they needed.

CHAPTER THREE

'WHAT have you got to tell me?' Silas asked.

'I…' She was nervous; her voice got lost somewhere in her throat.

She moved more into the centre of the room, but, indicating one of the easy chairs, 'Come and sit over here,' Silas invited calmly. If he was aware of how mixed up inside she felt, he was not showing it.

With him towering over her, to sit across the room from him seemed a good idea. Colly went and took a seat—then found that Silas had no intention of going over to sit behind his desk when he came and took the easy chair opposite hers.

'I'm sorry to have intruded on your day.' She found her voice. 'I know how busy you are!'

If she had expected him to say that it did not matter she would have been in for a disappointment. For he said nothing of the sort, but, getting straight to the point, 'You couldn't wait until tomorrow to give me your answer?'

'My answer was no,' she replied promptly.

'On Friday.' He immediately got down to business. 'On Friday it was no. You've had time to think about it fully since then.'

She had thought of little else. 'My answer was still no this morning,' Colly answered. 'Only…'

'Only?' he took up when she hesitated.

'Only—well, to tell you the truth, I found myself weakening when this morning Nanette—um—mentioned—well, to be honest— This is extremely embarrassing for me!' she broke off to exclaim.

'You're doing well,' Silas stated calmly. 'Carry on.'

44

'Well, it would seem I soon won't have anywhere to live.'

'That "lady" wants you out?'

Colly coughed slightly. 'By the weekend,' she agreed, not missing that he did not seem to have much time for her 'lady' stepmother. 'I said this was embarrassing,' she mumbled. 'Anyhow, my trawl of just a few rental agencies has shown that I'm going to be hard put to it to find the rent.'

'So on that basis you decided, yes, you'd change your mind and agree to marry me?'

'No,' Colly denied. 'I'm being as honest with you as I know how,' she added quickly. 'My answer first thing this morning was still no,' she went on openly, explaining, 'When you and I are virtually strangers to each other, it goes against everything in me to allow you to, in effect, keep me while I undertake whatever training I need to make a career for myself.'

She paused for breath and looked at him. But he said nothing, just sat quietly listening—and assessing.

'Anyhow,' she continued, 'in the light of this morning's happenings—my imminent homelessness and inability to afford anywhere to live—I found I was weakening in my decision to—er—not take you up on your offer.' She took a shaky breath. 'So I thought I shouldn't wait until tomorrow to tell you, but tell you today. But I couldn't get you when I phoned earlier. Then I was close by, so I thought I'd better come and tell you in person.'

'Before you weakened further?' he suggested.

'Yes,' she replied. And hesitated again. Never had she felt so totally all over the place as she did then. 'But…'

'But?' Silas prompted when she seemed momentarily stuck to know how to go on.

'But—I've just met your cousin.'

Silas moved his head fractionally to one side, alert, interested. 'And?' he enquired.

'Oh, Silas,' she said in a rush, 'you can't possibly allow him to take over the company!'

Silas looked at her levelly for ageless seconds. Then, quietly, he let fall, 'You, Colly, have the power to stop him.'

She stared at him, her heart thundering. She felt she was teetering on the biggest decision of her life.

'Forget your pride at taking assistance from me,' he urged after some moments, 'and think of what you will be doing for me, and this company. I, in turn, will benefit far more than you,' he reminded her.

That made her feel a whole deal better. But it still did not make it right. 'Why me?' she asked as the question suddenly came to her. And, looking at him, seeing everything about him shrieking sex appeal, 'You must know any number of women who would agree to this?'

He did not deny it but gave her question a few seconds' thought before replying. 'You because you, like me, have a need, and we would be helping each other. And you, if I'm to be as honest as you, mainly because you don't want to marry me and would prefer any other way if you could find one.'

'Ah!' she exclaimed, as it suddenly dawned on her. 'Me because you know I won't get in your hair afterwards and try to make capital of it?'

He stared at her. 'Precisely,' he acknowledged, and with entire spontaneity they both burst out laughing. It was good to laugh with him—it lightened the serious atmosphere.

Then the intercom buzzed and Ellen Rothwell, apologising for the interruption, was informing him of telephone calls queuing up and reminding him of an appointment he had to keep.

Colly stood up. It seemed to her that she had intruded on his day for long enough. 'You still want to—um—do this?' she asked as Silas, on his feet too, looked down at her.

'Most definitely,' he replied, his eyes on her fine green eyes.

Colly took a long breath. She could hardly believe she was about to commit herself to marry this handsome virile man, but, 'You'd better say when,' she consented.

Silas did not take a moment to comprehend that she had just agreed to be his wife. Nor did he waste words, but stated, 'The sooner the better,' and, at once decisive, went over to his desk, wrote something on a piece of paper and returned to hand it to her. 'You'll want to have a look at your new home,' he said. 'We'll have matters to discuss too. I can be there around nine this evening. Is that all right with you?'

Grief, when she was committed she was committed, she realised. Silas was not hanging about. 'Fine,' she said faintly, and made for the door.

She left the Livingstone building in something of a daze. Had she just done what she thought she had? Had she just done what she had not intended to do? Was she, in effect, engaged to marry Silas Livingstone?

Over the following few hours her all-over-the-place feelings settled down. One way and another there had been quite an upheaval in her life lately. First her father had died. Then, before she could come to terms with his passing, she had learned that there was no way her father's wife was going to let her continue to live under the same roof. And now, Colly mused, she was going to have to come to terms with being— a wife!

Though not a proper wife, she hastily amended. She would meet Silas tonight and sort out any and all loose ends. They would no doubt agree on a wedding date, then it would be that half-hour in front of a registrar, and that should be it.

With so much whirling around in her head she only just remembered that she had promised to ring Rupert Thomas, who owned the art gallery where she helped out on Tuesdays.

'Tell me you're coming in tomorrow,' he pleaded. And,

prone to exaggeration, 'I missed you dreadfully when you didn't come in last Tuesday.'

Rupert was forty, and had been married twice but was currently single. He was a good friend. 'I'll come in tomorrow,' she agreed. 'How's business?'

'Terrible, terrible!' he replied, but it always was, according to Rupert, so there was nothing new there. They chatted for a few minutes, then Colly ended the call.

She supposed she should go and see about getting something to eat, but did not fancy another of Nanette's mean-spirited comments should she be around.

She did bump into her, though, when, in ample time to get to the address Silas had given her by nine, she left her room. 'Where are you going?' Nanette demanded.

In truth, Colly was finding her more than a little tedious, and was tempted to tell her to mind her own business. But politeness cost nothing, and this woman had brightened the last few years of her father's life—even if she had not stayed true to him.

'I'm going to take a look at an apartment,' she replied, and felt quite pleased to see that Nanette looked more taken aback by that than she would have done had she told her to mind her own business. But she was not taken aback for long, and was soon there with another of her spleenish remarks.

'I hope for your sake it will be vacant by Saturday!'

Saturday! Colly left her home unhappily aware it could no longer be called a home. She thought of her mother and could have wept. It had all been so different when she had been alive. So much love...

Colly put love out of her mind. She was getting married without love. Silas was too, and that suited her fine. Which reflection brought a previously unthought question to mind. Silas had said they would have matters to discuss. And he was right there!

Until now she had not thought there would be so very much

for them *to* discuss. But, for a start, what happened if one of them fell in love with someone? And how would they go on about a divorce? She supposed that that was the way their marriage would end—in divorce—with neither side battered or bruised by the experience. But what if Silas fell in love with someone and wanted out? What then?

Most oddly, she experienced a small niggle of impatience with the thought that he might fall in love with someone. Odd really was the word for it, she mused as she pulled up outside a newish-looking apartment block. She most certainly was not interested in him herself!

Colly was the first to arrive. She stayed in her car and observed the smart entrance to the building. It seemed incredible that she might soon be moving in here, but so far she liked what she saw.

A short while later a long sleek car pulled alongside, and as her heart suddenly missed a beat she recognised Silas Livingstone behind the steering-wheel so her insides joined in and did a churn.

Leaving her car, she went with him, waiting while he unlocked the entrance door. The apartment block was over three floors; the apartment owned by his grandfather was on the ground floor.

'It's lovely!' she exclaimed as Silas took her from room to room. It was small, as he had said, but only in that it consisted of just one bedroom, a sitting room-cum-dining room, a bathroom and a kitchen. All the rooms were otherwise spacious. Colly came from a very nice home herself, but had nothing to complain about in this her new home.

'Any of the furniture you can't live with can be put into storage,' Silas offered when they returned to the sitting room.

'Everything's fine,' she responded. Some of the furniture was antique, and beautiful, though there were some very pleasing modern pieces too.

'If you want to, bring some of your own furniture,' he suggested. 'I should like you to feel at home here.'

'That's kind of you,' Colly replied, smiling at him while thinking him most considerate. Without doubt the man had a great deal of charm. 'But I'm quite happy with the apartment the way it is.' She forbore to tell him that Nanette would probably call the police if she saw one stick of her inheritance making its way into any furniture van.

Silas took her at her word and handed the keys to the apartment over to her. 'Move in as soon as you like,' he instructed.

'You don't think we should stand in front of that registrar first?' she questioned, but could not deny that she felt pleased at this show of his trust in her.

'There seems little point in you spending a couple of weeks in some hotel when this place could benefit from someone living in it. Shall we sit down?' he suggested.

'I'm missing something?' she queried, confessing, 'Where does "hotel" come into it?'

'It doesn't,' he answered, and began to enlighten her into the working ways of his mind. 'Ellen has been able to shunt my diary around in order for me to have some time off tomorrow.'

'Yes?' Colly murmured, supposing that what he was talking about would become clearer.

'You're free tomorrow morning?' he asked.

'I promised Rupert I'd—'

'Rupert?' Silas cut in, his expression stern.

'It's not a problem,' she replied. 'Rupert owns the art gallery I help out in on Tuesdays. I said I'd be there tomorrow, but if I need to I can ring and cancel.'

'Cancel!' Silas instructed bluntly.

What happened to charm! 'Because…?' she queried stiffly.

'Because we both need to attend to make arrangements for the nuptials.'

'Oh!' she exclaimed, a little bit startled. She had already

formed an opinion that Silas Livingstone was a 'have it done by yesterday' kind of man. But—and she supposed she had not got around to thinking about it too much—she had rather thought their marriage would happen some time. By the sound of it he was keeping to that 'the sooner the better' comment. 'What time do you…?'

'I'll call for you at ten-twenty. You'll need either your birth certificate or your passport.'

'Er—I'll be ready. Um—when were you thinking of…?'

'Doing the deed?'

That was one way of putting it. 'You don't want to delay, by the sound of it?'

'No point,' he agreed. 'Though, since we apparently have to wait fifteen clear days after tomorrow, and a non-work day would suit me best, I'd suggest we marry two weeks on Saturday.' He looked at her questioningly.

'I've no objection to that,' she agreed faintly. His remark with regard to her not spending a couple of weeks in some hotel was starting to make sense. What he had been saying was that, since she would be without a roof over her head come the weekend, she might as well move in straight away rather than spend time in a hotel prior to their marriage.

'Good,' he said.

She started to feel a little panicky. 'This marriage…' she said in a rush. Though when she saw that she had his full attention had difficulty in continuing.

'This marriage?' he asked.

This was absurd. Spit it out, Colly, she fumed, irritated with herself. 'It wouldn't… I mean, I wouldn't have to—er—do anything—er—else?'

'Anything else?'

Oh, surely he wasn't that obtuse! For a moment she hated him that he was making her spell it out. 'Live with you—I mean.'

'You have your own apartment,' he replied urbanely, and she felt like boxing his ears.

'You said you occasionally spend a night here.' She dug her heels in stubbornly. She needed it all cut and dried now, and could not leave any question unanswered. 'And, while you may have given me a set of keys, I don't doubt that you still have a spare set.'

'True.' He did not deny it.

'Well…' She could feel herself going pink, but it had to be said. 'I wouldn't want anything—er—physical between—'

'You're blushing,' he interrupted, seeming fascinated at the tide of colour that flowed to her face.

And that annoyed her. 'I mean it!' she said stubbornly. 'I don't want a husband—' She broke off, looked at him, and everything suddenly righted itself in her head and settled. 'And you don't want a wife,' she ended, it being plain to her then that 'anything physical' was way off his agenda.

'You obviously needed to work that through,' he remarked casually.

She began to feel hot all over that she had ever brought the subject up. 'You're sure you need to do this?' she questioned hurriedly to cover her embarrassment. And, when he looked unsmiling at her, 'I mean—' she glanced from him and around the graciously appointed room '—I seem to be doing very well out of this.'

He nodded. 'Drastic circumstances call for drastic measures.' She had known that he would not be taking this 'drastic' action if he could find some other way out. And while drastic action was not very flattering to her, it was also fine by Colly. It was the same for her too. Her impending homelessness, her joblessness, her inability to earn sufficient to make her independent, made drastic action the only way possible for her too. 'I know my father,' Silas went on. 'Unless he was absolutely certain that my grandfather meant every word rather than cause me disquiet my father would have kept their conversation strictly to himself. You,' Silas said, looking straight into her green eyes, 'are my insurance.'

She looked away, uncertain how she felt about that. But considering all that had gone on, all that would go on, she realised that now was not the time to get picky because, not dressing it up, her intended was telling it as it was. Her intended! Oh, heavens!

Then she recalled how earlier that evening she had pondered on the question of their divorce. But when she looked at him it was to see he was taking out a card and handing it to her. 'My home address and phone number,' he informed her. 'I cannot see a situation arising when you'd need either, but—'

'I can,' she interrupted.

'You can?' He was looking stern again, whether because he did not care to be interrupted or because he was not too happy that she might have a complication that would see her wanting to phone him every five minutes, Colly could not tell.

'We've discussed the legal aspects of—um—what we're about.' Ridiculously, the words 'our marriage' stuck in her throat. 'But what about at the end of it?'

'End of it?'

There he was again, making her spell it out! 'Divorce. What—?'

His expression darkened. 'They'll be no divorce!' Silas stated harshly.

'No divorce?' It was her turn to echo his words this time.

Silas shook his head. 'My grandfather has very old-fashioned views on the sanctity of marriage. To him divorce is a dirty word. I have no idea of how he intends to word his new will, but I can be certain, from what I know of him, that there will be a clause in there somewhere to the effect that should any such marriage I have contracted end in divorce prior to his demise—Kit's marriage too for that matter—then the other cousin inherits the shares.'

'He's got you pretty well sewn up, hasn't he?' she commented.

'He has,' Silas admitted. 'And I resent it.'

'Er—you're not going to tell him you're married—when you are?'

'Hell, no!' Silas said forthrightly.

'Because you're—aggrieved with him?'

Silas shook his head slightly, though owned, 'A bit of that, perhaps, but mainly because he would want to meet my bride.'

'Oh, grief. I hadn't thought of that!' Colly exclaimed, mentally backing away fast from the very idea.

Silas favoured her with one of his rare smiles. 'While I know little about you, Colly, other than using my instincts, from what I *do* know about you I'd say you won't be telling anyone of our marriage either.'

'For my part, there's no one who needs to know,' she answered. He really had quite a superb mouth when he smiled. 'Um—shall we keep it between our two selves, then?' she asked. Good heavens, what was the matter with her? Abruptly she switched her gaze from his mouth to his eyes.

He gave a small nod. 'I may have to give my father some kind of hint that he has no need to worry. But you can rely absolutely on my discretion.'

'I'm sure,' she murmured. And from nowhere the words came rushing from her mouth. 'What if we marry but you fall in love with someone?' She had his full attention, and felt a touch awkward, but rushed on, 'What if you want to marry someone else?'

'I won't.'

'How do you know?' she exclaimed, not a little amazed by the confidence in his statement.

'She'd have to be more than a bit extra-special for me to

think so much of her that I'd be prepared to divorce you and so risk my inheritance going to my cousin.'

'You don't know anyone—er—that extra-special?' Colly found herself enquiring.

His mouth quirked upwards. 'She doesn't exist,' he returned pleasantly.

Colly mulled that over for a moment, then concluded, 'I'll marry you, because it suits us both, but I think we should have some sort of time limit.'

'You think you may fall in love and want to marry elsewhere?' he demanded, every bit as though he thought she was deceiving him—and that was before they started.

'No!' she denied hotly, her green eyes sparking at this hint he thought she might not be being absolutely honest with him. 'I've told you. I'm more interested in making a career for myself than in matrimony. I just—just need to cover all bases, all eventualities, that's all. And I—I think it's best to have these matters sorted out now, rather than on the registry office steps in a couple of weeks' time.' She ran out of breath, and owned to not being too enamoured that he had turned her question about him and his love-life around and fired it back at her.

Silas stared at her, his gaze on the spirited look of her, his glance slipping briefly to her mouth before he fixed on her eyes once more. Then he told her seriously, 'I'm afraid I cannot agree to any time limit in the length of our marriage,' explaining, 'To do so would be to speculate on my grandfather's demise, and that is abhorrent to me.'

'Oh, I couldn't agree more,' she said impulsively, suddenly wondering why it had been important to her anyway—Silas had more or less stated that he would not want to divorce during his grandfather's remaining years. 'I'm sorry,' she apologised. 'It was insensitive of me to push the issue.'

Silas looked at her contemplatively. 'Do you know?' he began a moment later. 'I do believe I'm getting me a very nice wife.' Colly could only look at him, but at once she realised that there was absolutely nothing intimate or anything for her to worry about in his remark when, in the same breath, and as if to take anything personal out of what he had said, he followed up with, 'You'll be dating, I expect, during our marriage?'

Her lips twitched. 'You're saying that you won't?' she bounced back at him. And, impossibly, they both laughed.

'That seems to be everything, I think,' he said a few seconds later. 'Unless there's anything else you'd like to ask?' She shook her head, finding that she enjoyed sharing laughter with him. 'Then I'll just show you where to garage your car, and we'll be off.'

Silas Livingstone was in her head the whole of the way home. He was still there when she went in and searched around in the drawer where personal papers were kept for her birth certificate.

'What are you nosing around in here for?' Nanette asked on coming into the study and seeing her with a rolled up piece of paper in her hand. 'What have you got there?'

'Nothing that belongs to you,' Colly replied evenly. And she realised that she did not have to put up with this woman for very much longer, that, in fact, now that she already had the keys to her new abode in her bag, she could move out tomorrow if she cared to. 'Since I shall soon be living elsewhere, I'm taking papers personal to me with me.' With that she escaped to her room.

Colly was about to go to the drawing room to wait and watch for Silas the next morning when she belatedly remembered that she had not telephoned Rupert. She was not surprised she had forgotten. The fact that she was going to marry Silas Livingstone two weeks on Saturday had kept her thoughts elsewhere. But Rupert would have expected her at the gallery twenty minutes ago.

She was on the hall phone to Rupert when her housecoated

stepmother floated past on her way to fix herself a cup of coffee. But while Colly was attempting to console Rupert—all 'his' women were against him, apparently, and his latest lady-love had last night dumped him—the doorbell rang.

'I'm sorry about that, Rupert,' Colly said, wanting to get to the front door before Nanette got there first. 'But I'll…'

Too late. Nanette was there. Colly heard her delighted coo of surprise, and was not listening at all to what Rupert was bending her ear with as Nanette invited Silas into the house.

'All I said to her,' Rupert was complaining, 'was that…'

Nanette took Silas into the drawing room and closed the door.

'I'm sorry, Rupert, I really must go. I have some business to attend to, but it shouldn't take me too long.'

'You liked her, didn't you?'

Meriel? He must be referring to his dumper. 'She was very nice. Look, Rupert, I must dash. I'm sorry I didn't call earlier, but…'

It seemed to be all of five minutes before she was able to put down the phone and hurry to the elegant drawing room, where Nanette was acting out the sad, but available, widow.

'Here you are,' she trilled sweetly as Silas got to his feet. 'You forgot to mention that Silas was calling.'

Colly ignored the question in her voice. 'I almost forgot to ring Rupert too,' she answered lightly. And, turning to Silas, 'I'm sorry to have kept you waiting.'

'You're sure I can't tempt you to coffee?' Nanette enquired of him.

'Thank you, no,' he replied urbanely. 'Ready, Colly?'

Nanette gave her a frosty look that said she would be asking questions later, and Silas escorted Colly out to his car. 'I was ready on time,' Colly commented as they crossed the drive to his car.

'And then you remembered Rupert?' Silas filled in.

'I've—er—had other things on my mind,' she mumbled as he held the passenger door open for her.

'Will you mind very much having to leave here?' he asked, looking back at the substantial house with its fine furnishings.

'I…' she began, then shook her head. 'It—isn't home any more.' And was aghast that her voice should unexpectedly go all wobbly.

To her surprise Silas stretched out a hand and touched her arm in a moment of sympathy. 'It will get better,' he comforted softly.

She was suddenly ashamed of herself. 'It has already,' she said brightly, and got into his car, telling herself she must guard against such weak moments, but starting to like this man she was going to marry. She liked especially this more sensitive side of him.

Their business at the register office was dealt with without fuss, and in no time they were back in his car and Silas was returning her to the only home she had ever known but which on Saturday she would leave for ever.

'I can't think of any reason for you to contact me but you have my phone numbers should you find a need,' he said, when at her home she went to open the car door. 'Just a moment.' He halted her, and took a ring-sizer from the glove compartment. 'Better get the size right.'

A tingle shot through her as he took her hand to get the measure of her wedding finger. 'I can use my mother's wedding ring,' she said hurriedly.

'Are you calling me a cheapskate?' he teased—and she found she liked that about him as well, his teasing, just as if he sensed she was suddenly uptight and, when she was nothing to him, easing her through it.

She got out of the car to find that he had stepped out too and was coming round to her. 'I'll—um—see you two weeks on Saturday,' she said by way of parting.

He nodded. 'Move into the apartment as soon as you're ready,' he suggested, and that was it. He was gone.

Nanette was avid to know how she knew Silas Livingstone and what he was doing calling for her, and where had they gone?

'He's in the engineering business like my father,' Colly replied offhandedly, and decided Nanette could make of that what she would because it was all she was getting.

Colly then went to the gallery and listened to Rupert going on and on—and on—about the ingratitude of Meriel. When he had for the moment paused to seek fresh charges to lay against Meriel's door, Colly told him that she was moving to an apartment.

'I don't blame you!' he exclaimed, obviously having no idea that she had been left penniless and of the opinion that she could afford to rent or buy. 'What your father saw in that Nanette creature, I shall never know!' he dramatised, having met her once, fancied his chance, but received short shrift when Nanette had her eyes set on more lucrative game.

Colly went home late that afternoon and began putting her belongings together. She moved to her new home on Friday—and was not bitterly disappointed that Nanette had taken herself off clothes shopping and was not there to say goodbye to. Colly left her house keys on the hall table—and went quickly.

The weeks leading up to her wedding went in turns fast and then slowly, fast and then slowly. She was soon settled into her new abode, and liked where she was living and its surrounds, but experienced a feeling of edginess. Perhaps it was through the speed with which everything had happened and was happening. She owned to a few panicky moments too whenever she thought—that day creeping nearer and nearer, galloping nearer and nearer sometimes—of how she was going to marry the tall, distinguished-looking Silas

Livingstone. Sometimes it seemed more like a dream than reality.

She did not find any reason to contact him. Though would not have minded some reassuring word. Reassuring? Get a grip, Colly, she lectured herself, you're twenty-three—and life is going to get better. It already had. While she still missed her father, grouch that he had been a lot of the time, at least she didn't have to spend time being picked on by his widow.

When, with two days to go before she married Silas, the telephone in the apartment rang, Colly nearly jumped out of her skin. For several fearful seconds she was too alarmed to answer it. What if it were Silas's grandfather, the owner of the apartment?

Common sense settled that one. Why on earth would he ring what he thought was an empty apartment? She picked up the phone, said a tentative, 'Hello,' ready to say, Wrong number, if indeed it were Grandfather Livingstone. Then with utter relief she heard Silas's voice and realised, by the same token as she had his home number, he had the number of the phone in the apartment should he find a need to contact her.

'Any problems?' he enquired evenly.

'Not one. But I'm glad you phoned,' she said impulsively—and wished she hadn't because, while Silas politely waited for her to tell him why she was so glad, she started to feel a little foolish. 'It doesn't seen real somehow,' she explained lamely.

'Trust me. It's real,' he answered, but there was a smile in his voice.

'I know,' she said, and felt better. 'Any problems your end?' She batted his enquiry back at him.

'None that Saturday won't see secured,' he replied easily, and, getting down to the purpose of his call, 'I'm about to transfer some funds into your account,' he informed her, going matter-of-factly on when she felt too awkward to have anything to say, 'Can you get me your bank details? I'll hang on if you need to find you account number.'

Wanting to tell him not to bother with that now, that he could see to all that once they were married, Colly, realising he was too busy to want to call her again on this issue, obediently went to find her cheque-book—unused of late.

But, having given him the details he required, she just could not hold back from saying hurriedly, 'There's no rush! If you don't want to—'

'I want to,' he cut in, that smile in his voice again. And, about to ring off, 'Does your bank know your new address?' he enquired.

She hadn't given that a thought. 'I'll do it tomorrow,' she replied.

'Then I'll see you on Saturday,' he said.

'I won't be late,' she replied as evenly as she could manage.

Nor was she late. January had given way to February: not the most exciting month of the year. She had wanted to buy something new to be married in, and had then lectured herself that this was more a half-hour in front of a registrar than a marriage. In any event, funds would not run to anything new—even though she supposed that by now Silas would have seen to it that her bank balance was the healthiest it had ever been.

But that money was not for some extravagant clothes-buying session, but as a base to get her started on some sort of career training—Colly knew she would never ask him for more, for the subsequent top-ups he had mentioned. So she went out to her car dressed in a pale yellow biscuit-coloured suit she'd had for some while but which still looked good.

She was some minutes early arriving at the register office, and was relieved to see that Silas was already there. He came towards her, and seemed to like what he saw. For her part she had to admire the way his suit fitted him to perfection, the way he effortlessly wore clothes.

'You look lovely,' he said by way of greeting, and if he'd had any idea how sorely her confidence needed a booster just then, he could not have said anything better.

She wanted to say something bright such as, You're not looking so bad yourself, but the nerves that had kept her sleepless last night were attacking again, and all she could say was a husky, 'Thank you.'

She had spent a tormented night having last-minute doubts. And, having arrived at the register office, having decided to go through with it, had done nothing to dispel her nerves. But if Silas had picked up something of how she was feeling he did not refer to it, but stated calmly, 'I've roped in a couple of witnesses,' and, looking steadily into her worried green eyes, 'Ready to make a fresh start?' he asked.

And suddenly his words, his steady look, made everything fall into place. She knew why he was marrying her—to secure the future of the company he headed. And, by marrying him, she in turn was securing her own future, securing for herself that fresh start she so sorely needed.

And, looking at him, she liked what she saw, and just had to beam a smile at him. 'Let's do it,' she agreed.

Not so long after that she stood beside him in front of the registrar and, in front of the witnesses he had found, took him as her lawful wedded husband. The strange feel of his wedding ring on her marriage finger brought home to her that, as Silas was her lawful wedded husband, she was his lawful wedded wife.

Emotion gripped her at the end of the ceremony when, by tradition, the marriage certificate was handed to her as her property. Colly turned to Silas and, the certificate of marriage being all that he was interested in, she handed it over to him. He took it from her, looked down at her, and smiled his wonderful smile.

Her insides were already having a merry time within her. But when he bent and gently placed his lips on hers her heart joined in the general mêlée. 'Thank you, Colly,' he mur-mured.

He had kissed her! This was not a love-match but—Silas had kissed her. A second later, however, and she was realising that they were not alone. Aside from the registrar, they had witnesses. Should questions be asked at some later date as to the romance or otherwise of their wedding, then any witness could state that there had been 'romance in the air'.

Colly swiftly got her head back together. For goodness' sake, anyone would think she wanted his kisses! She gave him a smile of her own—two could play at that game—and waited nicely while he thanked their witnesses—she gathered he had settled any financial arrangements in advance—and, Saturday a busy day for weddings, apparently, they left so that the registrar could go and check through details with the next couple.

From the register office Silas escorted Colly to where she had parked her car. And suddenly it all seemed just a little too much. She looked at him as they stood by her car. She had married him, this man. This man was her husband, yet it was unlikely that after today their paths would ever cross again. She did not know what to do, whether to shake hands or just get into her car and drive off. She certainly wasn't going to kiss him. She opted to unlock her car.

'Would you like lunch?' he asked abruptly, almost as if the question had been dragged from him.

She opened the driver's door. Oh, my word, her insides were on the march again. 'You haven't time,' she replied—this man never had a minute to breathe.

'Today I could find time,' he replied.

She didn't thank him. He obviously felt he should give her lunch rather than allow her to just drive off. She shook her head. 'I only signed up for a half-hour,' she told him, and saw his lips twitch the moment before he stood back to allow her to get into the driver's seat. Her lips twitched too. 'Bye,' she said and, looking at him, saw that they were both grinning.

'Bye—wife,' he said, and as she got into her car and he closed the door he began walking away.

She passed him, drove by him; they both waved. Somehow she had never imagined that her wedding day would be like this. That the last she would see of her husband on her wedding day would be through the rear-view mirror of her car, the distance between them getting further and further apart.

She remembered the happy way they had grinned at each other. Yet suddenly she could have burst into tears, and had to acknowledge that one Silas Livingstone was having a most peculiar effect on her.

CHAPTER FOUR

By Monday, having removed her wedding ring, though unable to remove the lingering memory of the touch of her husband's lips on hers, Colly had got herself back together again. By then she was scorning any such notion that her emotions were in any way affected by Silas Livingstone. Still the same, an involuntary smile came to her mouth that she was married to the man, his name was now her name and, if she cared to, she could use it. Which, of course, she did not care to. Though she could not resist saying 'Colly Livingstone' out loud to hear what it sounded like.

She abruptly turned her back on such nonsense and reached for the telephone book. A short while later she had taken the first steps towards enrolling for a foundation course.

Disappointingly, although an application form would be put in the post, to be then followed up by an interview, she had been told that it was unlikely she would be able to start before the September term.

Which meant, since pride reared and made it impossible to use Silas's money while she spent the next six or seven months in idleness, that she must get a job. Now what? She decided against secretarial—she still blushed when she thought of her nerve in going for that secretarial interview.

Only then did it come to her that it was perhaps from some inner instinct that had warned she would not get that secretarial job that she had not previously told Rupert that she had been looking for work. But when she went to the gallery on Tuesday she felt that to be fair to him she ought to warn him that her circumstances were a little different from what they had been and that she was going to have to look for temporary full-time paid employment.

Rupert, as ever with his head in the clouds, took that 'temporary' to mean that the lawyers were dragging their feet over settling her father's estate and that they had temporarily frozen all assets.

'I expect your dear stepmama will make sure she gets her grasping fingers on some of it.' Unasked, he gave his opinion. But straight away was thinking of his loss rather than that of his unpaid helper as it dawned on him that he stood to be without his Tuesday helper. 'You can't leave!' he exclaimed. 'You're so good with the customers! And who else can I trust to look after this place when I'm out buying?'

'You'll find someone,' Colly tried to reassure him.

'I'll have to *pay* them!' he replied. But, his eyes lighting up, 'I'll pay you!' he decided. Though, as ever covering his back, 'It won't be very much, of course. But at least it will be enough for you to be able to keep your head above water.'

This was Rupert in full skinflint mode. But, in considering his offer, Colly realised since she had no work experience other than housekeeping, plus the little bit of work she did for him, that in those circumstances to work for him full time in a poorly paid job was quite a good deal.

'You do know that there's a minimum wage allowed by law?' she thought to remind him. She just could not afford to work for nothing. And, while Rupert was always moaning about his lack of funds, it was she who mainly kept his books, so she knew that financially he was doing quite nicely, thank you.

'You drive a hard bargain, Miss Gillingham,' he grumbled, for the look of it, but stuck out his hand to shake on the deal.

Mrs Livingstone, she mentally corrected him, and had to smile at how ridiculous she was being. Thankfully Rupert thought she was smiling at the done deal. They formally shook hands.

The very next day she received a statement from her bank showing that her account was in excess of ten thousand pounds in credit. Even though she knew about it, she still felt shocked to see it there in black and white. But, as she started to adjust to the fact that Silas had paid ten thousand pounds into her bank, she still knew that she would continue to work full time for Rupert and use Silas's money only when she had to. It still did not feel right to take his money—even if it had been all part of their bargain.

Colly, her application for the foundation course posted off, was two weeks into her paid employment, and was busy in the small office, when someone called at the gallery to collect a picture his mother had bought. 'I'm double parked,' she heard him tell Rupert. There was only one picture awaiting collection. She picked up the carefully wrapped painting and, thinking to save him a second or two, took it out to him.

'Mr Andrews?' she enquired—and discovered that Mr Andrews was not in that much of a hurry.

'Tony Andrews,' he introduced himself. And, obviously liking what he saw, 'Miss…? Mrs…?' he enquired. 'I'm sorry, I don't know your name.'

What could she do? She was a paid member of staff. Besides which, there was no mystery about her name. 'Colly Gillingham,' she supplied. 'Um, they're a bit hot on double parking around here.'

'I shall return,' he promised, and went.

He did return too—to ask her out. Colly was unsure, and reflected for a moment that neither she nor the man she had married had placed any restriction on dating, but she said no. Tony Andrews was undeterred and returned a few days later to ask again, with the same result.

Then on Tuesday of the following week something astonishing occurred. She was working at the gallery when the door opened and her father's old friend, Henry Warren, came in.

'Uncle Henry!' Colly cried, and, feeling quite choked suddenly, she went speedily over to him and was given a fatherly hug. 'How was the holiday…?' she began.

'We came home on Saturday. But it wasn't until last night that I went to my club.' He looked at her sadly. 'I was so sorry to hear about Joseph.'

'It must have been a great shock for you,' she sympathised, realising that someone at his club would have told him of his friend's death.

'Last night was my night for shocks. I went straight round to see you, only to hear from a gloating Nanette that you'd moved out without leaving a forwarding address. Luckily I was able to remember your father mentioning something one time about you having a little job in this gallery.' A smile came to his lined face then, to be joined by a look of utmost satisfaction as he added, 'The dear Nanette wasn't gloating after I'd told her what I had to tell her.'

'You told her off about something?' Colly asked, feeling a little mystified.

'That creature thought she was sitting pretty,' he replied. 'It was my happy duty to inform her that, shortly before I went on holiday, your father contacted me and made a new will.'

'My father…'

'Your father had started to realise that, apart from being very unfair to you, he had been something of an old fool.'

Colly just stared at him. 'Good heavens!' she said faintly.

'As you probably know, he was so besotted with Nanette that he was blind to anything else. But by and by he began to come to his senses and to be appalled by what he had done—the way he had willed his affairs. He came to the club, seeking me out.'

'But—you're not his legal representative.'

Henry Warren smiled again. 'Poor Joseph. He was too embarrassed at realising his foolishness to go back to the firm he had always dealt with. I drew up his fresh will in secret.'

He paused, then announced, 'He left everything equally between the two of you.'

Colly looked at him disbelievingly. 'My father left me...'
She could not continue.

'He left you half of everything. The house, his money, his
shares.'

That word 'shares' brought Silas to mind, but she tried to
concentrate on what Henry Warren was saying. 'Er—come
into the office. I'll make us some coffee,' she said, trying to
gather her scattered wits. But coffee was forgotten when, in
the office, she asked, 'It's—legal, this new will?'

Henry Warren gave her a reproachful look. 'You should
know better than to ask such a thing,' he said with a smile.
'I made certain it is totally watertight,' he assured her. 'It goes
without saying that neither your father nor I had any idea that
he would so soon depart this life.' He halted for a solemn
moment, as if remembering his friend, before going on. 'But
I know he would want me to look after your interests, Colly.
To that end I have taken steps to have all your father's assets
frozen.'

Colly confessed herself little short of stunned. 'Does
Nanette know—about everything being frozen?'

'If she doesn't, she soon will,' he replied cheerfully.

Colly was having difficulty taking it all in, her mind a jumble. 'Coffee,' she remembered, but more from some kind of
need to do something practical.

It was over coffee that he asked for her new address. She
did not want to lie to him, but did not feel able to tell him
the facts of her marriage to Silas. Their marriage was private,
secret between her and Silas, so she simply gave Henry
Warren her new address and phone number.

He assumed she was renting the apartment and jovially told
her, 'You'll be well able to afford to buy somewhere to live
now. For that matter you'll have funds enough to buy out

Nanette's share of the house, should you want to move back in there.'

'There's that much?'

'Oh, yes.' He nodded. 'Given that that woman is going to take half of everything, you'll be quite moderately wealthy once the estate is settled.'

Several things struck Colly at one and the same time then. One was that she was happier living in Silas's grandfather's apartment than she had been living with her father and his second wife. And two, she did not want to go back to that house. Life after her mother's death had been pretty bleak—she only then realised just how bleak. But more important than anything was the realisation that she had money of her own now. She did not have to use Silas's money!

'I've no idea how long it will take for my father's affairs to be wound up,' she commented, and just had to ask, 'Is there any chance I might have…?' She felt embarrassed asking.

'Of course.' Henry Warren, as if aware of her embarrassment, cut in at once. 'I don't doubt that Nanette has managed to talk your father's previous executors into allowing her to draw something on account.'

Colly went home that night with her head in a spin from these latest developments. But a week later she was in a position to take action on a matter that had troubled her from the beginning. She had accepted Silas's ten thousand pounds because of the deal she had made with him. But she had never been truly comfortable about taking his money; it had never seemed right. It had gnawed away at her from time to time, even before Uncle Henry had called at the gallery last week. Since his visit the fact that she had taken that money had started to become untenable.

That night she wrote to Silas, telling him of her father's lawyer friend Henry Warren, and how he had returned from holiday and had come to the art gallery with the astonishing news of her father's newest will. She wrote that, while she was extremely grateful to Silas for his support when she had so sorely needed it, she no longer had need of his money. She enclosed her cheque for ten thousand pounds. Added to that she stated how she loved living in the apartment and how, if he was agreeable, she would like to stay on as a rent-paying tenant. She wished him well, and signed it 'Colly'.

She posted her letter on her way to the gallery on Wednesday morning. She had addressed it to Silas's apartment, about twenty minutes away by car from where she was living. With any luck, if he replied straight away—say he received her letter and cheque tomorrow—she might have a response from him in the post by Saturday.

His response came sooner than that, and in person. She had finished her evening meal on Thursday and was tidying up in the kitchen when someone knocked on her door. She realised at once that it must be one of the other occupants in the building, otherwise her caller would have buzzed from the outside door so that she could let them in.

So far, apart from exchanging a morning or evening greeting with her fellow apartment dwellers, she had not had anything to do with her neighbours. Ready to be friendly, she went to the door, opened it and stared in quite some surprise. Somehow she had fully expected a written response.

'You've got a key to the outer door?' she said witlessly.

'We established that,' Silas replied, his eyes going over her trim shape in trousers and light sweater. 'And to this door—but I thought you'd prefer me to knock rather than walk straight in.'

She smiled at him, realising with more surprise just how very pleased to see him she was. 'Come in,' she invited. And, as he crossed the threshold, 'You received my letter?'

'I did,' he confirmed. But did not seem too ecstatic about it. In fact he sounded quite tough as he demanded, 'You're saying you want to divorce?'

Colly stared at him, her jaw dropping. 'When did I say that?' she gasped, startled.

'You wrote in terms of ending our agreement!'

'No, I didn't!' she retorted, facing him on the sitting room carpet. 'I merely mentioned that I've money of my own now. And, to be blunt, I have never felt very comfortable about taking yours.'

'You agreed—'

'I know. I know!' she butted in, feeling all het-up suddenly—and who wouldn't with those dark blue eyes glittering at her? 'But I'm no longer in need of your financial support.'

'But you otherwise intend to keep to our agreement?' he demanded.

'Of course,' she replied, and, a grin starting to break because he looked so fierce, 'It's sheer bliss being married to you.'

'We seldom, if ever, meet,' he commented and, his eyes on her sparking eyes, his lips twitched. 'The perfect marriage,' he endorsed.

Her heart gave a peculiar kind of leap. 'But since we have met—and you are here,' she took up, striving to be sensible, 'is it all right for me to stay on here now that...?'

'I find it offensive you need to ask!' he replied curtly.

Pardon me for breathing! 'Will you allow me to pay rent, then?' she tried.

His answer was sharp and unequivocal. 'Not a chance!' He chopped her off before she could finish.

'At least think about it!' she bridled.

'It doesn't need thinking about. We made a contract, you and I. Paying rent never came into it.'

'But I didn't know then—'

'No!' he said, the matter closed as far as he was concerned, his tone brooking no argument, and, before she could try anyway, 'You're comfortable here?'

'Who wouldn't be? I love it here.'

'Good.'

'And that's your last word on the subject?' she protested.

'It is!' he returned brusquely.

That did not please her. She turned and led the way to the door. 'I would have offered you coffee,' she informed him shortly, but opened the door so he would know he could die of thirst before she would make him a drink.

'I would have refused it!' he answered in kind. And she just did not know what it was about the wretched man—she just had to laugh.

'Bye, Silas,' she bade him.

She saw his glance go to her laughing mouth—and she felt her knees go weak when he smiled. 'Bye,' he said, and added, 'Wife.' And, before striding away, he bent down and lightly kissed her.

He was much in her head after that. She quite liked his light kisses, she discovered. Not that there had been so many of them. Only two, in fact. One possibly to seal the deal of their marriage. And the other probably to pay her back for not making him a coffee. It was, she owned, quite a nice punishment.

She then scorned such a ridiculous notion. But recalling his 'You're saying you want to divorce?' and his 'You wrote in terms of ending our agreement,' she then realised the reason he had called in person in preference to writing. It was their agreement he was concerned about. He needed to establish, now that she no longer needed his help, exactly where he stood with their agreement and their marital state, with regard to his future concerns in connection with his grandfather. Why else would he have called in person for goodness' sake? She had invited his visit by breaking their unwritten 'no communication' clause and writing to him.

Colly decided the next day that she was thinking far too much about Silas, and determined not to think about him any more. To that end she accepted a date with Tony Andrews.

Tony was in public relations, and was quite amusing with his various anecdotes, but she was not sorry when the evening was over.

He tried amorously to kiss her—much too amorously. She had been kissed before, but discovered a sudden aversion to being kissed—amorously or any other way. 'Goodnight Tony,' she bade him, pushing him away. For goodness' sake!

'Never on a first date, huh?'

Nor second or third. She went indoors half wishing she had not gone out with him—and wondered how mixed up was that. Then saw that she had gone out on a date more because she thought she should than because she wanted to.

Tony asked her out again, several times, but she told him she didn't consider it a very good idea. 'I'll behave myself,' he promised. She told him she would think about it.

Colly still found herself drifting off to think about Silas. It was two weeks now since she had last seen him. She wished he would allow her to pay rent, but had to accept that free use of the apartment was part of their agreement. She had to accept also that Silas was the kind of man who disliked being indebted. In the circumstances, she supposed she must be grateful that he had accepted her breaking their agreement to the extent of returning that ten thousand pounds.

Only the very next day she discovered, when another bank statement arrived, that Silas had not accepted it. Her bank balance was ten thousand pounds better off than it should have been. Silas had not cashed her cheque!

Feeling winded, Colly stared at the figures on her statement as if to magic the removal of that money. But, no, it was over two weeks ago now. She rang her bank; perhaps the transaction was in the pipeline. It was not.

She heaved a sigh. She did not feel like writing to Silas a second time, and went to the gallery wondering what, if anything, she could do about it.

'I'm just popping out for an hour,' Rupert said when he came in.

'You've only just got here!' She made the effort to rib him. There was a new woman on his scene.

'Busy, busy, busy!' he chortled, and was off.

They were not particularly busy, as it happened, and, after doing a few chores, Colly, with Silas in her head, went and made some coffee and took up the newspaper Rupert had discarded before going out.

She was several pages into it when, with alarm shooting through her, she saw a possible reason for why Silas had not banked her cheque. He had been out of the country. He had been in the tropics on business—but had returned home and was now gravely ill.

Shocked, stunned, and with fear in her heart, she read on. Apparently Silas had been struck down with some tropical bug and was hospitalised in an isolation ward. It gave the name of the hospital. She felt dizzy with fear—and had to ring the hospital. As did everyone else, it seemed—press included. She learned nothing.

Colly just could not settle, and when Rupert returned she had her car keys at the ready. 'I have to go out,' she told him without preamble, and guessed he could see that she was going to go whether he gave permission or not.

'Will you be long?' was all he asked.

'I don't know.'

'Take as long as you need,' he replied, and she was grateful to him that he did not ask questions but simply held up her coat for her.

Never had she felt so churned up as she did on that drive to the hospital. She afterwards supposed that it must have been sheer determination that got her as far as the doors of the isolation unit.

'Can I help?' enquired the stern-looking nurse who blocked her from going any further.

'Silas Livingstone?' Colly queried. 'How is he?'

'He's doing well,' the nurse replied, her eyes taking in the look of strain about Colly, her ashen face.

Tears of relief spurted to Colly's eyes. 'He's getting better?' she asked huskily.

'He's doing well.' And, a smile thawing the nurse's stern look, 'And you are?'

'Colly Gillingham,' Colly replied. 'He really is doing well?' She had to be sure.

'Are you and Mr Livingstone—close?' the nurse wanted to know before she would disclose more.

Married was close. 'Yes,' Colly answered.

And then learned that they had been able to sort out the bug and, while Silas would continue to be hospitalised, once that morning's test results were through they were hoping to release him from the isolation unit to another part of the hospital. Colly let go a tremendous sigh and a little colour started to return to her cheeks.

'Thank you,' she said quietly, and turned away.

'Would you like to see him for a few minutes?'

Colly turned swiftly about. She knew she should say no. Against that, though, she experienced a tremendous need to see for herself that he was better than that 'gravely ill' that had scared the daylights out of her.

'May I?'

'You'll have to wear a gown and all the gear,' the nurse warned. It was a small price to pay.

To be swamped by a cotton gown, wearing a cap and face mask, was insignificant to Colly when, with the nurse showing the way, she entered the isolation room.

Colly's heart turned over to see Silas, his eyes closed, propped up on pillows. 'A visitor for you, Mr Livingstone,' the nurse announced—and stayed to make sure that they really were known to each other.

Colly went forward. Silas opened his eyes as she reached

his bed and just stared at her. He looked washed out, she thought, but, realising that dressed as she was she could have been just about anybody, 'It's Colly,' she told him.

'Who else do I know with such fabulous green eyes?' he returned. Her green eyes were about the only part of her visible.

The nurse was convinced. She went from the room.

'Sorry to intrude on your illness,' Colly apologised primly, much relieved to see Silas looking better than she had anticipated. 'I saw a report in the paper that you'd picked up some tropical bug and…' she racked her brains for a reason '…and I thought I'd better come and check that I'm not a widow.'

She had no idea where those words had come from. But, to her delight, Silas thought her comment funny, and as he leaned against his pillows—washed out, exhausted as he seemed to be—he laughed, he actually laughed—and Colly accepted at that moment that she was heart and soul in love with him.

'I'd better be going,' she said, wanting to stay and to stay and never to leave him. 'Your nurse said I should visit for only a few minutes. You should be resting.'

'I've done nothing but rest since I got here.'

'You'll be on your feet in no time,' she encouraged.

'Why did you come?' he asked, but his eyelids had started to droop. Colly thought it was time to tiptoe out of there.

She did not go to see him again. She wanted to. Days trickled by, and some days she did not know how she held back from going to the hospital to see him. But to go to see him again was just not on. The only requirement in their agreement was that she stand with him in front of a registrar and make the appropriate responses. No way could she go to the hospital a second time and risk Silas again asking, 'Why did you come?'

So she stayed away, though she fretted about what sort of progress he was making. She daily scanned the paper for some sort of progress report, but saw nothing in the pages of print about him.

Then suddenly, early on Friday evening—a week since she had been to see him—her telephone rang. Silas, she thought! But that was because Silas was always in her head. Both Uncle Henry and Rupert also had her address and this phone number.

'Hello,' she said down the instrument. It was neither Henry Warren nor Rupert Thomas.

'I've a bit of a problem!' She would know that voice anywhere. Silas! Her heart started to thunder.

'Where are you?' she asked, striving hard to take the urgency out of her voice.

'For the moment, still in hospital.'

'For the moment?' Her concern antennae went into action. 'They say you can go home?'

'I'm going home,' Silas replied.

There was a subtle difference between 'They say' and 'I'm going'. Colly picked up on it. 'You're signing yourself out, aren't you?' she questioned, trying to hold down her feelings of anxiety.

'In the morning.'

Don't panic. Stay calm. 'Are you well enough to leave?' she enquired, amazed she could sound so even, when she was inwardly a ferment of disquiet.

'I'm fed up with this illness, not foolhardy about it,' he responded. 'I've had enough. Another day in here and I'll be climbing the walls. The problem is,' he went on, getting down to the reason for his call, 'while I've promised my father I won't return to the office until my physician gives me the nod, my mother has threatened to come and nurse me if I *do* sign myself out. Unless,' he added, 'I can do something about it.'

'That sounds reasonable to me,' Colly said with a smile.

'You don't know my mother. She's wonderful,' he said,

'but memory of her attempts to mollycoddle me at the first childhood sniffle makes me know she'll fuss and cosset me to death if I let her an inch over my doorstep. She'll want to take my temperature every five minutes and feed me every ten.'

'Perhaps you'd better stay where you are,' Colly said sweetly.

'Not a chance!' he fired unhesitatingly back, then paused and said evenly, 'Actually, it was my mother who gave me the answer.'

'What answer?' Colly fell straight in.

And she was sure she could hear a smile in his voice because of it, as he began to reveal, 'It was while I was resisting all arguments that she move in, with my mother insisting that she was the natural choice for someone to come and "watch over" me—that on its own was threatening enough—that when she attempted to settle her argument with the words "It's not as if you have a wife to look after you" I had an idea.'

'You didn't tell her you had a wife?' Colly exclaimed in shock.

'I wasn't *that* panicked!' Charming! 'I just thought, if you're not busy with anything else just now—purely to keep my mother off my back—you might care to come and stay for a night or two. Naturally, without question, you'd have your own room. I just...' His voice seemed to fade, and she guessed he was far from back to his full strength yet.

She loved him too much to put him through further strain. It did not take any thinking about. 'I'll come and see you at the hospital at ten tomorrow,' she said decisively. And, bossily, 'Now go to sleep.'

'Yes, Mother,' he responded meekly—but Colly just knew that his lips were twitching.

She sat for ageless minutes after his call, just thinking about him. She supposed that for a man who was always up to his eyes in work, always so very busy, that to be so incarcerated would truly drive him up the wall. Particularly now that he had started to mend and was no longer as gravely ill as he had been.

Colly had no idea of what was involved in 'watching over' him, but, while obviously not back to top form yet, he must be feeling well enough to leave hospital. And if Silas needed someone to be there so that he was not in his home alone overnight, or during the day, for that matter, then Colly knew that she wanted that someone to be her and no one else.

CHAPTER FIVE

WITH Silas her first priority, Colly rang Rupert at his home that Friday night and asked if he'd mind if they reverted to her previous hours of work.

'Ah, your money's come through and you no longer need to relieve me of my hard-earned cash,' he replied.

'My heart bleeds,' she joked with him. 'Will that be all right?'

'I shall miss you,' he answered, adding soulfully, 'Nobody makes coffee like you.'

'I'll be there to make you some next Tuesday,' she said, and rang off.

When she left the apartment the following morning Colly was carrying an overnight bag. That to stay with Silas and keep any eye on him as he recovered had never been part of their agreement was neither here nor there. She loved him, was in love with him, and if he was in trouble—in this case still unwell—with him was where she wanted to be.

He was already dressed when she arrived at the hospital, and was sitting in a wooden-armed chair. Colly's heart went out to him—he looked far from well.

'You've lost weight!' she observed when, impatient to be off, he got to his feet.

He adopted a kind of sardonic look of pathos. 'I've been poorly,' he sighed.

As ever, he made her laugh. But she still was not too happy about him leaving hospital. 'Are you sure you should be—?' she began.

'I've already had this lecture,' he cut in sharply.

'You just wait until I get you home!' she threatened

toughly, and turned away when she saw him trying to suppress an involuntary laugh of his own. 'Sit down again while I go and check up on your medicines,' she instructed, and went quickly to find someone in charge.

Armed with a mental list of dos and don'ts, Colly went back to Silas. 'Now?' he questioned, rising from his chair. He *had* lost weight Colly fretted, but clamped her lips shut so not to make another comment. She must keep her anxieties to herself.

Stubbornly he walked unaided to her car—it was quite some way. It was a cold day; she turned up the heater. Silas was asleep five minutes later.

She knew his address, and fortunately found it without too much trouble. Silas stirred as they arrived outside the stately building where he had his apartment. 'It's impossible to park around here,' he said, and was alert as he directed her to where his garage and the parking area was.

From there she took charge and drove round to the front of the building again. 'You go in while I park,' she suggested.

That he did not argue showed her that he was not feeling as strong as he might have thought he was. Colly parked her car, grabbed her overnight bag from the boot, and hurried to him. He had left the door ajar; she went in.

'Not in bed yet?' she enquired mildly, on finding him seated in a beautiful high-ceilinged drawing room.

'You don't know how good it is to be back,' he replied.

'Coffee?' she suggested, and found her way to the kitchen while she wondered on the best approach to get him to go to bed. She did not want to argue with him, or say anything in the least contentious that might see him pulling the other way. But in bed seemed the best place for him.

She returned to the drawing room with a tray of coffee, handed him a cup and took hers to the seat opposite. 'You'll probably want to rest in bed after you've drunk that.' She tried the power of suggestion.

'Why? What have you put in it?'

She wanted to laugh—and hit him at one and the same time. Hints, she saw, were going to be a waste of time. 'You may be out of hospital, but you still need your bedrest.'

He gave her a disgusted look but forbore to tell her that she was worse than his mother. 'How have you been?' he enquired instead.

'Me? Fine!' she replied, not caring to be the subject under discussion. 'Better than you, I'd say.' She attempted to put the conversation back where she wanted it.

'If you need any help winding up your father's estate, my people will—'

'Thanks for the offer, but everything's going smoothly,' she butted in. 'Nanette wants to sell the house and I've no objection.'

'She has your present address?'

'No, but I've been working full time at the gallery and Uncle Henry pops in whenever there's anything new I need to know. I told you about Henry Warren, my father's friend?'

Silas did not answer her, but questioned something else she had just said. 'You're working full time? I thought you only helped out there one day a week?'

'I did,' she agreed. 'But when I discovered that the foundation course I'm interested in doesn't start until September I realised I'd better find some paid employment, so I—'

'We agreed I was to fund you!' Silas cut her off, sounding annoyed.

'It didn't seem right that I should sit idly back and use your money while waiting for my course to start,' she explained. 'But, since I'm not qualified to do anything in particular, I told Rupert I need to find paid employment, and he said he'd put me on his payroll.'

Silas still did not look overjoyed. 'So you've had to ask for time off in order to spend two or three days here?'

She shook her head. 'With my father's new will my financial position has changed. I rang Rupert last night and told him I'd like to go back to our old arrangement.'

What she expected Silas to reply she could not have said, but a kind of grunt was what she did get, coupled with something that sounded very much like, 'You're too proud by half!'

'Look who's talking!' she retorted. 'You're dead on your feet but won't give in!' And, guessing from the set of his jaw that she was going to get nowhere with him with that attitude, 'Come on, Silas, give me a break.' And, when he looked obstinately back at her, 'I shall have to pop to the shops in a little while. I shall feel much happier in my head if I know you're lying down regaining your strength.'

'What have you to "pop to the shops" for?' he wanted to know.

'You have to eat. If I'm to cook meals for you—'

'You don't have to cook my meals!' he objected—and Colly stared at him, and started to get cross.'

'Look here, Livingstone. I've given up my job—not much of a job, I admit, but all I'm likely to get until I'm trained—to come here and keep an eye on you. But if I'm not allowed to cajole you to bed, and nor am I allowed to see to it that you take proper nourishment, then would you please mind telling me just what exactly I am doing here?'

'You're here to answer the phone when my mother rings—which she is going to any minute now, if I'm not mistaken. And—' he gave her a wry look '—you shouldn't talk to me like that. I've not been well.'

Laugh or hit him? She was tempted. Laughter won. She turned away so he should not see. Though she soon sobered, to turn back and quickly ask, 'Your mother knows I'm here? Who I am? I mean, that we—um—got married?'

'Hell, no! If she knew I'd married she'd be round here to meet you quicker than that. I just told her a kind, close friend, who had nothing else on at the moment, was coming to stay for a few days.'

And that annoyed Colly. Though, as she was well aware, jealousy was the root cause. 'You have many ''kind, close'' women-friends with nothing else on at the moment?' she asked shortly.

He shrugged. 'None that I'd care to give that sort of advantage.'

Colly thought about his answer and realised he was meaning that, because he knew she had no ulterior motive in answering his SOS, he could trust her not to want to get too domesticated with him. The fact that they were already married to each other, but only married for expediency and no other reason, made her, in his eyes, nothing of a threat.

'I think—I'm not sure—but I think you've just paid me a compliment.'

He did not tell her whether he had or he hadn't, but informed her, 'Mrs Varley was here most of yesterday. She—'

'Mrs Varley?' Colly interrupted him. He might be physically weakened, but she knew she would have to stay on her toes to mentally keep up with him.

'She's the good soul who comes and housekeeps five mornings a week. When she's not cleaning, washing or ironing, she cooks. She also shops. She said when I rang that she'd leave a pie ready for today's dinner.'

'Presumably I'm allowed to heat it up?'

The phone rang before she received any answer. 'Tell my mother I look well and that—'

'I'm expected to answer your phone?'

'She'll be here jet-propelled if it goes unanswered,' he hinted, not moving.

'Go to bed.' Colly openly blackmailed him.

'I could always tell her we're married, I suppose.' He bounced her blackmail with blackmail of his own. Colly decided not to risk it.

She went over to the insistent telephone and picked it up. 'Hello?' she said, feeling more than a touch nervous.

'Hello,' answered a warm-sounding voice. 'I'm Paula Livingstone, Silas's mother,' she introduced herself. 'And you're—Colly?'

'That's right,' Colly replied.

'You got that son of mine home all right? How does he seem? He won't tell me if I ask him, so I just have to use your eyes.'

Colly cast a glance over at him. 'He seems much improved from the last time I saw him.' She thought that was a nice safe answer.

Only to realise she had invited more questions and no small speculation when Paula Livingstone enquired, 'You saw Silas when he was in hospital?'

Somehow Colly did not feel she could lie to her. 'Only for a short while—when he was in the isolation unit.' Colly saw Silas give a 'tut-tut' kind of look at what she had just said. She turned her back on him.

'They let you see him? Oh, that is nice,' Paula Livingstone remarked warmly. 'They said that only family members were allowed in when…'

Oh, heavens. Colly realised that Silas had straight away seen this development in the split second she had owned to seeing him in that particular department. 'I saw him on his last day there—I believe Silas was transferred out of the isolation unit soon after.' She had to turn and take another look at him—he was shaking his head from side to side. Colly felt a laugh bubbling up, and wondered if she was growing slightly hysterical. 'We're just having a cup of coffee, then Silas is going to go to bed for a little while,' she volunteered.

'Oh, good. I'm so glad you're there with him,' Paula Livingstone said genuinely.

'Would you like to speak with him?'

'No, no. He'll only accuse me of being a fusspot. I'd come

over in person, but he always did have a rigid independent streak. I naturally dropped everything when Silas was so ill. Which means I'm way behind with my committee work. But if you need me for any reason—no matter how small—I'll be there. Just give me a call.'

Colly came away from the telephone having warmed to Silas's mother but hoping that she would not have to speak to her again. It was too fraught with holes for her to fall into. 'I didn't handle that too brilliantly, did I?' she said to Silas unhappily.

'You did well,' he answered.

Colly knew that she had not done well. 'I'm no good at subterfuge,' she remarked. 'All I've done now is let your mother believe I'm almost as close to you as family.'

'We're still not getting divorced,' he countered, pulling a face that made her laugh.

'Oh, shut up,' she ordered. 'And, if you don't want to make a liar of me, go to bed.'

Silas gave her a long steady look, but to her amazement he got up and, without another word, went from the room. That alone told her that he was more tired and used up that he would ever admit to.

Moving quietly so as not to disturb him, Colly stacked their cups and saucers onto the tray and took them to the kitchen. As silently as she could she washed the dishes and investigated the cupboards. He would need a light meal of some sort shortly.

Having taken a look in the fridge and the freezer, she saw that Mrs Varley had been extremely busy. There was enough food there to last through a siege. Colly prepared some vegetables for the evening meal, and began to wonder where her room would be.

She felt a little hesitant to investigate, but would not mind knowing where she was to sleep that night. Taking her overnight bag with her, she went along the hall. There were several doors to choose from.

Anticipating that one of them would be the door to Silas's room, she tapped lightly on the wood panels of the first door and quietly opened it. It was a bedroom. Silas's bedroom.

He was neither asleep nor in bed, but, fully clothed apart from his shoes, he was lying on top of the bedcovers reading. He lowered his book and glanced at her over the top of it.

'Sorry to bother you,' she apologised, feeling suddenly all flustered—how very dear to her he was. 'But I was wondering—looking for my room.'

'I should have shown you,' he said, and before she could stop him he was off the bed and coming over to her.

'I'll find it!' she protested. 'Just—'

'I'm not *totally* debilitated!' he butted in harshly, and led the way along the hall to a room at the end. 'This do?' he questioned brusquely, opening the door and allowing her to enter first.

For a few seconds Colly was in two minds about staying at all. She was doing *him* a favour, not the other way round! Then she looked at him and realised that he hated being ill, hated being weakened, and hated like blazes having to ask anyone for help. And her heart went out to him.

So she smiled at him. 'You're a touchy brute, Livingstone,' she told him sweetly. 'And this,' she said, going in and looking round, 'is a lovely room.' A grunt was her answer as he left to return to his room.

After unpacking her bag Colly went to the kitchen. She decided on a ham omelette with some salad, and would very much have liked to take it to Silas on a tray—she doubted very much that he possessed a bed-tray. But, in view of his scratchiness not so long ago, she decided to treat him as he wished to be treated. She laid two places at the kitchen table and, when everything was ready, went to his room.

'I've laid the table in the kitchen. Lunch is ready when you are.' She turned about and went back to the kitchen. When less than thirty seconds later he joined her, she felt he had been nicely brought up not to let the cook's efforts go to waste.

He had eaten only half his omelette, though, when he put down his knife and fork. 'Sorry,' he apologised. He plainly could eat no more.

Colly smiled at him because she had to. 'You're forgiven,' she assured him. And, apologising in turn, 'I'll try to be more understanding,' she added.

And loved him the more when, his mouth tweaking at the corners, he told her, 'My wife really doesn't understand me.' She had to smile again, but could not deny a small glow to hear him call her his wife.

With lunch out of the way, she saw to it that he had his medication. She thought he was looking a trifle worn again, and began to wonder if she was the best person to look after him. She was having difficulty in being objective where he was concerned.

She was relieved when he took himself off to his room, and, guessing he had no intention of getting into bed, felt that at least just by lying on top of the covers he would be resting.

He wandered into the kitchen while she was cooking the evening meal—one of Mrs Varley's chicken and mushroom pies, with duchesse potatoes, broccoli and glazed carrots.

Colly saw that his appetite had not fully recovered, in that there was quite some of the meal left, but she guessed he had enjoyed what he had eaten when he asked, 'Where did you learn to cook?'

'Given that dinner was mainly Mrs Varley's efforts, my cooking skills came from what I think is called "on the job training",' Colly answered.

'You had no formal training?'

She shook her head. Their housekeeper had walked out the week before Colly had been due to leave school. She left school one day and was housekeeper the next. 'There's sponge pudding if…'

'Thanks, no,' he refused. Colly did not push it. 'It's hot in here. I think I'll go to my room,' he volunteered.

It did not seem unduly hot to her. 'You're very hot?' she asked, trying not to look as concerned as she felt.

'Hot, cold—it's all part of the fever territory. It will pass,' he said confidently, and left the table.

Colly busied herself clearing up after he had gone, but determined to keep a watch on him whether he liked it or not. To that end she went to his room at just after ten. He was in bed this time, and although propped up on pillows had his eyes closed. His shoulders and arms were uncovered, so she had to assume that he either slept without pyjamas or that he was still feeling hot.

'I've brought you some water. You may be thirsty in the night,' she said pleasantly as he opened his eyes. 'I was just about to make myself a drink—can I get you anything? Tea? Not coffee. You'll never sleep if—'

'Come and talk to me,' he interrupted her.

'You're bored?'

'And some!'

'Poor love,' she said softly, the endearment slipping out before she could stop it. She was going to have to watch that. 'Still feeling hot?' she asked in her best professional manner.

'Not now,' he replied, and, as if trying to remember that he was the host here, 'Have you everything you need?' he asked. 'If you…'

'I've absolutely everything I need,' she told him hurriedly and, when it looked as though he might sit up and take charge, she went quickly to the side of the bed and sat down on it beside him. 'I believe you're looking better already,' she said encouragingly. 'If you could bear to rest as much as possible over the next few days—' She broke off when he gave her a look that said she was adding to his boredom. 'Right,' she said snappily, 'I'll relieve you of my company!'

'What did I say?' he protested.

She looked at him, and loved him so much. 'Try to get some sleep,' she said gently, and as she went to stand up she felt such a welter of compassion for this strong man who had been flattened by some tropical bug that she just could not hold back on the urge to bend over and kiss him.

The feel of his lips beneath hers brought her rapidly to her senses—what on earth did she think she was doing? She straightened quickly, and was about to wish him an abrupt goodnight—only he found his voice first.

'Was that part of the nursing package?' he asked, his eyes solemnly on hers.

Oh, help! 'Just pretend I'm your mother,' Colly brought out from an awkward, embarrassed nowhere.

'My imagination isn't that good!'

'Goodnight,' she bade him crisply, and went from his room, knowing that she was never, ever going to do that again.

Indeed, away from him, she could hardly credit that she had done such a thing. He had not asked her to kiss him, and certainly did not want or need her kisses. Though, having worked herself up into something of a state, Colly recalled how, unasked, he had kissed her—twice. And her het-up world righted itself. It wasn't his sole prerogative to go around kissing folk! Still the same, she would not be doing it again in a hurry.

Colly was awake several times in the night, and having to hold down the urge to go and check on Silas. Although he was mainly recovered from the more serious effects of the illness that had befallen him, he was still prey—to a much lesser degree—to attacks of hot and cold as the fever petered its unfriendly way out.

But she found it impossible to stay in bed beyond five the next morning, and got out of bed. Wrapping her cotton robe about her as she went, she could no longer hold down the urge to go and check on Silas.

She snicked on the hall light and went to his door. Just in case he was sleeping soundly she decided against tapping on his door, but, making no noise, slowly opened it. She stood in the doorway, but even with the light behind her she could make out little. She went further into the room.

Silas was lying on his back with his bare chest free of his duvet. All too clearly he had been hot again in the night. She stood looking down at him and wanted to place a hand on his forehead to gauge his temperature. But he was sleeping peacefully and she did not wish to disturb him.

Denying her need to pull the duvet up and over his shoulders, Colly turned away. Then, just as she reached the door, 'If you're making tea...?' an all-male voice hinted, addressing her back.

Laughter bubbled up inside her, but she did not turn around. Dratted man. He had been awake the whole time she had been looking down at him. She carried on walking—kitchenwards.

Silas was sitting up in bed with his bedside lamp on when she returned. 'Sleep well?' she asked lightly, handing him the tea he had requested.

'I was about to ask you the same question,' he responded.

'Very well,' she replied.

'You normally get up at five in the morning?'

'"Normal" disappeared when I collected you from the hospital yesterday.'

'Am I such a trial?' he asked seriously.

Looking at him, she had to smile. 'Not when you do as you're told.' She tried for a stern note—and failed.

'I'm famous for my biddable ways,' he blatantly lied.

Colly gave him a sceptical look. 'You're going to have breakfast in bed?' She challenged his protest, but could see the idea had absolutely no appeal.

'Must I?'

She folded. 'Oh, Silas. You're trying so hard.'

'Does that mean I don't have to?'

They breakfasted at seven, in the kitchen. At half past seven the telephone rang. 'My mother,' Silas stated, not needing second sight, apparently.

'She'll want to speak to you,' Colly replied.

'I know,' he accepted, and went to take the call.

A couple of hours later word seemed to have got around that he was now out of hospital, and he appeared to spend the rest of the day taking telephone calls.

He spoke to his father too, and also his cousin Kit. And, for all he may have promised his father that he would not return to his office before his physician advised that he could, and for all it was Sunday, it did not prevent Silas from having long and involved business conversations with his PA and also some of his directors when they rang to wish him well.

But at the end of that day, when Colly took a jug of water to his room, she felt that Silas was looking very much better than he had. She guessed that the stimulus of talking over complicated work issues was partly responsible.

'You've had a good day today,' she commented as she visually checked him over. He had recently showered and was sitting robe-clad against his pillows. 'But you won't overdo it tomorrow, after I've gone?' she dared.

Instead of agreeing that he would take care, 'Gone?' he demanded. 'Where are you going?'

Colly stared at him in surprise, her heart hurrying up its beat. It sounded for all the world as though he did not want her to leave! Logic, cold icy logic, hit that notion squarely on the head. He may not want her to leave, but only because if she was not there his mother might drop everything and come and fuss over him.

'You asked me to stay for a night or two,' she reminded him. 'Tonight will be my second night.'

'Have I been such a dreadful patient?' he asked.

'Well, given that you go your own way, regardless of anything I say, you have taken your medication when you should, so...'

'Stay another night?'

Willingly. 'You're just scared your mother will come and take over and make you eat your greens,' Colly managed to jibe.

'Please?' he asked nicely. Then, frowning, 'You're seeing someone tomorrow?' he demanded. 'You've a date and—?'

'Just because your love-life's out of bounds just now...' Colly began, and then gave him a smile of some charm, pleased by the thought that he was not physically up to—um—'tom-catting' just now. 'I suppose I could cancel my arrangement,' she conceded, there being no arrangement, and knowing she would not have to so much as lift the phone.

His frown cleared. 'You really should put your husband first, Mrs Livingstone,' he replied, his charm swamping hers.

Her heart lifted to be so addressed. 'Goodnight,' she said shortly—and went to her room almost dancing. He had called her Mrs Livingstone, and she was to have an extra day with him.

Her normal sleep patterns went haywire in her caring for him, and Colly was up again at five the next morning and going to check on him. He appeared to be sleeping peacefully, but she had been fooled before. 'Tea?' she asked, her voice barely above a whisper.

'Please,' he answered, but did not open his eyes.

That day followed a slightly different pattern from the previous day, in that although they again breakfasted in the kitchen, Paula Livingstone left it until seven-forty-five before she rang. Colly tackled the breakfast dishes, but Silas had not closed the door, and she could hear his side of the conversation.

'I'm all right!' she heard him repeat. 'There's absolutely no need... Yes... But... Fine, I'll see you tomorrow.'

'Your mother's visiting tomorrow?' Colly guessed when he returned to the kitchen.

'I should have known better than to argue,' he said, and looked so glum Colly burst out laughing. She was not laughing a moment later, though, when Silas smiled too. 'My mother is looking forward to meeting you,' he mentioned pleasantly.

'No way!'

'You'll like her,' he promised.

It was clear, despite his objections to the threat of being cosseted, that Silas loved his mother dearly. 'I'm sure I would,' Colly replied. 'She was lovely when I spoke to her on the phone. But I've already told you—I'm no good at subterfuge. In my efforts not to reveal the truth about us, I'd only go and say something I shouldn't. I just know I would. And anyway—' Colly began to slow down from her first flush of panic '—you can't want me to meet her. Ours is a secret—um—marriage.'

'True,' he replied. 'Though events we could not have foreseen have rather overtaken us.'

'You couldn't help being ill.' She found she was defending him.

'True again,' he responded. 'Though perhaps I shouldn't have asked you to come and collect me from the hospital.' He paused, his look thoughtful as he suggested, 'But perhaps you started it when—entirely unexpectedly—you decided to come to the hospital and pay me a visit.'

Steady, Colly. She was ready to panic again. By no chance did she want him speculating on why she had taken it into her head to do so. 'From that exaggerated newspaper report I thought you were gasping your last,' she trotted out cheerfully.

What he would have answered was lost when they were both alerted by a ring at the doorbell. 'Mrs Varley, come to "do",' Silas supplied at Colly's startled look. And, as Mrs

Varley used her own key to let herself in, a minute later Silas was introducing them. Mrs Varley was anxious to know how he was, and Silas told her he was all but recovered, adding, 'I'll make myself scarce.' A second later he was on his way to his bedroom.

'Is there anything I can help you with?' Colly asked Mrs Varley. The apartment looked immaculate as it was, but she could hardly sit around idle while the other woman set to.

'I have my own system that I like to keep to, thank you just the same.' Mrs Varley refused her offer cheerfully—and Colly wandered back to her room.

With her room tidy, and feeling uncomfortable at the idea of sitting doing nothing while a woman some thirty years her senior wielded a vacuum cleaner, Colly surveyed her options. She could sit twiddling her thumbs where she was, or alternatively she could go and sit with Silas in his room. He had complained the night before last about being bored, tempted a small voice. Against that, he had a telephone in his room. If yesterday were anything to go by, he would most likely be relieving his boredom by conducting some business.

Realising that he would not thank her for interrupting the smooth grinding cogs of industry, Colly saw her only option was to busy herself elsewhere.

Donning her car coat, she picked up her shoulder-bag—and paused. Her wedding ring was in her purse. She took it out, knowing she had no right to it. But—and she knew she was being weak—she just had to try it on one last time.

She looked at it on her hand and felt so emotional just then that she knew she needed to be away from the apartment for a short while. Taking the ring off, she left her room, found Mrs Varley and, after chatting for a minute or two, told her she would be gone about an hour or so. Then Colly went to impart the same information to Silas.

He was just putting the phone down, after either making or receiving a call when she went in. But, on noticing she was dressed for the outdoors, and before she could say a word, 'Where are you going?' he demanded.

'We need some salad things.'

'Mrs Varley can go out for any shopping!'

'Mrs Varley has enough to do!' Colly answered. 'Though if you ask her nicely I'm sure she'll make you a coffee when she has hers.'

He wasn't having that. 'I'll come with you,' he stated categorically.

'No, you won't!' Colly returned swiftly. And, ignoring the thrust of his chin that she thought she could tell him what to do, 'Mrs Varley says it's bitterly cold out—and you're still suffering extremes of temperature. You need to stay in the same environment.'

'Who told you that?' he questioned belligerently.

'Nobody had to tell me,' she replied, and, with a superior look, 'It's just something that women know. Now,' she went on tartly, 'is there anything I can get you while I'm out? Anything—' She broke off, then, eyeing him fixedly. 'Any cheques you would like me to pay into your bank?' She refused to look away—he did not bat a guilty eyelid. 'You *do* intend to bank that cheque I sent you, I hope?' she challenged knowing she'd want to thump him if he dared to ask what cheque.

He did not ask. But made her cross just the same when he bluntly retorted, 'I don't consider I should. We made a bargain, you and I—that money was part of it.'

'Agreed,' she said, purely because she could not deny it. 'But I have money of my own now, and I don't feel comfortable about taking yours.'

His look said tough, and that was before he forthrightly told her, 'Likewise! To take your money makes it too one-sided.' She opened her mouth to argue, but he went steam-rollering on, 'I have that piece of paper I need, that marriage certificate, that insurance. You have nothing. And that puts me under an obligation—and I don't like it!'

'And you called me proud!' she erupted. Then, remembering how very ill he had been, and how he still needed to take care, she relented to say softly, 'Have you forgotten what you did for me when I was so not knowing where to turn? Have you forgotten that I'm living in a lovely apartment, totally rent-free?'

'I've forgotten nothing,' he grunted.

And her patience ran out. 'Oh, you're impossible!' she snapped, and, digging her hand into her pocket she pulled out the wedding ring. 'Here,' she hissed, 'have this!'

'What is it?' he wanted to know.

She came close to braining him. 'It went with the "I will" bit!' she retorted—though could not recall those two words featuring in their marriage ceremony. 'I always intended to give it back to you. I just didn't think it seemly to do so on the register office steps.'

He took it from her. 'What am I supposed to do with it?' he rapped harshly.

She looked at him and wanted to box his ears. 'Keep it— as a memento of the good times!' she flew, then turned her back on him and marched to the door.

She heard his short bark of laughter—she had caught his sense of humour. Oddly, as she let herself out from the apartment, she realised that she had a grin on her face. She loved him so much. Even arguing with the wretched man made her feel alive!

Knowing that Mrs Varley was in the apartment, Colly stayed away for nearly two hours. Mrs Varley would make him coffee and anything else he might require. For herself, Colly knew she was getting too close to him. While she loved him, and wanted to be near him, she at the same time felt nervous about that closeness.

She supposed, as Silas had said, she had started the whole

thing rolling by going to see him in hospital that day. But to be with him was not part of their agreement, and, while it had been his idea that she come and stay, she could not help but feel that he might start to regret having asked her once his health was back to normal. Once he was back to his full strength, she had a feeling that he was going to dislike very much the situation she had instigated by that hospital visit.

When Colly returned to the apartment she felt calmer. It had done her good to get away for a short while—even if she'd had to make a determined effort to keep from returning. And while she intended to quietly savour every moment she spent with Silas, she also knew that she would not see him again after tomorrow. Tomorrow, before Paula Livingstone arrived, she would leave.

Since she had no key to the apartment, Colly rang the doorbell. Mrs Varley let her in and, after a few minutes spent in friendly chat, returned to her chores. Colly took her bits of shopping into the kitchen and, despite her strictures on keeping her distance from Silas, had to give in to an overwhelming need to see him.

She looked in at the drawing room on her way to seek him out in his bedroom. But he was in neither room. 'I'll come with you,' he'd said when she had told him she was going out. Oh, surely he had not gone out on his own! Trying not to panic, Colly went looking for him.

She found him in a room she had not been in before—it was a study. He was *working*! 'What do you think you're doing?' she demanded.

He looked at her—and grinned. Actually grinned. Did not look shame-faced, but *actually* grinned. Her fierce expression amused him, apparently. 'You wouldn't let me go out,' he replied innocently—a man who would do exactly as he wanted without bothering to ask her permission, thank you. 'I didn't think you'd mind if I found something to occupy myself with while you were gone.'

Colly calmed down, outwardly. 'Does that mean you intend to go and rest somewhere now?' she enquired evenly.

'My father called just after you left,' he ignored her question to announce unexpectedly. And, while she was getting over her surprise, 'He was sorry he missed you.'

Colly was not sorry. One way and another Silas's family were closing in. True, Silas had been extremely ill and was still recovering. Which meant that they must have been exceedingly alarmed and had more or less lived at the hospital until he had turned the corner, as it were. There was no way that they were not going to keep a check on his progress now.

'You said I was out?'

'I told him you went out looking for a lettuce—and might be some while.'

Her lips twitched at his hint that if it had taken her two hours to run some salad to earth, then it must be some pretty special salad. 'You didn't tell him anything else?'

Silas shook his head. 'What we have is personal to us, Colly.'

Her heart turned over at how wonderful that sounded, even though she knew full well that the only thing personal to them was their secret marriage. And in any event, while she instinctively knew that Silas would never lie to his father, Silas did not want anything more personal between them than those facts on that marriage certificate.

She turned away when the phone rang. She had an idea she would be wasting her time were she to insist that he rest. He was in the thick of business before she left his study.

And, in her view, he paid the price for not resting. Mrs Varley left at lunch-time. But Silas did not have any appetite for lunch. Colly took him some soup—in his study. He was not hungry at dinner-time either. Though he did insist on joining Colly at the dinner table.

'Why don't you go to bed?' she suggested when she saw he had eaten all that he was going to eat.

He looked drained, but even so she was sure he was about to say no. Worryingly, after a minute or so, he got up from the table.

He was in bed when Colly went in a short while later. He was not reading, but was just lying there. She grew more worried. 'As head nurse, is there anything I should know?' she asked lightly.

'I'll let you know,' he replied, and closed his eyes. Colly went quietly from his room.

But she could not settle. She felt marginally less worried when she heard plumbing sounds that indicated he was taking a shower. Still the same, she could not resist taking another look at him before she retired for the night. She tiptoed into his room. He had switched his light off and appeared to be asleep. She silently retreated.

She showered and got into bed—but she was awake at one, and awake at two. When the clock said three and she was still awake Colly gave in. It was no good. She just knew that she would get no rest until she had been to check on Silas.

Calling herself all sorts of a fool, she still the same got out of bed, slipped on her cotton wrap and, unable to deny the instinct that propelled her, went silently along the hall and, as silently, opened the door to his room. And at the sight that met her eyes she was never more glad that she did.

His bedside lamp was on and Silas was huddled up in bed—shivering. 'You're supposed to be asleep!' he admonished when he saw her.

She hurried into the room, not knowing what to do for the best. 'Where do you keep your hot-water bottles?' she asked, reaching him and pulling the duvet up closer around him.

'Don't have any,' he responded, his body shaking with cold.

That figured. 'I'll be back in a minute.'

'Don't you dare go calling out a doctor!' he instructed

shortly. And, when she stared at him obstinately, 'This is nothing to the attacks I had in hospital.'

That made her feel better, but only marginally. 'I'll just go and turn the heating up,' she said, and went looking for controls. Discovering that the system was programmed to shut down overnight, she switched it on full belt and then hurried to her room to grab up the duvet from her bed.

Back in his room, she wrapped the duvet around him. 'I'll just go and make you a warm drink,' she told him.

'A brandy would be good.'

'I'm unsure,' she answered. 'It might clash with your medication.' And, guessing he would probably gag if she made him some hot milk, 'I'll make some tea.'

She was still undecided about whether or not to call out a doctor, but decided to leave it a half-hour to see if Silas's shivering got worse. But in any case, after she took the tea into him she had no intention of leaving him.

She eyed his silk robe at the bottom of the bed, but didn't think there would be very much heat obtained were she able to get the robe around him. 'Sit up and drink this,' she said, and, first placing the tea down, she pulled her duvet closer around him.

In fact she still had an arm about his shaking form as he took a few swigs of tea, wanted no more, and leaned back against her.

'Put your arm in and try to get some sleep,' she urged gently.

He obediently put his arm under the covers, but more she suspected because he was cold than because she had told him to. 'You must sleep too,' he answered.

'I will—soon,' she replied, and, half sitting, half leaning on him, she secured the covers up and around him once more. 'Try to relax,' she murmured, realising he was tensing against the cold of his fever.

'Keep me warm,' he mumbled, and moved over so she should get closer to him.

It did not require any thinking about. Silas was her first priority, her only priority. She stretched out beside him on top of the covers, her head on the pillows, close to his head. 'You'll be all right soon,' she whispered softly.

'Don't get cold,' he mumbled, and said nothing more, but snuggled against her as though seeking her warmth.

And Colly lay against him, her arms around him. A few minutes later and she was of the view that she should be ringing a doctor or the hospital he had been in. A few minutes after that, though, and she thought his shivering had started to subside.

When another ten minutes had passed and, while Silas was still racked by the occasional shudder, he was not otherwise shaking, Colly thought and hoped that he was over the worst. But, mainly because she was unsure, she stayed with him. Stayed with him and held him, her love.

And gradually the shudders that had taken him began to pass. She felt him begin to relax, heard his even breathing, and she began to relax too, so much so that she closed her eyes.

She stirred in her sleep, moved—and bumped into someone! Her eyes shot wide—she always slept alone. 'Good morning, Mrs Livingstone,' said her bed companion.

'Silas!' she exclaimed croakily, a hundred and one emotions shooting through her. 'Er—how are you?' she asked witlessly, already attempting to scuttle urgently away. Where last night, or in the early hours, she'd had her arm about his shoulders, Silas was now sitting half propped up in bed and had an arm around her shoulders, holding her there. 'I'm s-sorry,' she stammered before he could answer. 'You were shivering,' she explained hurriedly. 'I tried to keep you warm.'

'In the time-honoured way.'

'Yes—well...' She wasn't sure what he meant by that. 'I'd better go.'

'No hurry,' he replied, to her amazement. And, with a grin that she absolutely adored, 'I'm nowhere near back to my former strength yet.'

That was quite some admission, coming from him. And she checked her agitated movement to stay and look into his face for signs of the exhaustion she had witnessed there yesterday. There were none. 'Let's be thankful for small mercies,' she replied.

'For that,' Silas said, and bent over and lightly kissed her.

She adored him some more. And then made a serious attempt to move. And that was when her foot came up against a bare leg! She shot Silas a startled look: she was *under* the duvet with him! 'I didn't get into bed with you. I swear I didn't!' she protested distractedly.

'You didn't,' he agreed. 'When I woke up around six, your duvet was on the floor. You were sleeping so soundly it seemed a shame to kick you out. I covered you over.'

'You're too good to me,' she muttered, and again went to get out of bed—but his face was so near that on impulse— her brain anywhere but where it should be—she moved those extra few inches and kissed him. 'Sorry,' she mumbled. 'I'm going to have to restrain my wicked ways.' She laughed then, hoping to cover her guilt. 'Only you were so poorly, it's a relief to know you're okay and that, regardless of you ordering me not to, I did do the right thing in not calling a doctor.' She was gabbling. She broke off. 'You are all right, aren't you?'

His very dark blue eyes were looking good-humouredly down into hers. 'You tell me,' he suggested, and, his head coming down, he kissed her long and lingeringly.

'Oh!' she said on a gasp of breath when he raised his head again. Her body was all of a tingle. 'I—um—think you're stronger than you're trying to make out,' she said on a cough. Somehow the will to leave his bed has disappeared.

'I think you could be right,' he answered, and loosened the duvet so she should be free to go.

She sat up—their bodies collided. 'S-sorry,' she stammered again, made valiant efforts to leave, and got cross. 'Why am I apologising?' she exclaimed. 'You're the one who's trying to lead me astray!'

'Outrageous accusation!' he denied, and suddenly they were both laughing. Then, breaking off, they were staring at each other. And then—kissing.

And it was all too wonderful. Silas had his arms around her, she had her arms around him, his lips were seeking hers, parting her lips with his own, and his hands were holding her, warm and burning her skin. There was thunder in her ears and in her heart.

She clung to him, and kissed him as he kissed her. 'Oh,' she sighed blissfully, and quite adored him, was in another world entirely as his hands began to caress over her back. 'I'm not s-sure this is good for you,' she murmured in one isolated sane moment.

'I'll be the judge of that,' he breathed against her throat, and the next she knew she was lying half beneath him and his hand was somehow beneath her nightdress, stroking upwards.

Shock hit her—his caressing hand strayed higher. *'No!'* she cried urgently, her head in panic—but surely she'd got that wrong; she'd meant yes. She wanted him.

'No?' he queried.

'This isn't... You... Stop!' she ordered, when once more his caressing hand began to adventure.

His hand stilled. Stayed on her upper thigh—but stilled. He bent and tenderly kissed her—and she was lost. 'This could be the best medicine so far for the both of us—wouldn't you agree?' he asked against her mouth.

The words 'yes, oh, yes,' were already forming—but that was when the doorbell sounded. Colly shot a startled look to the bedside clock. Half past eight. *Half past eight!* 'Mrs Varley!' she cried, with a strangled kind of sound, and leapt out of bed, galvanised—and hurtled to her room.

Mrs Varley had her own key and would let herself in. To ring the bell was a mere courtesy because she knew there was someone there, Colly realised, as she rushed to get showered and dressed.

She was almost dressed when a whole barrage of complications hit her. Had Mrs Varley not arrived when she had then she and Silas might well have made love. On thinking about it, Colly knew there was no 'might well have' about it. She had put up all the resistance of which she was capable and, as Silas had said, he was feeling stronger than he had believed. But where would that have got them? Their marriage would have been consummated. And, while Silas still wanted that marriage certificate, what he definitely did not want was a wife.

That thought stirred her pride into action. Complications aside, she felt it incumbent on her to let him know that as he did not want a wife so she did not want a husband.

She remembered his kisses and could not lie to herself— she wanted more of them. To be in his arms... But this would never do. She recalled her response, the way she had clung to him—she had more or less offered herself to him! She recalled the way her lips had so willingly, so urgently met his—and died a hundred deaths. Oh, how was she ever to look him in the eye again?

That was when, too truly het-up to bear it, Colly decided that she did not have to look him in the eye again. She had intended to be away before his mother got here this morning anyway.

It seemed to Colly that, later than she had meant to be, she had better get her skates on. Paula Livingstone could arrive at any moment. If she hurried, Colly realised, she might be able to be away without having to see Silas again either.

Colly did not merely hurry—she flew!

CHAPTER SIX

COLLY did not see Silas again. She heard from him, though. The next day. Flowers arrived. 'Thank you—for everything', the card said, ending 'Silas'. How final was that?

She wanted to hate him that he could cast her off with a few flowers, and owned she was not best pleased. Even so, she just did not have the heart to toss his flowers in the bin. And, since they filled two vases, she supposed that 'a few flowers' was a bit of an understatement.

And, in all honesty, what had she expected? She had left his apartment without a word. Had he wanted to thank her personally, she had denied him that chance.

Day followed day just the same, she discovered, when a month had dawdled by since that day she had walked out of Silas's apartment. While her chief concern was to know how his recovery was going—and, after the finality of his flowers, to ring and ask was totally out of the question—other matters, minor in comparison, were about.

For one, Colly had her interview for the foundation course she'd applied for, and was accepted to start in September. For another, Nanette sought her out at the art gallery and bluntly stated that, since Colly was going to benefit when the sale of the house went through, she could come and help clear everything out.

That, apart from calling in antiques valuers, Nanette had small intention of lifting a finger was neither here nor there. Colly was glad to be busy. It was a large house—her days were fully occupied. Her evenings less so.

Tony Andrews continued to ask her out, and, while she had no intention of going out with him, she started to form the opinion that he was not so bad after all. He hadn't pushed it when she had let him know that the evening ended on her doorstep, had he?

And, anyway, with a month passing since she had zipped up her overnight bag and rocketed out of Silas's apartment, she felt that Silas had to be better by now. And a well-again Silas, when she recalled the virile look of the man, meant that no way was he sitting at home evenings; well, not by himself, he wasn't.

The next time Tony Andrews phoned and suggested they dine together somewhere, Colly agreed.

'You said yes!' he exclaimed.

Already she was half regretting her decision. 'I should love to have dinner with you,' she said quickly, before she could change her mind.

She knew, though, when twenty-four hours later she waited for him to call, that her acceptance had stemmed from being pricked by spiteful barbs of jealousy that Silas would have renewed *his* dating activities. She had to admit, too, that the hope of dislodging Silas from being so constantly in her heart and her head had something to do with her decision to go out with Tony.

Which effort was totally defeated when, on entering the smart eating establishment Tony had chosen, the first person she should cast her eyes on was none other than Silas Livingstone!

The restaurant was crowded, dozens of other people were there. So why should he stand out from the crowd? It was a question she had no need to ask. He was her love, her life— pure and simple.

Silas had spotted her too; she knew that he had. He was with a party of other people; she refused to try and pinpoint which of the attractive women in the group he was with. But as her eyes locked on him, so for a split second his eyes seem to lock with hers.

She turned away and looked at Tony, who was beaming his best smile down on her. Then the head waiter was leading them to their table and her fast-beating heart slowed down to a sprint. From what she could see Silas looked fully recovered from the bug that had flattened him. And she could not have been more pleased about that. She could not deny, either, that even if jealous darts were giving her a bad time she was still the same glad to have seen him.

Colly bucked her ideas up. Tony was doing his best to be an ideal dinner companion. She had agreed to dine with him, and politeness, if nothing else, said she should forget the party of six who appeared to be having a splendid time.

So she ate, while barely knowing what she ate. And she chatted and responded cheerfully to any comment Tony made. But, oh, how she heartily wished that the evening were over.

She knew that she was not going to completely relax until Silas and his party had gone. But she had struggled through to the dessert stage of her meal before she glimpsed some of the people Silas had been with making their way to the exit.

She determined to keep her eyes fixed either on her plate or Tony. She might want to look her fill at Silas, but, on the rarest chance he might cast a glance over to her, he would not find her looking at him again.

'Hello, Colly.'

So much for her decision not to look at him. She looked up, realising that Silas must have left the people he had been with to come and stand right next to her. But while her heart pounded, and before she could find her voice, he, to her astonishment, did no more than bend down and kiss her cheek in greeting!

Feeling too stunned to be able to think, let alone think straight, 'Hello,' was all she was capable of mumbling.

Silas was not a bit fazed. 'How have you been?' he asked pleasantly.

Since the last time he had seen her—when she had run from his bed? 'Er—busy,' she answered.

'Busy?' he queried, quite well aware that she now worked only one day a week.

'The house is being sold,' she replied, guessing he would know she meant her old home. 'I'm spending a lot of time there—er—clearing up.'

Plainly he was bored with such detail. She saw his glance go to her dinner companion. 'Aren't you going to introduce us?' he enquired.

It passed her by totally that he was upbraiding her for her lack of manners; she was still feeling flabbergasted that not only had he come over to their table, but he had actually kissed her.

By this time Tony was on his feet. 'Tony Andrews,' he introduced himself.

'Silas Livingstone,' Silas supplied, and the two shook hands.

She saw Tony register that Silas was *the* Silas Livingstone of Livingstone Developments, and realised that with Tony being in public relations perhaps it was part and parcel of his job to know who anybody was. But at last she found her voice, to quickly butt in, 'You're well again now, Silas?'

Both men turned to her. 'Thanks to your—personal—nursing,' Silas replied smoothly. And she wondered how she could love him so much yet at one and the same time want to punch his head. All too obviously that 'personal' was a reference to the way she had lain with him when he'd had the shivers.

'I didn't know you included nursing in your many other talents?' Tony queried, sounding curious. She wondered which hat he was wearing: his PR hat, where he soaked up any useful snippet, or if it was just idle interest.

'I should have been lost without Colly there to keep me warm,' Silas answered before she could reply.

She stared at him, stupefied. 'Silas had a fever. You may

have read about it.' She smiled at Tony while at the same time speculating if it would cause very much of a scene if right there and then she handbagged this man she was married to. 'I should think you'll consider it very carefully before you venture to the tropics again.' She smiled at Silas.

He looked her straight in the eyes. 'It had its compensations,' he murmured, nodded to Tony—and went to rejoin his party.

'I didn't know you knew Silas Livingstone?' Tony questioned the moment he was out of earshot.

'He knew my father,' she replied. 'My father was in engineering too.'

'So that's how you know him,' Tony documented. 'Um—you sound very well acquainted?'

'I was at a loose end when he was sick,' she explained, as though casually. 'I haven't seen him in ages. How's your mother?'

Tony took the hint. Then took her home. And, she was glad to note, was on his best behaviour. Though whether that was because he was remembering the last time he had brought her home, and the ages it had been before she'd agreed to go out with him again, she did not know. Or maybe he was just trying another tack. Or maybe, she mused, he had just gone off her.

Colly had proof that Tony Andrews had not gone off her when the very next evening he rang, ostensibly for a chat, but in actual fact to see how she felt about going out with him again.

While she supposed it was flattering to have someone that keen, she had barely finished thanking him for a pleasant evening the night before and thought it was too soon. No way was she looking for a steady boyfriend—though she did not doubt that she was not the only female he asked out.

'I'm busy with the house just now,' she excused, having

last night explained about her involvement with clearing her old home.

'But that's during the day,' he pointed out.

Colly had no intention of arguing. 'I'll call you, Tony,' she said decisively.

Barely had she put the phone down than it rang a second time. She suspected that it was Tony again, perhaps about to enquire just when he might expect her to ring. She just did not need this, and almost let the phone ring until he got tired. But, against that, she had dined with him last night, and he had behaved himself when he'd brought her home.

She picked up the phone. 'Hello,' she said.

'Who were you talking to?' asked a voice that set her heart-beats pounding.

'When?' she asked, striving to get herself together. Silas!

'You've been on the phone for an age!' he accused.

'Well, you know how it is when you're popular!'

'Tony Andrews?'

His question sounded like another accusation. 'Tony,' she confirmed.

Silence, then, shatteringly, 'You have remembered you're married to *me*?' Silas demanded.

Her mouth fell open. 'Get you!' she exclaimed, stunned. But, recovering fast, and feeling not a little cross at what she thought he was hinting, 'I haven't committed adultery, if that's what you're asking!' she flew. And, starting to feel angry that he'd dared to ring to say what he had—this was all too one-sided as far as she was concerned, 'I trust you can say the same?' she snapped spiritedly, knowing darn well that he could not.

But, to shatter her further, 'Believe it or not, I take my vows seriously,' Silas replied. Her mouth fell open again in shock. Marriage vows, did he mean? She realised that he did—must do. Vows encompassed marriage vows—which must mean that he had not been to bed with anyone since their marriage? Strangely enough, she believed him, and suddenly she was glad he could not see her—she would hate him to see the delighted smile that that information had wrought. She tried for something either witty or sharp to say, but found she was stunned into silence, until, 'Have dinner with me?' Silas invited.

'No!' It did not take any thinking about. Theirs was not a 'have dinner with me' relationship. He knew that too. So why was he suggesting it? 'Why?' she asked bluntly, suspiciously.

There was a pause, then—and she was sure she heard a smile in his voice— 'I might have a proposition to put to you,' he hinted.

Yes, yes, yes. He had proposed they marry. He had also proposed she go and stay at his apartment for a few nights—and look what had happened. 'I've had some of your propositions!' she retorted sharply, and, knowing that the yes, yes, yes part of her was within an ace of taking over, she promptly slammed down the phone.

No sooner was it done than Colly regretted doing so. But she went to bed smiling and knowing that she loved Silas more than ever. Which seemed to make it a good idea to keep well away from the man. But, oh, how she would dearly love to have dinner with him.

Silas did not ring again. She did not expect him to. That did not stop her heartbeats from racing, though, on the few times when the phone did ring. She wondered why he had phoned at all, and doubted that he'd had any proposition to put to her, or that he had telephoned with the sole purpose of asking her to have dinner with him. Which meant, then, that he must have rung only to remind her that she was married to him.

She would have liked to get excited at how possessive that 'You have remembered you're married to *me*?' had sounded. But in reality she knew that Silas, perhaps thinking that she and Tony were closer than they were, had only phoned to remind her that their marriage was secret and that there was an unwritten 'no immediate divorce' clause to it.

It was a lovely June morning when Colly looked out of her window at the bright sunlight—and felt that life seemed somehow to be unutterably dull. She had not seen or heard from Silas in weeks.

She reminded herself that theirs was supposed to be a non-communications type of marriage, and tried to count her blessings. Nanette was currently away, holidaying with 'a friend', and the house was in the process of being sold; once all the legal work had been completed she'd no longer need to have any contact with her.

Tony Andrews was still asking her out. He'd obviously decided not to wait for her call and frequently phoned her. She still worked every Tuesday at the gallery—and Rupert was still bending her ear with the tragedy of his love-life.

And that was the crux of the matter. The reason why she felt so down. She did not crave a love-life; she just craved to see Silas. But he never got in touch, and he would think it mightily peculiar if, for no especial reason, she took it upon herself to contact him.

Colly gave herself a short sharp lecture on how she was going to beat this thing. She was not, not, not going to let her feelings for Silas ruin her life. Maybe when she had started that foundation course she would meet other people, get to know other people, let her life take a new direction.

But for now she was going to start a new life—with the people she knew. She rang Tony Andrews. 'Colly!' he exclaimed, sounding pleased to hear her.

Already she was regretting what she was about. But that was not the way it was supposed to go. 'I wondered if you'd like to have dinner with me?' she invited.

'Would I ever!' he accepted eagerly. 'At your apartment, do you mean?'

No, she had not meant that at all. But she hesitated—get a

life. 'If that's all right with you,' she answered. 'We can eat out if you prefer…'

'I'll bring a bottle. What time?'

He thought she meant tonight! Colly was about to put him off when her new-found self asserted itself. Why was she dithering? What better than to start her new life *now*? Tonight? This very Monday? What was there to wait for?

'We could eat about eight?' she suggested.

'I'll be there at seven-thirty,' he accepted readily.

Colly was still squashing down that part of her that was not too happy about having Tony in the apartment when, punctually at seven-thirty, bottle of wine in hand, he arrived.

It was the first time she had entertained in the apartment, and as the evening wore on so she began to lose any small feeling of apprehension; the evening seemed to be going rather well. Tony appeared impressed with her cooking— though she did confess that the stilton and celery soup was not home-made, but came from the delicatessen.

The rest of the meal was home-made, though, and it pleased her to see Tony tucking in. He seemed thoroughly relaxed, and that made her feel relaxed too. She thought she had got to know him quite well over these past months of phone calls and his visits to the gallery. But she knew she would never regard him as more than a friend.

Something she rather belatedly realised he had not taken on board when, insisting despite her protests that he wanted to help her with the dishwashing, and taking no heed of her, 'Honestly, I'd much prefer to do it later when you've gone,' he carried their dessert plates out to the kitchen and started to run the hot water.

'Let me try my hand at being domesticated,' he requested, giving her his most charming smile.

Perhaps she was too intense. To her way of thinking he was a guest, and this was his first meal in her home. Should there be subsequent meals, then perhaps to let him clear away might be in order, but...

'If you're sure.' She gave in, and took over at the sink. But only to grow immediately uptight when he passed behind her and she felt him drop a kiss on the back of her neck.

Instinctively she took a sudsy hand out from the dishwashing water to wipe his kiss away. 'Now look what you've done,' he teased, and, taking up a hand towel, he stepped closer and dabbed at her damp nape.

'That's fine. Thank you,' Colly said as lightly as she could, half turning, her instincts suddenly on the alert as she took a step back from him. She at once came up against the kitchen sink—Tony moved in closer.

He took the towel and dried her hands. 'You're beautiful— you know that, don't you?' he said, to her amazement his tone suddenly gone all seductive. She was still staring at him mesmerised when he reached out and took her in his arms.

'This—isn't getting the washing up done,' she reminded him, staying the polite hostess.

'We can, as you suggested, do it later,' he replied, and kissed her.

Colly felt a soul in torment. She wanted a life, had to have a life without Silas. But the wretched truth was there undeniably before her—she did not want anyone's kisses but his.

'You can do better than that, can't you?' Tony coaxed— and she wondered if she was being fair to him, fair to herself?

'Of course,' she replied, and tried. She put her arms around him and offered him her lips. But he was alien to hold, his lips alien. It will get better, she attempted to tell herself, in despair about the new life she was going to make for herself if only she could put some kind of effort into it.

He came closer, pressing her against the sink. She tried hard to keep calm, to respond; did she really want to do this? She was wedged in between him and the sink with no way out when he placed his hands on her hips and pulled her into him.

She pushed him away and knew then that, new life or no new life, she would much rather do the washing up. 'Er—I think…' was as far as she got before Tony grabbed her and clamped his moist mouth over hers, his body pressing into her while his hands moved up, seeking her breasts. *'No!'* she yelled, and, giving him a push, meant it.

He knew she meant it too. It was there in her tone, her look, her stance. 'Why not?' he argued. 'Hell's bells, I've given you miles of rope to get you to this pitch. You invite me to dinner and then…' He grinned suddenly—she saw it as a leer—'You still playing hard to get, Colly?' he questioned, and made another grab for her.

She was determined not to panic, but knew she was losing it when, forcefully, she ordered, *'No!'*

'Oh, come on.' He made another lunge for her.

'No!' she said again.

'Why not?' he repeated, a wheedling kind of note there in his voice. 'What's to stop us? I'm unattached. You're free and…' he leered again '…I'm sure I could make you willing. Relax, sweetie,' he pressed, his breath hot against her face, and in the next moment he had fastened his lips on hers again.

Her agitation was growing as again she pushed him wildly away, while wondering at the same time how, when she now felt revolted by his kisses, she had allowed him to kiss her in the first place. And suddenly, her composure shot when he would not take his wet mouth from hers, she gave him another shove, and, picking up on what he had just said, cried, 'I'm not free!'

That seemed to stop him in his tracks. He stared incredulously at her. 'You're—engaged—married?' he asked in disbelief.

Oh, Lord, her head was spinning. She did not know where the devil she was. All she could think then was that no one must know about her marriage. Panic set in with a vengeance. 'We're getting divorced!' It was out before she could stop it.

Tony heard what she had said, for all she had gabbled it out in a panicky rush, and sifted through what she had just told him. 'So where's the problem?' he came back, without so much as a blink. But even as he went to make a grab for her again, so part of his brain appeared to be putting two and two together. 'Where's your husband?' he asked, and, more pertinently, 'Who *is* your husband?' he prodded further. And, his two and two swiftly adding up to a correct four, before she could halt him, 'Silas Livingstone!' he exclaimed, sounding staggered, though still able to replay in his mind that time when Silas Livingstone had revealed that she had 'personally' nursed him when he had been ill. How she had been there to keep him warm. 'You're married to Silas Livingstone!' he concluded, and, as if shaken anew, he actually took a step back.

Colly wanted to repeat that they were getting divorced—but suddenly a whole welter of complications were crashing in. She immediately wanted to deny that she and Silas were married at all. And from there at once grew terrified that any other panic-stricken comment she might make would see her saying something else to Tony that could lead just about anywhere.

Without another word she went smartly from the kitchen. Tony followed. 'It's true, isn't it?' he questioned, but seemed to know it for a fact.

'I—think you'd better go, Tony,' she replied, trying to keep her voice from shaking.

'That's a bit steep, isn't it?' he complained. 'You invite me for an intimate dinner…'

Intimate dinner! Was that the way he had read her invitation? She shook her head. 'I've enjoyed your company,' she told him—which, up to a point, she had. 'But I never intended it to be more than dinner.'

'I don't suppose your husband would approve,' Tony, his tone changing, offered sourly. There wasn't any possible answer to that. So she just stood her ground. After a few belligerent moments, 'Don't call me—I'll call you,' he said huffily. Colly went and opened the door for him. Seriously annoyed, he took the none-too-subtle hint.

She closed the door after him, reeling. What had she done? Just what…? It all played back horribly in her head. 'Silas Livingstone!' he had guessed. 'We're getting divorced,' she had lied. Oh, save us!

In need of something to do, Colly went to the kitchen and carried on with the dishes from where she had left off. But her head was spinning even more when the used dishes had been washed, dried and put away, and the kitchen once more immaculate. Because by then she had recalled that Tony Andrews worked in public relations, and, from conversations she'd had with him, she had also recalled that he seemed well acquainted with people in the news media.

Oh, heavens. What was to stop him making capital in any way he could from what she had so unintentionally revealed? She doubted that after tonight's little episode Tony would feel any loyalty to her.

Needing action of any kind, she went and brushed her teeth. Then ran a comb through her hair. But she was so unable to settle she began to pace up and down. For herself she could not care less what Tony told his press contacts. For Silas… She could not think. The whole thing was a nightmare.

She continued to pace up and down, but as the hands on her watch neared half past eleven it came to her that there was only one thing she could possibly do. She had to warn Silas! There was no way around it; she had to warn him.

Hoping that he was in—and for all his statement that he took his vows seriously it would not stop him from living it up somewhere—Colly went and found his home number.

When the phone was not answered straight away she was sure he must be out. But then, doing nothing for the agitated mass she was inside, the phone was picked up and, 'Livingstone,' he answered.

'It—it's Colly,' she stammered.

Silence for a moment, before, 'You make a habit of telephoning men when they've gone to bed for the night?' he questioned tersely.

And she was glad he was being vile. It made some—not all, but some—of her nerves subside. 'I have it on good authority that you're in bed alone!' she retorted snappily. But was immediately unsure, sick inside with jealousy, and nervous again. 'You are, aren't you? I m-mean, I haven't...?' She could not finish.

An agonising moment or two of silence followed, until, 'You haven't,' Silas confirmed, and his tone thawing a little, 'To be quite honest, petal, I have to get to the airport for a business trip very soon—I wouldn't mind a few hours' sleep before then.'

'Oh, I'm sorry—I'm sorry,' she apologised. But, as the import of what he had just said hit her, 'You're going away!' she cried.

'Don't upset yourself—I'm coming back.'

Smug pig. 'This isn't funny!' she exclaimed furiously.

'Presumably you're going to get to the point of this call—before my plane takes off.'

'You weren't smacked enough as a child!' she flew, feeling very much like redressing the balance had he been near.

His tone changed again, was warmer again. 'You're in a tizz about something?' he guessed.

Colly promptly folded. 'Oh, Silas,' she mourned. 'I've done something so dreadful I hardly know how to tell you.'

'Sounds—serious,' he commented.

'It is. It—um—won't wait until you get back.'

Silas was decisive. 'I'd better come over.'

'No, no,' she protested. 'I've enough guilt without adding

any more. You get what sleep you can. I'll come to you.' She put the phone down before he should persuade her differently.

A short while later she was ringing the doorbell to his apartment, and still had not been able to find a way of telling him what she knew she urgently had to share with him.

He was wearing shirt and trousers when he opened the door. 'You needn't have dressed,' came tripping off her tongue, she having assumed that, having got up from his bed, he would be robe-clad.

'Now, there's an invitation,' he said dryly, leading the way to the drawing room.

She gave him a speaking look, but as he indicated she take a seat and then took a seat facing her, so Colly saw the opening that she needed. 'That's the thing about invitations,' she began, searching for words and finding a few, 'I invited a friend to dinner tonight—and got things very badly wrong.'

'Tony Andrews?' Silas guessed, a hard kind of glint all at once there in his eyes.

'I do know other men,' she stated, a touch miffed that he seemed to think Tony was the only man who asked her out. But she was in the wrong here and she knew it; this was not the time to get shirty. 'But, yes, Tony.'

'Where did you eat?' Silas wanted to know.

She suspected he already knew. 'At the apartment,' she owned.

'My grandfather's apartment?' he asked toughly.

'It's where I live!' she snapped.

'Andrews often dines there with you?'

There was no let-up on Silas's toughness, she noted. But after what she had done she wasn't in a position to take exception to anything. 'It was the first—and the last—time,' she confessed.

Silas had an alert look in his eyes, but his tough tone was fading as he commented, 'It sounds as if you sent him home with a flea in his ear?'

'I—it…not quite. But—' on reflection '—similar.' Then suddenly she wanted this all said and done. If Silas was going to rain coals of fury down on her head, and she was sure he would go ballistic, then the sooner it was done the better. 'Well, the thing is, I—er—invited him to dinner out of friendship. But he—um—seemed to think I'd invited him for an—er—intimate dinner, and…'

'It didn't occur to you that dinner for two at your place might be construed as a touch intimate?'

'Well, if you're going to take his side!' she erupted heatedly. But again remembered that she was the one in the wrong here. 'No,' she changed tack to answer, 'it didn't cross my mind that—that I was on the menu with the *petit fours*.'

'He came on strong and you didn't like it?' Silas guessed, his expression stern.

Colly flicked her glance from him. She did not want to tell Silas how she had tried to respond to Tony. But in all honesty she could not make Tony out to be the villain of the piece. 'It—er—was all right at first,' she admitted, but hurried on, 'Then I said no, and…'

'You said no?' Silas questioned. Her ears felt scarlet. 'Because you didn't want to? Or because you're married to me?' he persisted.

By no chance was she going to let Silas know that other men stood no chance—because of him. But she could feel herself getting het-up again at the thought that Silas might guess at her feelings for him.

Unable to sit still, but with no idea of where she was going, she was on her feet. 'Would you like me to make you some coffee?' she offered.

'Because you didn't want to or because of your marriage vows?' Silas insisted.

She felt cornered. 'Because I just don't sleep around!' she said heatedly, and saw that Silas looked somewhat shaken by her confession.

'You don't?' he queried, on his feet too. 'Hmm—you have, though?' She would not answer, but then found he was persistent if nothing else. 'At some time you have—experimented—fully?'

She still did not want to answer. Silence reigned until, dumbly, she shook her head, finding the carpet of great interest. 'How old-fashioned is that?' she asked, and, expecting some derisive remark that at twenty-three she still hadn't left the starting blocks, she turned her back on him.

But to her surprise Silas made no derisive remark, but came over to her and, taking hold of her upper arms, turned her to face him. Gently then he drew her against him. 'Don't be embarrassed,' he instructed softly.

'I feel stupid,' she confessed, and for long wonderful seconds was held in his gentle hold.

Then, unhurriedly, he lowered his head and gently kissed her. 'You're not stupid, you're lovely,' he assured her, and led her back to her chair. 'So what happened when you rejected Andrews' advances?' he asked.

Feeling a little bemused—Silas's light kiss just now had had far more effect than the assault of Tony Andrews' kisses—she endeavoured to think straight. 'Well, he wouldn't take no for an answer—' she began, but was stopped from saying more when, on the instant enraged, Silas cut her off.

'He assaulted you? He sexually assaulted you?' he roared. 'Where does he live?' he demanded, on his feet and seeming about to charge off to Tony Andrews' address and flatten him.

'No. No,' Colly said quickly, realising that Silas's protection of her stemmed only from the fact that he had given her the right to use his name. It was the reaction of any decent man, but there was nothing more personal in it than that. Though she did so hope that Silas liked her. 'I think I told him no a couple of times, and he wanted to know why not—he thought I was playing hard to get,' she rushed on. 'I should never have invited him to the apartment, I can see that now.

Anyway, he couldn't see why I wouldn't. Oh, heavens, this all sounds so sordid.'

'You're doing fine,' Silas encouraged, his fury in check. 'You're getting there,' he added, as though recalling how over the phone she had said that *she* had done something so dreadful. And, as though to encourage her further, he retook his seat and stayed quiet until she was ready to go on.

'Well, Tony was—well, you know—and wanting to know what was to stop us. He said that he was unattached, and that I was free, and... Well, anyhow, I was starting to feel a touch out of my depth, so I must have grabbed at that "out", and I told him I wasn't free.'

'You told him you were married?'

'Not in so many words, I don't think. But then I got all over the place in my head, and all I knew was that no one must know about our marriage.'

'You weren't making a very good job of it,' Silas butted in.

'It gets worse.'

'I'll brace myself.'

'By then I was panicking.'

'Poor love,' he said, as she at one time, she clearly recalled, had said to him.

She felt a little heartened. Sufficiently, anyway, to be able to carry on. 'I knew at once that I'd said the wrong thing. Instinctively knew, I suppose, that I had to say something to counteract that I'd just as good as said I was married. She swallowed. 'I then went and dug myself into an even bigger hole.'

'You told him you were married to me?' Silas guessed.

She shook her head. 'I didn't have to. Tony guessed. He must have remembered that night you two met. You know, that night when...'

'When I commented on the fact that you'd had a hand in nursing me?'

'Such as it was—my nursing, I mean,' she said, thinking how all she had done was dole out his medication. But as she recalled waking up in bed with him, so she blushed scarlet. 'A-anyhow…' she tried to rush on.

'Anyhow, from that Andrews deduced that the man you were married to must be me,' Silas took up, with a not unkind look at her blushing face. 'Is that it?' he wanted to know.

'I said it gets worse,' Colly reminded him quietly. And, wanting it all said and done, she hurriedly added. 'Tony works in PR. He knows all sorts of press people—' She broke off when she spotted the sharp look that came to Silas's eyes.

'You foresee a problem?' He was ahead of her; she knew that he was.

This was it. She had to tell him. She took a deep breath, but had she been hoping it might steady her, she knew it had failed. She was shaking inside as she blurted out, 'I was panicking, and I knew I had to do something to counteract that I'd as good as told him that I was married. I just wasn't thinking,' she confessed, 'and I told him that we were—um—getting divorced.'

Silas stared at her as if he could not believe his hearing. 'You told him that you and I were going to divorce?' he questioned harshly. 'You actually told this man with press connections that you and I were divorcing? When you know, have always known, that that is the last piece of information I want broadcast—'

'I'm sorry,' she cut in miserably, watching as Silas, as if needing to be on his feet, left his chair. 'I was in panic, as I said—trying to make good something I'd inadvertently let slip—that I wasn't free.'

Silas seemed gone from her, his look thoughtful. She would dearly love to know what was going on behind his clever forehead. 'What chance is there that Andrews won't make capital out of this?' he wanted to know.

'I've no idea. He was pretty mad at me when he left, so I

don't suppose he's likely to want to spare me. Shall I ring him?' she asked. 'Appeal to him not to—'

'No!' Silas answered decisively. And, his thoughts and conclusions soon reached, he resumed his seat, and looked her straight in the eye as he informed her, 'I want you to have nothing whatsoever to do with Andrews in the future.' And, his chin jutting slightly, 'Is that understood?' he stressed.

'I'm not so keen myself,' she agreed, and was rewarded with a near smile. 'Is there anything I can do?' she asked, hoping Silas would not say that in his view she had done more than enough.

He did not say anything of the sort. But nor did his smile make it when he let her into his deliberations. 'All things considered, there is only one thing we *can* do if I'm to be able to continue to make long-term plans for Livingstone Developments.' Her eyes were fixed on nowhere but him when, coolly, he brought out, 'Thanks to you, my dear, I believe the time has come to reveal that we—you and I—are married—happily married.'

Her mouth went dry. She had no idea what any of that might mean, yet knew that figuratively she hadn't a leg to stand on. She had known the rules when she had married Silas—she had known in advance that divorce was a forbidden word. She it was who had broken the rules, and it was she who had messed the whole of it up.

'Y-you intend to tell your grandfather?' she asked hesitantly.

'My father,' Silas corrected. 'He's an early riser. I'll phone him from the airport and ring my grandfather when I get back. By then he'll know from my father that you and I are married, and that despite what they might read in the press neither of us has any intention of being divorced.' And, having told her how it was to be, he stood up. She guessed he was keen to get to bed and get what sleep he could before he went to catch his early flight. Colly stood up too, and Silas escorted her to the door. 'Agreed?' he thought to ask.

Colly stared unhappily up into his searching dark blue eyes. She had no idea what sort of complications this turn of events might bring. But she had brought this sorry state of affairs about, so how could she not agree?

'Agreed,' she answered, and again wanted to apologise for whatever chain of events she had set in motion by her agitated 'I'm not free' to Tony Andrews. She did not apologise, but felt so down just then that she would dearly have loved it had Silas held her for a moment or two in a gentle hug.

But Silas did not give her a hug. Nor did he attempt to kiss her cheek. She supposed he must be as fed up with her as she was with herself.

'I'll be in touch when I get back,' he told her.

'Whatever you say,' she replied, and left.

CHAPTER SEVEN

COLLY spent the next two days searching the various newspapers for any reference to the fact that she and Silas Livingstone were married—there was none.

But, oh, what had she done? By now Silas's father, and his mother too, of course, would know that their son was married. And, by the look of it, Colly realised, she had panicked unnecessarily. With nothing in the papers there had been no need for any of his family to know that he had a wife! By now Silas's grandfather probably knew as well—but there had been absolutely no need for anyone to know! And Silas would hate her.

In an agony of torment from not knowing what, if anything, was going on, Colly felt very inclined to ring Tony Andrews and ask him if he intended to use that snippet that Silas Livingstone was married. Against ringing Tony, though, was her fear that if he had not already been in touch with his press pals, any call she made might prompt him to do so. And anyhow, Silas had been adamant that she should have nothing more to do with Tony; she supposed Silas knew more about these things than she did.

She left her bed on Thursday, wishing she had some idea of when Silas would be coming home. Oh, what a hornets' nest she had stirred up! And yet she'd had to warn him, hadn't she? And it had been his decision to, as it were, go public. And in all fairness, looking back to last Monday, when she had gone to see him, Colly still did not see how she could not have told him what she had.

To add to her inner turmoil there was nothing in the papers that day either. She had no idea if Silas would call or phone.

'I'll be in touch when I get back,' he'd said. She wished now that she had thought to ask when that would be. As it was, not wanting to miss his call, she had spent most of her time since yesterday more or less glued to the apartment.

He did not phone that day either, but it was around nine o'clock that evening when someone knocked on her door. Silas! It could be one of her neighbours, of course. She was acquainted with several of them by now, but as her heartbeats raced she somehow knew that it would be Silas.

Which caused her to take a very deep breath before she opened the door. It was him! They stared at each other. Colly sought to find her voice, but the 'Hello' she found came out sounding all husky and, to her ears, weird. 'Come in,' she invited, and left him to follow her into the sitting room. She turned. He was business-suited. 'You've come from the airport?' she enquired politely.

'I got in this afternoon. I thought I'd better spend some time in the office.'

'Have you eaten?'

If he could tell she was nervous he did not refer to it. 'I have, but I wouldn't mind taking you up on your offer to make me a coffee,' he replied pleasantly.

Colly was relieved to escape to the kitchen. They had been at his apartment when she had volunteered to make him coffee. Her relief was short-lived, though, because a few seconds later Silas joined her in the kitchen.

'Andrews been in touch?' he asked conversationally.

She shook her head. 'I don't think I'm flavour of the month there,' she responded.

'Does that upset you?'

'You know better than that!' she replied shortly. But then folded completely and blurted out, 'Oh, Silas, I got it all wrong, didn't I?'

'You did?' he asked, seeming not to know what she was talking about.

'You won't know, being out of the country and everything, but there's been nothing in the papers about—about us—being married!'

'I know,' he surprised her by saying. So she could only suppose he had read the foreign editions while abroad. Either that or he had found time to scan them since his plane had landed that afternoon.

She sighed heavily. 'I'm sorry. I rather jumped the gun, didn't I—coming to see you like that? But,' she excused, 'I felt you had to know.'

'You did the only thing possible,' he assured her.

'I did?'

He smiled then, and it so lit his face that her heart turned over. How dear he was to her. 'There hasn't been anything in the press yet, but there will be tomorrow,' he said succinctly. 'Shall I carry that in?' he suggested, taking up the tray of coffee.

They were back in the sitting room—she seated on the sofa, Silas having taken the chair opposite, with the highly polished table in between. He relaxed back, seemingly enjoying the coffee he had apparently been parched for. She ignored her own coffee; there were things here that she felt she ought to know.

'You—um—seem pretty certain the—papers will be printing—'

'Just the financial ones, I suspect,' Silas chipped in, and went on to dumbfound her as he explained, 'I got in touch with my PA first thing on Tuesday. I suspected that before our marriage—or divorce—was made news, someone would contact my office for verification. At the end of my instructions Ellen knew to confirm, if pushed, that I was happily married, to laugh at any suggestion that a divorce might be in the offing, and to then transfer the call to my own PR department, who would quote that which I had dictated to Ellen.'

Colly stared at him. 'Forward planning has nothing on you,' she said faintly. And, endeavouring to recover, 'And someone did ring?'

'Several people,' he confirmed.

'Am I allowed to know what this piece of dictation was?'

He shrugged. 'I kept any details about us to a minimum by saying that Columbine Gillingham and I had married quietly on account of your father's recent demise. And from there I took the limelight off you and me by giving details of your father's brilliant engineering brain and mentioning some of his more spectacular achievements.' Silas paused. 'I hope that doesn't offend you, Colly?'

How could it? It was true that they had married quietly, shortly after her father's death, even if his recent death was not the reason for their quiet wedding. Nor could she be offended that Silas had referred to her father's brilliant engineering brain; it heartened her that her father's engineering achievements were not forgotten.

'No,' she said simply, 'I'm not offended.' And, realising then that with the press having contacted Silas's office she had done the right thing after all in contacting him, she reached for her coffee and took a sip. A trace nervously, she had to admit, she moved on to enquire, as calmly as she could, 'You—rang your father from the airport? You—um—said you would.'

'I rang him.' He nodded, and his lips twitched a little. 'My mother was ringing my hotel in Italy before I got there.'

Oh, crumbs. 'They—your parents—they're all right about it?'

'You mean their not being present at our wedding?'

She had not meant that, though supposed they had a right to feel a touch annoyed. 'I mean more about you being married.'

'They couldn't be more pleased. Not to put too fine a point on it, my mother is overjoyed.'

'She is?'

'She is,' he confirmed. 'She remembers speaking to you on the phone—and says you have a lovely voice.' Colly stared at him. 'My father,' he went on, 'is just pleased that I'm happy.'

'You—are happy?' Colly queried.

'Why wouldn't I be?'

Why indeed? The future of Livingstone Developments appeared secure, and the future of the company was what he cared about. 'Have your parents told your grandfather yet, do you think?'

Silas looked at her solemnly, and she felt he hesitated a fraction before he confirmed that his grandfather did indeed know that he had taken himself a bride. 'My grandfather is delighted,' he revealed.

But Colly had a strange feeling that there was more than that. 'And?' she pressed, a touch apprehensively, she had to admit.

'And,' Silas replied calmly, 'my grandfather wants to meet you.'

'No!' She did not even have to think about it. 'No,' she said again, though less forcefully this time. Silas said nothing, but just sat watching her. And then Colly did start to think about it, even if she did not like the idea any better. 'When?' she asked.

'He'd like us to visit this weekend.'

This weekend! *Weekend?* 'Weekend?' she questioned faintly. 'You mean a *whole* weekend?' Well, that wasn't on. Whatever excuses Silas had to make, he could jolly well get them out of it.

'He's very lonely since my grandmother died.' Silas, whether he knew it or not, jangled her heartstrings. 'But, in view of our other commitments, I said we'd arrive on Saturday—rather than the Friday he suggested—and stay just the one night.'

Stay one night: Colly did not feel any happier, but something else Silas had just said caused her to forget that for the moment and follow this new trail. 'Our—other commitments?' she queried warily—and was right to be wary, she very soon discovered.

'Quite naturally my parents will be most offended if they don't get to meet you first,' Silas explained.

Colly did not think very much of his explanation! She owned that her brain did not seem to be working at full capacity just then, but it very much appeared that if she was to meet Silas's grandfather on Saturday—and bearing in mind that today, or tonight, was Thursday—then at some time between now and then she must first meet Silas's parents.

'This is getting much too complicated,' she complained, casting a belligerent look over to the man she had 'quietly' married.

He bore her look pleasantly. 'What's complicated?' he asked, and sounded so reasonable she could have truly done with hating him.

Particularly since she could not come up with much of an answer. 'Why can't we just tell your parents the truth? That we are married, but—'

'Because to do so would put them under an obligation not to tell my grandfather the truth,' Silas cut in heavily. 'This is my situation, not theirs.'

Reluctantly Colly could see that. To involve his parents in the way she had suggested would just not be fair to them. But she protested just the same. 'I don't like deceiving people,' she said woodenly.

'How are we deceiving anyone?' he asked, and she truly did hate him that while she was starting to feel all stewed up he could continue to sound so reasonable. She gave him a look of dislike. It bounced off him. And he was still insufferably reasonable when he drew her attention to the facts.

'My grandfather wants to meet my wife—you, Colly, *are* my wife.'

You are my wife. She found it hard to hate him while her heart took a giddy trip at those words. But, though those lovely words sounded beautifully possessive, she knew full well that Silas stated them as merely fact. Colly pulled herself sternly together. 'I didn't sign up for any of this when I agreed to marry you,' she reminded him snappily.

'Neither did I!' he returned bluntly. And, his expression harsh, 'As I recall, it was you who let the cat out,' he reminded her.

He had her there. If she had not let Tony Andrews know she was not free, and then gone on to compound that error by telling him she was getting divorced—giving him space to speculate on whom she might be married to—none of this would be happening. As it was, Silas had been forced into taking what action he had to when she'd triggered off that which could have led to disaster.

She was in the wrong, and she knew it. Colly took a defeated breath and, as graciously as she could in the circumstances, enquired, 'When do I meet your parents?'

His harsh expression faded. 'We're having them over for dinner tomorrow evening.'

'Over at your place?' she asked, her voice barely audible—keep reminding yourself that you're the one in the wrong, Colly.

'Over at *our* place,' he corrected.

'You're not expecting me to move in with you?' she asked in sudden alarm.

He looked cheered. 'Oh, your face!' he exclaimed, but sobered to let her know, 'As far as anyone else knows we live together, but at this stage I see no need for us to go that far.'

Why did she feel miffed at what he said? She did not want to live with him, for goodness' sake—well, not under the present circumstances, she qualified.

'We must be thankful for small mercies, I suppose,' she offered dryly, and saw his lips twitch, felt a moment's weakness where he was concerned, but hurried on, 'I'm cooking?'

'Mrs Varley will attend to that. My parents will be at my place around seven, but just in case they should be half an hour early, if you could be there around six?'

'You'll be there—at six?'

'I'll finish work early,' he said, and suddenly Colly was feeling dreadful.

'I've caused one almighty giant upheaval, haven't I?' she said apologetically.

'Oh, Colly, don't be too upset,' Silas said gently, leaving his chair and coming over to take a seat on the sofa with her. And, his tone friendly, not sharp, as she felt she deserved, 'One way and another you have done me a favour.'

She turned in her seat to look at him, her heart pounding to have him so close. 'How?' she asked with what sign of normality she could find. 'If I hadn't—'

'I find it next to impossible to tell lies to my family,' Silas cut in. 'So when my father asked me outright if I'd thought any more about what he'd confided about grandfather altering his will I was able to calm his anxieties and truthfully tell him I was seriously involved with someone.'

'You meant me?'

'You,' Silas confirmed. 'By then you and I were married.'

'I don't suppose you can truthfully get more seriously involved than that,' she mumbled.

'Everything slotted in for both my father and my mother when they recalled how, when I was in hospital, you were allowed in to see me. How, when I got out of hospital, you were at my apartment staying with me. My mother really started to get her hopes high then, by the way. When, less than a couple of months after that, said cat bolted out from the bag, it didn't seem so far-fetched to them when I explained that we had quietly married.'

'They didn't think it at all odd that we didn't invite them to our wedding?'

'Not so much when I told them your maiden name—who you were. My father at once recognised your name. He had been with me, paying his respects at your father's funeral. My mother, while a triftle put out, it has to be said, at the same time understood when I said I didn't want to wait but wanted to marry straight away. That, with your father's death so recent, we'd agreed we did not want a big tell-the-world type of wedding.'

Colly knew, for all her heart had given a little flutter, that she could not get excited about that 'I didn't want to wait'. Silas had wanted that marriage certificate with all speed—she, his bride, was incidental to his forward planning.

'Um…' she murmured, and saw she had his full attention. 'Er—this dinner tomorrow…' she began, hardly knowing how to continue. Silas looked at her, but was not saying another word, and she felt forced to continue, 'I mean, do your parents think ours is a love-match?' There—it was out.

'I haven't said so in as many words. But my mother certainly will be sure that ours is a love-match. Or—' suddenly he was grinning a wicked grin '—or at least that no woman could know me and not love me.'

'Which just goes to show how terribly blinkered mothers really are!' Colly said acidly. And because it was so true that she did love him, so very much—only he was not to know it—she got up from the sofa commenting, 'I just thought I ought to know—er—whether I'm supposed to—um—show a bit of affection for you.'

'Well, if your feelings really do get too much for you, and you feel you just have to hold and kiss me…' he began to tease. Then, seeing how tense she suddenly seemed, he left the sofa and came to stand next to her. 'Nervous about tomorrow?' he asked kindly.

Petrified, if you must know. 'You could say that,' she replied, and suddenly found herself in the loose hold of his embrace.

'Don't be,' he said softly, as her heart went into overdrive. 'My parents will love you. Just be yourself and everything will be fine.'

She wished she could believe him. The truth was, she did not feel she knew what was herself any more. She shook her head in some kind of bewilderment. 'All I did on Monday night was say I wasn't free, add that I was getting divorced— and now look where we are!'

'Things have moved on at something of a pace,' Silas agreed quietly.

'Something of a pace! They've positively galloped!'

'Don't fret about it. What's done is done.'

And she was the one who had done it. 'I'm throwing you out,' she told him, knowing she quite desperately needed to get herself more of one piece. Just being held in the loose circle of his arms was making her head chaotic.

'I thought you might be,' he replied, lightly kissed her cheek, and then walked to the door.

Colly did not sleep well that night. In her head she imagined all sorts of disasters at Friday night's dinner—when she would meet her in-laws. The only way she was able to get any rest at all was by repeatedly reminding herself that Silas would be there too. She would have his support.

But it was while she was showering on Friday morning that the trepidation of her thoughts about that evening let up to let in an even bigger cause for worry. And it had nothing to do with that evening—but the following one.

Because only then did something she had been too preoccupied to think about suddenly jump up and hit her. What about tomorrow evening? Or, more specifically, tomorrow night? Only then did it dawn on her that, unless Silas Livingstone Senior lived in a house that had a separate suite for overnight guests, tomorrow night she was going to have to share a room with Silas!

There was one thing about this new source of inner conflict, she discovered, it certainly transferred some of her agitation away from that evening's dinner party. She hoped with all she had that Silas had plans to sleep elsewhere. But, bearing in mind they'd barely been married four months, she could imagine his grandfather looking askance at the mere idea of them sleeping in separate rooms.

She was glad when later that morning her phone rang, and a difficult conversation with Henry Warren gave her head some respite from her concerns about meeting her in-laws—both in London and in Dorset.

'Is it true?' Henry Warren asked.

She knew what he was talking about and realised she should have guessed he would take a financial newspaper and might pick up that which Silas had dictated.

'Yes, it's true,' she replied. 'I'm sorry, Uncle Henry, I should have told you. But…' But what? He had been untold good to her, and must think her silence about something as important as this very strange. 'I've been a bit—um—mixed up,' she added lamely.

'Because of your father?'

'I—er—Silas was at my father's funeral.'

'You met him that day?'

Sort of. 'I'm sorry I didn't tell you.' She felt she had to apologise again. 'But Silas and I, we wanted a quiet wedding. His parents didn't even know about us until quite recently.'

That seemed to mollify him a little. But, maybe out of duty to his old friend, he still had questions to ask. 'But what are you doing living in that apartment alone?'

'The apartment belongs to Silas's grandfather, but he doesn't use it and doesn't wish to sell it so we sort of keep the place aired. Silas goes abroad on business from time to time, but for the moment when he's home he likes to sometimes stay here.' Colly was not at all happy about embroidering the truth the way she was doing. 'And,' she hurried on, forestalling what she anticipated would be his next question, of why she had been so relieved when he had got some funds through for her, 'Silas is more than generous,' she explained—she still had ten thousand pounds of his that he was refusing to take back— 'But I felt such a pauper going to him penniless; it was a pride thing, I suppose. I was so grateful to you when you were able to get me some money of my own.'

'You always were a proud little thing,' he commented when she had finished, and while she was swishing around in guilt he went on more warmly—perhaps he more than most was aware of the joylessness of her existence prior to her father's death. 'You deserve some happiness, Colly.'

She thanked him and, while regretting she could not be entirely open with him, felt better that their phone conversation had ended in a friendly and affectionate way.

By four that afternoon, however, thoughts of the impending evening had taken most other thoughts from her mind. She supposed it was usual for most women to be apprehensive on meeting their in-laws for the first time. Though everything, she felt, about this meeting was *un*usual.

Because of her fidgety unable-to-settle feelings, Colly left the apartment ten minutes before she should. She hoped to feel better once everything was under way. She was wearing an emerald-green chiffon-over-silk evening trouser suit and, having noticed an absence of flowers in Silas's home, was carrying a sizeable bouquet of flowers when she rang his doorbell.

She wondered who would answer the door—Silas or Mrs Varley. It was Silas. He had said he would leave work early, and had. But while she thought he looked absolutely wonderful, he seemed impressed that she had made a bit of an effort herself.

'You look just a touch gorgeous,' he said softly, not moving back to let her in, but just standing there, his eyes showing his admiration.

Theirs was a non-personal relationship—most of the time. But to hear that Silas thought she looked a touch gorgeous was what she needed to hear. 'Just something I threw on,' she murmured offhandedly, every bit as though she had not changed three times before deciding to stick with the first outfit she had tried on. And, feeling unutterably shy suddenly, she thrust the flowers at him, 'Here,' she said, 'take a hold of these before they die.'

His face was alight with laughter as he took the hint and invited her in. She felt good suddenly. Perhaps the evening would not be such a trial after all.

'Where do you keep your vases?' Colly asked as they went along the hall.

'Good question.'

She wanted to grin—it was good just to be with him. 'I'll try the kitchen,' she decided, and found he was right there with her when she went in that direction.

In the kitchen was where Mrs Varley was, putting the finishing touches to a smoked salmon and watercress starter. 'Oh, Mrs Livingstone.' Mrs Varley beamed before Colly could say a word, and Colly hid her small moment of shock— but owned she was delighted at being so addressed. 'Mr Livingstone has told me of your marriage.' And, clearly a born romantic, 'I know you're both going to be very happy.' She beamed again.

'Thank you,' Colly answered. She felt stumped to know what to say next, but beamed a smile back and asked, 'Am I going to be in your way if I arrange the flowers in here?'

It took longer for her to arrange the flowers than she had thought—they just did not go right—and Colly was glad she had arrived ten minutes early. But by a quarter to seven there were two flower arrangements brightening up the otherwise masculine-looking drawing room, and one arrangement in the dining room.

Her chores, if chores they were, completed, Colly was starting to feel more nervous than ever. Mrs Varley assured her she had everything under control, so Colly left her and went to the bathroom to check her appearance. She ran a comb through her hair, touched up her lipstick and left the bathroom. Wishing the evening were over, she went to the drawing room. Silas was there waiting for her.

Whether or not he could tell she was being attacked by nerves she had no idea, but he smiled a smile that warmed her heart, and, coming over to her, asked, 'What would you like to drink?'

How he could sound so unconcerned when she felt such a wreck, she had no idea. But she drew strength from his easy manner. 'Nothing, thanks,' she refused. She had warned him that she was no good at subterfuge, but if he still wanted this evening to go ahead, so be it.

He took her refusal to have a drink without comment, but continued to come towards her, halting barely a step away. 'Perhaps you'd better wear this,' he said, and, putting his hand into his pocket, took out the wedding ring she had returned to him.

'I forgot!' she exclaimed, realising that while some women might prefer not to wear a wedding ring, she was not one of them. And, as he had once before, Silas took a hold of her left hand and slipped the gold band over her marriage finger.

'You're shaking!' he remarked in surprise at her trembling hand.

She felt absurd. He was so sophisticated, so able to carry off any situation. 'It's all right for you!' she accused snappily. 'You know my in-laws. I don't!'

He burst out laughing. 'Oh, I do l—like you, Colly Livingstone,' he said, and while her heart raced at the sudden warm look in his eyes, so the doorbell sounded.

'They're early!' she gasped.

'It's the season,' he said, and to her gratitude did not leave her alone to wait while he went to let his parents in, but caught hold of her hand. 'Come on—let's go and get it done,' he said, and led her to the door.

The next few minutes passed in a haze of beaming smiles of hugs and kisses that left Colly, who had missed a mother's love, feeling very emotional.

'How beautiful you are!' Paula Livingstone exclaimed, tall, distinguished and all heart. 'And, oh, how pleased I am to meet you.' She was still bursting with joy when she pulled Colly to her and just had to give her another hug.

Silas's father, Borden Livingstone, was more subdued than his wife, though it was possible that he had not spent the last few years waiting for this very day the way his wife had.

Colly recognised him as the man who had been with Silas at her father's funeral, and warmed to Borden Livingstone when he offered his condolences and apologised that he had not spoken to her then.

'Would you like something to drink first, or are you ready to eat?' Silas asked as they ambled into the drawing room.

'We'd better eat,' his mother declared, her eyes approvingly flicking from one flower arrangement to the other. 'I've hardly been able to eat a thing all day. I'd better get something solid down before I attempt anything alcoholic.'

Colly liked her mother-in-law. She was such a warm and natural person and Colly felt it would be difficult not to like her. She wished she could be as natural in return, and did try her very hardest so to be. But she was aware that she had to be on her guard; any small slip and she could see they would have to confess the truth.

Though as they chatted all through the first course, and enjoyed each other's company, so Colly did begin to feel a little more relaxed.

It was midway through the main course, however—Mrs

Varley having excelled herself with crispy roast duck in a black cherry sauce—that Colly realised she just could not afford to relax.

Paula Livingstone made some passing reference to the tropical bug Silas had picked up, and said how heartily relieved she had been to know that someone he might be serious about was going to collect him from the hospital and would look after him. 'Of course I didn't know then that you and Silas were married,' she went on warmly, with a happy glance at Colly's wedding band before going smilingly on, 'We very nearly met then, when I came to check on him—but you'd already left.'

Oh, grief, what could she say? Colly recalled that she had left the apartment before nine that morning—she had no idea how soon afterwards Silas's mother had arrived.

'I don't think Colly will mind me telling you—she's been having a few problems in connection with her father's will,' Silas slotted in smoothly. Colly glanced to him and supposed that, given the problems that had faced her when she had thought herself left out of her father's will, Silas was speaking only the truth.

'Oh, I'm so sorry, Colly.' Paula was instantly sympathetic. And, turning to her husband, 'I'm sure our legal advisers would be—'

'It's no longer a problem,' Silas informed her.

How could he say that when the consequences of the action she had taken when thinking herself homeless, jobless and penniless were still reverberating around her? And what consequences! For heaven's sake, unless she could think up something close to brilliant, she was going to have to share a bedroom with him tomorrow night!

'I'm so glad you've been able to resolve matters,' Paula said kindly.

'The house is being sold.' Colly, not wanting to think about anything to do with that trip to Dorset, was ready to chat about anything to keep her mind off it. 'It's a large house, with years of accumulated impediments to sort through. I've been spending most of my days there.'

'I shouldn't know where to start should we ever decide to sell our house,' Paula sympathised. 'Borden has so much clutter.'

'Clutter?' he came in, effecting to look amazed.

'I swear he's hoarded every engineering magazine that was ever published,' his wife replied. 'He has years and years of back issues.'

When Mrs Varley served the last course, Silas, with a look to Colly as if to seek her confirmation, a gesture that was purely for his parents' benefit, thanked Mrs Varley and said that they would see to everything else themselves. Colly thanked her too. In her view Mrs Varley was a first-class cook.

All in all it had been a happy meal, Colly considered. If feelings of guilt had come along and given her a nip every now and then, she hoped she had been too well mannered to let it show.

She did not feel she could breathe easy, though, until, with hugs and kisses and a very firm suggestion that she and Silas should dine with them before too long, they went to wave his parents off.

'Was that so bad?' Silas asked as they came back along the hall.

'Your parents are super,' she answered, adding coolly as they headed towards the kitchen, 'The guilt I shall have to live with.' They went into the kitchen and she owned she felt somehow on edge with Silas. 'But if you can get me out of another dinner I'd be glad.' Ready to tackle the remaining dishes, Mrs Varley having already loaded up the dishwasher, Colly began to fill the sink. 'I'll leave it fifteen minutes, then I'll be on my way,' she commented, thinking to wait until his parents were well clear.

She began to wash the pots and pans, but to her surprise Silas picked up a cloth and began to dry them. 'You could stay if you like?' he offered equably after some moments. She looked at him, startled, and caught a glimpse of his smile as he added, 'I've a spare bedroom. It wouldn't…'

She knew he had a spare bedroom; she had used it. And she would love to stay, but… Was love always about denial? 'I think it's enough that I shall have to put up with you to-morrow night,' she said sharply, fearful that her need to be with him might yet see her give in. But, since the subject was there, just crying out to be addressed, 'I—er…' she murmured, her voice already losing its sharp edge. She looked away from him. 'I suppose there's no chance I'll have a room of my own tomorrow night?'

She had to look at him again. She saw he was unsmiling, but she heard a note of sensitivity in his tones when, his glance gentle on her, he answered, 'I'm afraid, Colly, that is very unlikely.'

Her heartbeats suddenly started to thunder at his gentle look. And all at once—perhaps it was partly to do with the strain of the evening; she could not have said—she just knew she needed to be by herself.

'Hard-hearted Hannah's leaving you with the dishwashing *and* the drying,' she announced, taking her hands from the water and drying them.

She went into the drawing room, where she had left her small evening purse, and picking it up took out her car keys. She heard a sound and looked up to see that Silas had come to stand in the drawing room doorway.

She went towards him. He did not move out of her way, and even though her heart was thundering she managed to find a little acid to tell him bluntly, 'Might I suggest that as soon as you've done the dishes you go and get as much sleep as you can?' He raised a mocking eyebrow. 'And it might be an idea if you had a lie-in in the morning.'

'You reckon?' he drawled.

Oh, she did. She very much did. 'From where I'm viewing it, unless that room in Dorset has twin beds, it very much looks as if you're in for a very uncomfortable night tomorrow,' she said sweetly, adding for smiling good measure, 'Sleepless in a chair.'

He was not taken in by her phoney sweetness. Nor was he put out by what she had said either. But he managed, effortlessly, to take the fake smile off her face when, as nicely as you please, he enquired, 'Did I say that to you when you insisted on getting into bed with me that time?'

Speechlessly she glared at him. It had not been like that, and he knew it. But, having effectively silenced her syrupy tones, Silas stood away from the door to let her pass.

She was already on her way when, 'I'll call for you round about two,' he said, going to the door with her.

Don't bother, sprang to mind—but, against that, she loved the man; she knew she could not let him down.

CHAPTER EIGHT

THERE were five minutes to go before two o'clock on Saturday afternoon when Silas called for her. Colly was ready and waiting. Although inwardly she felt that she would never be ready.

She swallowed hard before she could open the door to him. And had to again remind herself of the lecture she had given herself about forgetting her guilt, her feelings that she was deceiving some octogenarian. She must see the other side of this coin. Think of Silas. He had not been thinking of himself when he had decided he must marry, but thinking of the good of the company, its workers and its shareholders. As he had said, his grandfather wanted to meet his wife and she—she was his wife.

She opened the door. 'Sorry to have kept you.' She apologised for her delay in answering his knock. Silas was casually dressed in trousers and shirt and she was basically simply pleased to see him. 'I'll just get my overnight bag,' she murmured.

Silas carried her bag to his car, and a minute or so later they were on their way. 'My mother rang to thank you for a wonderful evening,' he thought to mention.

Obviously he had made the appropriate excuses for her not being there. 'On reflection, I think the evening went off quite well,' she commented.

'My parents loved you,' Silas answered.

'Oh, don't!' she cried, guilt having another stab at her. 'They were ready to love any woman you married before they met me.' She told it as she saw it, knowing in her heart that she would love to be a true daughter-in-law to Paula Livingstone. 'Your mother's so warm.'

'You've missed that,' he said softly, perceptively, and asked, 'How old were you when you lost your mother?'

'Eight,' she replied, but did not want to dwell on that. 'You will get us out of dining with your parents again, won't you?'

'You worry to much,' he said, which to her mind was no sort of an answer.

She fell silent, and as mile after mile sped by Silas seemed occupied with his own thoughts. Though he did think to ask after some while, 'Anything else worrying you, Colly?'

'Where would you like me to start?' she answered snappily. But was then instantly ashamed of herself. 'I'm sorry,' she apologised. 'All this is more my fault than yours.'

'What a sweetheart you are,' he replied, and her heart did a tiny kind of giddy flip—he had sounded as though he really meant it.

'I've been thinking only of myself and my guilt, but you too must be hating like blazes that you don't feel able to be open about our—er—relationship with your family.'

She did not know what she expected him to answer to that, but she was momentarily floored when, quite out of the blue, he quietly let fall, 'You know, Mrs Livingstone, I think I quite enjoy being married to you.'

Her mouth fell open in shock, and she was glad he had his eyes on the road in front. Silas quite enjoyed being married to her? A song began in her heart—until plain and utter common sense flooded in. Why wouldn't he enjoy being married to her? They were living apart. He had the marriage certificate he needed, but that was as far as his commitment went.

Which in turn had to mean that, of anyone he could have chosen to do a marriage deal with, he was happy he had made the right choice. Well, bully for him!

Realising she was getting nettled and uptight again—which

was no sort of mood to be in to meet her grandfather-in-law, Colly made a more determined effort.

'Uncle Henry phoned yesterday,' she said brightly.

'He'd read of our marriage?' Silas guessed. And, straight on the heels of that, 'You didn't tell him…?'

'Thank you for your confidence!' she snapped, but knew she was in the wrong and gave a heartfelt sigh. 'Why am I always apologising to you? I know, I know,' she went hurriedly on, 'I slipped up before with Tony Andrews. But I didn't with Uncle Henry.'

'Was he very put out?'

'He was very understanding, actually. I told him the apartment belonged to your grandfather, by the way. And,' she felt obliged to go on, 'that you go abroad from time to time, but that when you are home you sometimes stay at the apartment.'

'Have I made a liar of you?' he questioned with a kind glance.

'That's what you told me,' she defended. 'That you sometimes stay overnight.'

'Remind me to do it more often,' he responded dryly.

She laughed—this man did that to her.

Silas Livingstone Senior was tall, like all the Livingstone men. He had a thatch of white hair, was upright, and came out to greet them. He did not hug her, but after shaking hands with Silas took her hand warmly in his. His words were warm too, as he feasted his eyes on her, and demanded, 'How dare that grandson of mine run off and marry you without me there to wish you well?'

Colly smiled at him, a natural warm smile, as she replied, 'We didn't want to wait and we didn't want any fuss.' And, because they had done him out of attending his grandson's wedding, 'I'm sorry.'

'With a smile like that I'll forgive you,' he replied gallantly, and invited, 'Come in. Gwen's got the kettle boiling.'

Gwen, it appeared, was his housekeeper, a plump little lady

who had been with the Senior Livingstones for years. And Gwen it was who wheeled a trolley into the drawing room.

But it was Colly who poured the tea and, over tea and cake, accepted Grandfather Livingstone's regrets that he had not attended her father's funeral.

Colly realised that her father's funeral had not been all that many months after Silas Senior had lost his wife. And that, his age apart, perhaps he had not been emotionally up to attending a funeral.

'You knew my father?' she enquired.

'Not personally. But most people in the engineering world knew or had heard of him,' he answered, and spoke of several of her father's achievements.

Colly felt very proud, and suddenly realised that she felt quite relaxed. She was proud of Silas too, when he and his grandfather had a short conversation about something to do with engineering—all Greek to her—that cropped up as a side issue.

But, both men plainly thinking it not too polite to talk on a subject she could not join in, they swiftly abandoned the topic, only for her feeling of being relaxed to go plummeting when Grandfather Livingstone suggested to Silas, 'You'll want to freshen up, I expect. Your room's all ready for you. It's the one at the front.'

Oh, heavens! It was a large house, a house in its own grounds. But, as large as it was, there was no chance of their 'room' being a suite.

'We'll take our bags up, shall we, Colly?' Silas suggested easily, apparently aware which bedroom his grandfather referred to.

'Fine,' she answered, smiling, hoping her sudden feeling of tension was not showing to the elderly man who, she was fast realising, was thrilled that his grandson had married and brought his bride to see him.

Silas carried both their overnight bags up the stairs. She

was banking on twin beds. Wrong! As soon as the door was open she shot a speedy glance to the sleeping arrangements— it was a double bed.

As Silas stepped by her, and went to place their bags on the floor, so Colly stayed where she was. When thinking she might have to share a room with him she had been able to convince herself that, while preferring it to be otherwise, she would, for the sake of what they were about, be able to cope. But now, with the reality of it here, she did not feel convinced at all!

'What's wrong?' Silas had noticed that she seemed frozen over by the door.

'Nothing,' she answered stiltedly, her glance darting to the only padded chair in the room. She moved more into the room and Silas came and closed the bedroom door. When he un-expectedly placed his hands on her shoulders she jumped as though bitten.

'Nothing!' Silas scorned, turning her to face him. 'It looks like it!'

'Don't go on!' she snapped, pulling out of his hold.

If she had hoped he would leave it there, however, she discovered it was a forlorn hope. 'Look,' Silas began sternly, plainly not best pleased to have her so jumpy when he was anywhere near, 'as far as anyone knows you and I are married. But,' he went on, to lay it on the line, 'while I accept that you are a beautiful and desirable woman, you have to accept that I do not want to do anything that—in the long term— will bind you permanently to me.'

That well and truly did away with her tension. Not because of what he said, his attempt at reassurance, but because of his inference that she might give him half a chance should he try and test the water. 'As if—' she flared—who the devil did he think he was?

'So, whatever fears you have of anything happening between you and me,' he cut in before she could go for his jugular, 'forget it!'

She opened her mouth, ready with a few choice words, but with difficulty swallowed them down. 'Right!' she hurled at him, glaring at him. He stared back.

'Now what's wrong?' he demanded bluntly, his expression dark.

Let him whistle for an answer. But as she continued to glare stubbornly at him, so his dark expression suddenly cleared, and she knew she was not going to like what was coming even before it arrived. She didn't.

'Surely,' he began, 'you don't *want* anything to happen between us that will consummate—'

'Stop right there, Livingstone!' she erupted. 'I do not now, or ever...' Suddenly she ran out of steam. All at once she began to see the funny side of their non-argument—for what was there to argue about? Neither of them wanted the same thing. Her lips started to twitch, and while she became aware that his eyes were on her mouth she just had to tell him. 'In relation to your ''What's wrong?'' I suppose I'm just a touch miffed that you—or any man, given these circumstances— should be so immune to my charms.'

His lips twitched too, as she came to an end, and she guessed he appreciated her honesty when, honest himself, he took her in his arms and replied, 'Immune? I think you know better than that—don't you, Colly?'

She looked up at him, her heart pounding. 'So now we know where we stand?'

'Exactly,' he agreed, placed a light kiss on her lips and, his arms dropping to his sides, took a step back from her. 'Sing out if there's anything you need. I'll go and keep my grand-father company until you're ready to join us.'

Colly unpacked the few things she had brought with her after Silas had gone. She acknowledged that she felt better for what she could only think of as Silas's wading in to clear the air. Indeed, now that he was no longer in the room with her she began to wonder what all the fuss had been about. Silas had let her know point-blank that he wanted the state of their marriage to stay exactly as it was, and that she could sleep easy with him in the same room. But—a smile lit within her—it was nice to know that he was not totally immune to her.

She owned to feeling a touch apprehensive, however, when in the early evening she went down to dinner. But she discovered, with Silas there as a buttress and his grandfather being a man of courtesy and olde worlde charm, that she had no need to feel in the slightest apprehensive. The only small hiccup occurred—and she was sure that she was the only one who felt in any way awkward—when Grandfather Livingstone asked Silas, 'I don't suppose you've had time to check on the apartment recently?'

'I have,' Silas answered, having been there that very day. 'You've nothing to worry about there,' he assured him.

A short while later they left the dining room and returned to the drawing room, and Colly realised a little to her surprise, as the next hour ticked by, that all in all it had been a very pleasant evening.

When, during the conversation that followed in the next half an hour, she picked up that Silas's grandfather was usually in bed by ten-thirty, she thought the time might be right to make noises about retiring.

'I'll be up later,' Silas commented.

Nerves started to try and get a foothold again. 'I'll say goodnight, then.' She smiled as she got to her feet and both men stood.

Up in the bedroom she was to share with Silas, she blocked her mind to all save reliving the lecture he had given her: while not being immune to her, he had no desire to make theirs a full marriage.

On the plus side she discovered that her grandfather-in-law's household did not subscribe to the more modern duvet when it came to bedding. She showered and got into her nightdress and, leaving herself with sheets and a blanket, went and draped the over-large padded quilt over what she wincingly saw looked to be a not-very-comfortable chair. It still did not look very comfortable after she had draped the quilt over it. She added a pillow.

From there she went and switched on the bathroom light, and left the bathroom door ajar so Silas should have sufficient light to find his way around without banging into anything. Hopeful that she would be asleep before Silas came to bed, she put out the bedroom light and got into the big double bed. Just so that there should be no mistake, she opted to occupy the centre of the bed.

But so much for her hope to be asleep before Silas came up the stairs. She was still wide awake when, what seemed like hours later, she heard him at the door. She had her back to the bathroom her eyes closed, and was concentrating solely on making her breathing sound even when, almost silently, Silas came in, quietly closing the door after him.

If he knew that she was still awake he said nothing. She had nothing she wanted to say either. He must have taken her hint when he had seen the light from the bathroom, and did not turn on any other light. She heard him moving about, then, when the bathroom door closed, she opened her eyes to find the room in darkness.

Shortly afterwards there was light again, briefly. She closed her eyes, heard the light switch off, and knew that Silas was making his way to that not-too-comfortable-to-sleep-in chair. At least that was where she hoped he was making his way to; there would be all-out war if he thought he was sharing her bed!

It was a thought that, after an hour, or it might have been two, of listening to Silas trying to get his long length comfortable, she was having to review.

The chair creaked again as he once more adjusted his position, and she started to weaken, started to feel sorry for him. Just what had he done to deserve this? Nothing but try to do his best for the firm his grandfather had started.

Well, one sleepless night would not hurt him, argued her other self. He would probably have backache for a week, but... The chair creaked again as he attempted again to silently adjust his position.

'Oh, for goodness' sake!' she found she was erupting. 'Bring your pillow and that quilt over here and get on top of the bed! Feet my way up!' she ordered as an afterthought, and shunted over so he should have ample room.

She heard him move, and wished she had kept quiet, and was not at all appeased when, his voice near, 'For you, I bought a pair of pyjamas,' he informed her.

'I don't care if you're wearing a suit of armour!' she snapped. 'You're still sleeping with your feet my way up.'

She heard his low laugh and could not deny that all at once there was a bubble of laughter in her too. Sternly, she repressed it. Then felt the bed go down. Silas, sleeping his head to her toes, had joined her.

Though what sleep he got she did not know. For herself she was so overly conscious of him next to her she just could not sleep. He was so near, so dear—oh, think of something else, do.

Somewhere around dawn she felt him leave the bed. Either he was an early riser or he could not sleep either. She guessed it was the former. She heard the bathroom door close and surmised he was ready to shower and dress and start his day.

She closed her eyes and at last managed to get some sleep. But she did not sleep for too long; some inbuilt 'manners' alarm was there to remind her that she was a guest and that guests had certain duties. One of which was not to be late should breakfast be being served at some rigid time.

She sat up, hugging the sheet and blanket to her as she took a tentative look around. She relaxed. As she had supposed, Silas was up and out. Following suit, she slipped the fallen narrow shoulder-strap of her nightdress back in place and left the bed ready to take a shower.

She headed for the bathroom, wondering at what time they would leave. If— She opened the bathroom door and her thoughts, her body, everything, became motionless. She stared stunned, immobile. She had thought—no, not even thought, had just been certain that Silas had vacated the bathroom ages ago. She had thought she had been asleep for an hour or so— but realised that she could not have been asleep anywhere near that long, that her only sleep must have been the briefest of catnaps. Because the bathroom was not empty. Silas was in there. And—he was stark naked!

He was sideways on to her, half turned from her as he stood before the large mirror, having obviously just finished shaving. He had turned his head as the bathroom door opened, and simultaneously her yelp of 'Ooh!' had rent the air as her stunned glance took in his long length of leg, the well-muscled thigh, his right buttock, not to mention part of his broad naked back.

Then her eyes met his and scorching colour seared her skin. She was unsure who moved first, but, not lingering to have a debate about it, Colly found release from her rooted immobility and spun urgently about.

She had taken a couple of steps back into the bedroom but had still not got her head together, being unsure what to do— whether to take a dive back under the bedcovers or, totally unnerved as she was, what.

She stood there, crimson, striving hard to tell herself not to make an issue of it, that Silas was more sinned against than sinning. As far as he had been concerned she was fast asleep; the last thing he'd expected was that she would barge in and invade his privacy.

Then she heard him come and stand behind her. 'This gets worse!' she uttered croakily.

'I didn't think I looked so very dreadful stripped off,' Silas answered, plainly endeavouring to make light of it. But she could find no humour in the situation.

'Don't!' she said huskily. 'I didn't know you were in there!' she explained hurriedly. And she did not know just where she was when from behind his arms came around to the front of her in a loose hold. She glanced jerkily down and was overwhelmingly relieved to see from his silk-clad arms that he must have hastily donned a robe. 'I thought you'd showered and gone.'

'I rather think I know that,' he said to the top of her head. And, taking the blame totally on himself, 'Last time I looked you were sound away. But even so, bearing in mind that there's no lock on the bathroom door, I should have hung a note on the handle or something.'

'It—doesn't matter,' she replied.

His arms firmed a little around her. She was not sure that he did not drop a light kiss to the top of her head. Wishful thinking, she realised, and also realised all at once that she was clad in a thin shortie nightdress, and that, since she could feel the heat of his body, possibly all Silas had on was the fine silk robe.

She went to move away but his arms held her, and in all honesty she would by far prefer to stay just where she was. Soon they would be back in London, her closeness with him over; she needed these moments to treasure.

'You've been brilliant, Colly,' Silas said softly, bending to her ear. 'Just a few more hours,' he promised, 'and then we can say goodbye to the weekend.'

Just a few more hours! She wanted to stay like this for ever. 'I never wanted to make a fuss,' she replied, and whether he went to give her a bit of a hug or if she was just obeying some compulsion she could not have said—but Colly moved and leaned back against him.

He did not push her away from him, and the side of his face was almost touching the side of her face. 'You've been wonderful,' he applauded her.

Oh, help her, she was starting to feel all wobbly. She strove for levity. 'Is that what you say to all the girls after you've slept with them?' she asked with a light laugh.

He turned her then. His hands coming to her arms, he turned her to face him. 'You're special,' he replied, his own tone light.

Colly smiled, recalling the time when she had queried whether, married to her, he might want to marry someone else. She'd have to be more than a little extra-special, he had replied. 'Careful,' she warned. 'When you get to "extra-special" I'm bailing out.'

For answer Silas stared down at her, his dark blue eyes fixed on her green ones. And for ageless moments they just seem to stare wordlessly at each other. Then suddenly she felt him drawing her that little bit closer.

She thought it might be a good idea to resist. Only then his lips were over hers, gently over hers, warm over hers, and she had no hope of resisting him. She loved him. Why should she resist?

He broke his kiss. She tried to find her voice. But her brain seemed word-starved, and all she could think to say was a shy 'Good morning.'

He laughed. 'Good morning, wife,' he said, and seemed to so enjoy calling her his wife that any logic that tried to penetrate, to tell her nonsense, just did not stand a chance of getting through.

'You've got a very nice mouth, Mr Livingstone,' she thought to mention.

'You have my permission to kiss it, should its niceness become too much for you,' he suggested.

Logic at that point tried to get a toe-hold—this was not the way this weekend was supposed to go. But logic was a cold bedfellow, and she would much rather take her husband up on his offer.

Of their own volition her arms went round him. She felt his warmth, the cleanness of him. And she just had to kiss him. She stretched up invitingly. Obligingly he bent down, and responded fully.

They broke apart. Feeling a little breathless, she stared at him. 'I...' she said, but could not go on. Because what she wanted to tell him was that she loved him—and whatever else her mixed-up brain patterns were confusing her with, she somehow knew that to tell him that would be the height of folly.

'You...?' he prompted, his wonderful mouth quirking up-wards at the corners.

'I—um—think I'm feeling a touch confused,' she con-fessed.

He smiled gently at her, as if understanding. 'Would an-other kiss help, do you suppose?'

He had to be joking! It was those kisses that were partly responsible! But, even though she must refuse his most tempt-ing offer, she was finding she just could not. 'I shouldn't like you to think me greedy,' she murmured—and said no more.

How could she? Silas had drawn her to him again. Held fast against his heart, Colly was no longer thinking but was feeling, enjoying, and in utter seventh heaven as the man she loved with her whole heart kissed her not once but many times.

And she adored his kisses, returned his kisses without re-straint. Adored the way his fingers strayed through her long dark hair, the way his hands cupped her face. The way he transferred his hand to hold her in his arms.

'Silas!' She murmured his name when somehow, and she

had no clue how she had got there, all at once she found she was against a wall and Silas was leaning to her.

'You're…?' he began, his voice all kind of gravelly. 'I'm not alarming you?' he rephrased.

'Do you want me?' she asked huskily.

'Oh, sweet, innocent love,' he murmured, to thrill her. And, with a smile, 'Yes, I think you could say that,' he breathed, and as they moulded together so, wide-eyed, she stared at him.

'Oh!' she gasped.

'I'm—worrying you?' he asked, pulling back.

She shook her head. 'It's just I—um—think my—education in certain matters has just gone up another notch.' And as he grinned, seeming delighted with her, she wanted again to feel his wanting body against her, and pushed her wanting body against him.

'Colly!' he breathed, and kissed her, and it was such a kiss that she knew then that she was leaving the nursery slopes of lovemaking.

'Oh, Silas!' she cried, and wound her arms about him, loving every movement, every whispered kiss, as he traced tender kisses down the side of her throat, his hands caressing her all but naked shoulders.

She held on to him when, with one hand holding her close, his other hand caressed round to capture one of her breasts. A fire of such longing was leaping within her—she wanted more.

'Oh!' she sighed, as his sensitive fingers played and teased at the hardened tip of her breast. And again, 'Oh!' she cried, on a wanting kind of sound, when he bent his head and through the thin material of her nightdress gently pressed his lips to her breast, before once more claiming her lips.

Silas kissed her with long, slow, wonderful kisses, and his hands strayed behind her, to hold and caress her back, her waist, her buttocks.

When his searching hands found their way beneath her

nightdress, and those warm caressing fingers touched her naked buttocks, and he intimately pulled her to him, Colly thought she would faint.

She kissed him because she needed to. But her nightdress was all at once a hindrance. 'Do we need this?' Silas asked softly, his fingers on the thin cotton, her only covering.

And belatedly modesty—she could only afterwards suppose because she was as near naked as made no difference—suddenly woke up with a vengeance.

'No—I mean, yes.'

She did not know what she meant, other than that the idea of standing totally unclothed before him was completely alien to her—she just could not do it. This was all new ground to her, and love him quite desperately though she did, want him quite desperately as she did, there was just something in her that screamed out no. Perhaps it was something in her upbringing, some shyness at being the way she was with a man for the first time in her life. She just did not know.

But, 'No, I can't,' she said, panicking, swallowing hard, the idea of standing naked in front of Silas an entire anathema to her.

Silas, his skin slightly flushed—so she guessed her own face must be on fire—stared disbelievingly at her. 'You don't want to make love with me?' he questioned throatily, his hands falling away as he put some space between their two bodies, his eyes searching hers as he stepped back.

She did not mean that at all! Her whole body was throbbing with her need for him. But suddenly, despite the intimacy they had been sharing, and maybe because Silas had stepped back and was no longer touching her, she all at once hit a hard impenetrable wall of that belated and unwanted modesty. She just could not find the words to tell him, Yes, I need you, yes, I want you, please take me.

Dumbly she shook her head. Confusion? She was drowning in it. So why did her voice sound so composed, so apart, when, after taking a step to one side, 'Had you finished with the bathroom?' she heard a female stranger enquire.

She risked a glance at Silas. He was looking as if he could not believe it either. But there was no way he was going to force himself on her. He took another step away from her. 'My stars, you're a cool one!' he gritted.

Cool? If only he knew. 'I'll take that as a yes, then, shall I?' the female stranger asked. Colly went while she could, lest she should throw her arms around him and beg him to understand that no man had ever seen her naked, that while she was not ashamed of her body she seemed to have a hang-up about nudity.

They were silent on the journey back to London. Colly had plenty to think about, and Silas appeared to have much on his mind. Work, most likely, she assumed, quite certain that a man of his sophistication would not bother to dwell on what had happened between them.

She did not want to dwell on it either. She had stayed in the bathroom for a positive age after she had left him. He had not stayed around, though, and hadn't been in the bedroom when she'd eventually gone in. What, after all, had there been to stay around for? They had shared a few heady moments—*heady*—understatement of the year—but he had not tried to stop her when, misunderstanding her, 'No, I can't,' he had let her go.

Something she realised he must now be more than pleased about. He had not the smallest wish to cement their marriage, and was probably at this very moment thanking his lucky stars that when desire had sparked, though he had initially only meant to comfort her, she—so he had thought—had called a halt.

Well, she was glad too, she thought sniffily, because to make love with each other just was not in their contract. Oh, stop thinking about it, do.

'Are you all right?' The terse question cut through the strained atmosphere in the car.

Big of him to ask! No, she was not all right. Far from it. 'Why wouldn't I be?' she enquired, her voice proudly off-hand.

Silence settled in the car once more. She supposed he looked as grim as he sounded, but it was for sure she was not going to look at him to find out.

'I'll take half the blame if you'll take the other half,' he offered grimly.

'That's the least you can do!' she retorted, and, just so he should know, 'And if you don't mind I'd prefer not to discuss it.' She could feel herself getting all hot and bothered even before they went any further.

A grunt was her answer. Good. She switched her thoughts back to how she had discovered an unknown talent for acting when she had finally gone down the stairs to join Silas and his grandfather. Or maybe it had been just good manners in front of the elderly gentleman. But somehow or other over the next few hours she had managed to chat and smile with both men as though nothing out of the ordinary had so recently taken place in her life.

And when, shortly after lunch, Silas had said they should be on their way, and his grandfather had come out to the car with them and had commented, 'It has done my heart good to see you, Colly,' it had seemed natural that they should hold hands and kiss cheeks. Just as Silas had started up the car, 'Come again, *soon*,' he had urged.

If she had anything to do with it, that would never happen.

'Thank you for coming with me,' Silas said formally when he'd parked outside the apartment block and they got out of the car.

I wouldn't have missed it for the world, she thought acidly. 'That's all right,' she muttered, and felt as fed-up as Silas sounded.

'I'll bring your bag in.'

No way! She'd had one close encounter with him. She did not want him in her sitting room, where they might exchange verbal fisticuffs. 'No need!' she answered sharply. And, feeling close to tears suddenly, 'See you!' she mumbled. Taking her overnight bag, she went quickly from him before he should tell her, Not if I see you first.

She went to bed that night with her spirits at rock bottom. And, after a dreadful for the most part sleepless night, got out of bed on Monday morning with her spirits still down on the floor.

The situation, she felt, was hopeless. She and Silas could not have a proper marriage even should she want one—and it was for definite that he didn't—so what was the point of them staying married?

Well, she did not have to think about that very deeply. She knew the answer to that one. But from where she was viewing it, to get divorced from each other would suit her quite well.

Were they divorced then it would put an end to his parents inviting them to dinner and other family functions—which she could see might well crop up. And while Colly had truly liked Silas's parents, and while she would have loved to be a part of Silas's family, how could she be?

Look what had happened at the weekend? 'Come again, soon,' Grandfather Livingstone had urged when they were leaving. How could she go back there again with Silas?

She could not. Remembering how everything had got out of hand—to make love had never been in their agreement—Colly knew she dared not risk that again. Yet for how long could Silas stall his parents, his grandfather?

But, when to divorce seemed to be the only answer, Colly knew that she could not divorce Silas unless she wanted his feckless cousin to ultimately be in charge of Livingstone Developments and thereby ruin the work of three generations of Livingstones.

Colly knew she could not do that to Silas. She wished that she did not love him so much, and knew then that she should never have married him. But she also knew that she was glad she had known him. When all was said and done, he had never asked her to fall in love with him. And after the short way he had been with her on the drive home it was obvious he would be totally appalled at any such idea of them being any closer than they were. He did not want that sort of involvement.

The day dragged wearily on, with every hour seeming like ten. But, to show that she was not the only one in low spirits, Rupert Thomas phoned her around five that afternoon and sounded really out of sorts.

Colly had been tempted not to answer the phone when it rang. But it was then that common sense, pure and simple, stepped in to scornfully prod. Did she really think that after the dozen or so unfriendly words she and Silas had exchanged on the drive home it might be him calling for a chat? Get real!

'What are you doing tonight?' Rupert asked, his tone glum.

He'd been dumped again? 'Nothing in particular,' she replied, realising that tomorrow she was going to have to hide her own feelings while she listened, chapter and verse, to Rupert's latest tragedy.

'Can you have dinner with me?' he wanted to know.

She'd had dinner with him before—he was good company when he was up. 'Any particular reason?' she enquired. He was a pain when he was down, but he was a friend.

'You'll never believe it!' he launched in at her invitation. 'That wretched Averil Dennis has given me the elbow!'

'Oh, I'm sorry,' Colly sympathised, and for the next five minutes listened to a catalogue of the said Averil's faults.

'I badly need someone to talk to,' Rupert said as he came to an end. 'Say you'll have dinner with me?'

Colly was about to remind him that she would be seeing

him at the gallery tomorrow, when he would be able to talk his little cotton socks off, but abruptly, before she could say a word, changed her mind. What are you doing tonight? he had asked. Well, she wasn't doing anything tonight. Nor was she doing anything tomorrow night, or the night after that, nor, for that matter, any night in the foreseeable future. And it just was not good enough!

'I'd love to have dinner with you, Rupert,' she answered. And, forcing a bright note, 'Where are we going?' she asked, determined to rise above her down feeling. 'The White Flamingo?' It was one of his favourite haunts.

'Hmm—I thought I'd take you somewhere a bit more up-market than that,' he replied. 'Averil introduced me to this place. I'll pick you up about seven.'

'I'll be ready.' Colly guessed that Rupert was half hoping that Averil would be dining at that establishment, so he could either stick his nose in the air and ignore her—or introduce her to Averil as though she were his latest.

Colly did not mind. Rupert had lived and enjoyed a hard life, and though he was forty looked fifty, but he was harmless, and most of the time quite amusing, and besides, she was fond of him.

He was on time, and it was all Averil from the word go. He plainly had not read of her marriage to Silas, Colly realised, and realised too that, with the heartless Averil taking up central position in his head, he most likely would not have commented on it even if he had known.

Whether or not he knew of her marriage, however, suddenly became irrelevant. Because as Rupert drove on Colly was all at once filled with a feeling of apprehension. She had to be wrong. She had to! But, if she were not wrong, Rupert was heading for the same hotel where she had dined with Silas that night he had made that amazing suggestion that they marry!

'Rupert, I—' broke from her urgently when he halted his

car at the hotel. But he was getting in a fluster over a parking space that someone else was trying to grab, and either did not hear her or assumed she was taking him to task for being so bullish.

She calmed down. What did it matter? This hotel might have a favourite dining room for Averil, but it did not necessarily follow that it was a favourite for Silas too. For goodness' sake, there were dozens of restaurants in London! What about that restaurant Tony Andrews had taken her to that night Silas had come up to their table? Perhaps that was his favourite eating establishment.

Telling herself not to be ridiculous, Colly nevertheless scanned the dining room as she and Rupert went in. Then she realised that Rupert had been doing the same thing, though in his case he seemed disappointed that the object of his search was not dining there that night. For herself, Colly could not have said how she felt. She did not want to eat here. She knew well how idiotic she was being, but to her it was their place, hers and Silas's.

She was all tensed up, she knew that, and as it was relatively early she supposed Silas could still walk in—but did she want to see him again? Oh, to blazes with it—she positively ached to see him again.

'So I drove her home...' Rupert was saying. Colly tried to concentrate. '...and accidentally...' She was sitting where she could see the dining room door. It opened, and a tall dark-haired man came in; her heart thundered, then quietened. It was not Silas. '...think about that?' Rupert ended.

'Er—unfortunate,' Colly attempted.

And discovered she had said the right thing when Rupert took up, 'I'll say it was unfortunate! Averil swore I did it on purpose, but I...'

And so it went on through dinner. Colly tried not to look at the door every two minutes, and was glad to find she needed to make very little input as Rupert warmed to his 'heartless Averil' theme.

'...had enough?' he asked.

Colly felt out on a limb again, and hoped he was asking if she'd had sufficient to eat. 'That was a super meal,' she replied.

'We'll have coffee in the lounge, shall we?' he asked.

The lounge—where she and Silas had drunk coffee that night... Oh, Silas.

Not waiting for her answer, Rupert stood up. It was still early, not yet nine o'clock, but as they made their way to the lounge area so Colly felt she would much prefer to go home.

Less than a minute later she was wishing that she had said as much. Because as she and Rupert entered the lounge, so her eyes were immediately drawn to a good-looking dark-haired man seated, coffee-cups on the table before him, in deep conversation with a most attractive blonde!

Silas! Colly's spirits rapidly rose—only to hit the floor with an almighty crash. She had spent a good part of the evening watching every tall male who had come through the dining room door, whereas Silas was so engrossed with his coffee-drinking companion that he did not even look up when the lounge door opened.

Though even as a sick feeling battered Colly, and jealousy seared every part of her, Silas did take a moment to glance away from the blonde. His eyes met Colly's. She saw his glance go to her companion—he did not look too well pleased. All in less than two seconds, as he started to rise, so Colly was turning about and whispering to Rupert, 'I need to get out of here!'

She went speedily, and Rupert, to his credit, did not argue but followed her out. 'Feeling queasy?' he asked as he followed her to where he had parked his car.

Colly was too churned up to tell anything but the truth. 'I've just seen someone I don't want to see,' she said, though she wondered, as green barbs still pierced her, if it was not so much Silas she did not want to see, but Silas with another woman.

'Oh, I know that picture,' Rupert replied, and, as if fully understanding, 'Let's get going.'

Colly tried to remember her manners as Rupert drew up outside the apartment block. She had done him out of his coffee, and knew she should invite him in so she should make him a cup. But somehow she had not got the heart.

'Thank you for a lovely dinner,' she said instead, glad that Rupert had settled the account for their meal in the dining room, rather than leave it until after they'd had their coffee.

'It was good, wasn't it?' he replied, the defecting Averil having in no way affected his appetite, and, as Colly went to leave his car, 'See you tomorrow,' he said. 'I'll wait here until you get inside.'

Colly opened the outer door, turned and waved to him, and then went to the apartment. And she had thought she had been down before! She tried desperately hard to raise her spirits, but all she could see was Silas, deep in conversation with the pretty blonde.

Perhaps he was asking her to be wife number two, Colly thought with sour humour. But this was not a laughing matter. She hated feeling the way she did, and she hated him that he could make her feel that way.

She went and had a shower and got ready for bed. But sleep was light years away, so she returned to the sitting room—just as the phone started to ring.

Silas? As if! He'd got better things to do than remember he had a wife, she fumed sniffily. Rupert, then? Was she in the mood for more 'What Averil did'? Don't be mean. Rupert could not help it if he had a penchant for women who usually got their goodbyes in first.

She picked up the phone. 'Does he know you're not in line for a sugar-daddy?' Silas snarled grittily.

Shock, pleasure and hate fought for precedence. Jealousy romped in and flattened them all. 'Still keeping to your wedding vows, Livingstone?' she flew, and immediately wanted to bite out her tongue. Had she sounded jealous? Had Silas, shrewd, clever Silas, picked up that jealous tone? she wondered fearfully.

Whatever, there was a definite pause—but only so he could control his irritation with her, she quickly realised, when evenly, coolly, he had the nerve to ask, 'I wonder, Colly, if you'd care to have dinner with me tomorrow?'

And that made her mad! Furious! She just could not believe it! Only a little over an hour ago, definitely not more than that, he had been in deep conversation with a blonde! He was probably still *with* the blonde, Colly fumed, and that thought caused her fury to soar to volcanic proportions. Had he just excused himself from her to make this phone call? Was he still in that hotel with his blonde?

Vesuvius blew. *'Dinner!'* Colly exploded. 'I was thinking more of *divorcing* you than dining with you!' With that she slammed down the phone—and promptly burst into tears.

CHAPTER NINE

COLLY was at once ashamed. She dried her eyes and wondered where all that bad temper had come from. Oh, how
could she have been so awful to Silas? She had never used
to have such a temper.

She sighed as she realised that her emotions had been having a fine old time with her just recently. Well, ever since she
had met Silas, in actual fact.

Although, on reflection, perhaps to some extent she had
stepped on the roller-coaster of emotional upheaval starting
with the shock at the unexpected death of her father.

Tears spurted to her eyes again. Tears she could not control
ran unchecked down her cheeks. What with everything happening so fast—her father dying, followed by Nanette so soon
as good as throwing her out of her home—Colly felt as if she
had never properly mourned her father.

She again dried her tears, her thoughts on Silas and how
he had found a solution to her problems—and his problems
too, it had to be remembered. Oh, why had she to go and fall
in love with him?

Tears pricked her eyes again, but this time she held them
back. It was not the smallest good crying because she wanted
Silas. She could not have him because he preferred blondes.

Why had he phoned? She acknowledged that she did not
much care for his 'sugar-daddy' remark. But why had Silas
asked her to have dinner with him? She guessed he had not
been too pleased with her remark about divorcing him. But—

Her thoughts stopped right there when suddenly someone
came knocking at her door. Silas! Or one of her neighbours?
Silas—no! She'd got Silas on the brain. A neighbour, then?

Whoever. She was not going to answer the door. She was

not fit to be seen. Her eyes were most likely pink-rimmed from crying, and in any case she was in her nightdress and wrap and ready for bed.

If it were a neighbour who had seen a line of light under her door she would see them tomorrow and plead she'd had a headache. Were it Silas, then... Her breath caught—somebody was unlocking her door! Somebody—*was coming in*!

Silas had a key! In an instant she was on her feet, wanting to run, wanting to hide. But too late. As cool as you like, closing the door behind him, Silas was strolling into the sitting room.

Her reaction was immediate. In the absence of being able to hide, she turned her back on him. And, finding a snappy note, antagonistically suggested, 'Would you very much mind leaving? You're invading my personal space!' As if she thought that would work.

'We need to talk,' Silas retorted sharply.

'You sound as though you would rather quarrel than talk!' She stayed in there to erupt, still keeping her back to him.

'I don't—' he began, and to her dismay, plainly not a man who enjoyed talking to someone's back, he came round to the front of her '—want—' he added, but as she stared down at the carpet so he halted, a hand all at once under her chin, tilting her head up so he should see into her face. Abruptly he left what he had been about to say. 'You've been crying!' he accused.

'So?' she answered defiantly.

'Why?' he wanted to know. And, soon there with his conclusion, 'Who was that man you were with?' And, aggressively, before she could answer, 'Did he—?'

'No, he didn't!' she replied heatedly. 'That was Rupert.'

'From the gallery?'

'Look, Silas, I'm ready for bed, and—'

'I'll wait if you want to go and get dressed,' he cut in.

That stopped her in her tracks, and some of her defiance faded. 'You really do want to talk,' she commented.

There was a determined look about him, she noticed, but

his tone had lost its sharp edge when he asked, 'Why were you crying, Colly?'

She shrugged. 'A mixture of things, I suppose.' Silas waited. And when she did not want to tell him, most definitely did not want to tell him, she found she was going on, 'I never used to have a temper—then there I was yelling at you. Then...'

'You're saying that I'm the cause for your tears?' he asked, seeming not to like that idea one tiny bit.

'I think you're in there somewhere,' she understated. 'Probably the trigger,' she admitted. Having said so much, she felt she had to concede that. No way, though, was he going to know that he was the larger part of why she had given way to tears. 'Anyhow, with everything sort of exploding in my face, so to speak, I suddenly started to realise that, what with one thing and another, I never properly mourned my father when he died.'

'Your tears were for him?' Silas murmured, his tone so gentle she really had to protest.

'Don't go nice on me. You'll have me blubbering again!' she cried in alarm. But, gaining some control, added smartly, 'And if we're going to have a row, I prefer to—'

'I don't want to row with you,' Silas cut in. And, his voice now more matter-of-fact than anything, 'Things have sort of—got out of hand between us. I think,' he went on carefully, 'we should take time out to talk matters through.'

'It's nearly eleven o'clock!' she objected, just a little worried about where this talk would take them.

'You needn't go to the gallery tomorrow,' Silas decreed.

'Rupert will be thrilled,' she replied, but couldn't help being a touch pleased that Silas should remember that Tuesday was her gallery day.

'Shall we sit down?' he asked.

'This is going to take that long?' she queried as he led her over to the sofa and sat down beside her.

'As long as it takes,' he answered, as if—heedless of the fact he had to go to work tomorrow—he intended to stay all night if need be, until they had talked everything through. Colly was not sure that she wanted an in-depth discussion with Silas, when any unwary word she might utter might give him a hint of how she felt about him. 'You had dinner with him tonight?' Silas asked, which to her mind was hardly a subject for in-depth discussion.

'Rupert was feeling low. His latest girlfriend has decided she's seen enough of him for a while—Rupert likes to bend my ear on such occasions.'

'Some of your tears were for him?'

If she were honest she would have to say that, save thinking it might be him when her telephone had rung, she had not given Rupert another thought once his car had driven away. But, as that dreadful green-eyed monster gave her a nip, 'I don't remember seeing you in the dining room?' she remarked lightly, knowing without a question of a doubt that he had not been in the hotel dining room while she had been there.

'We didn't have a meal,' he replied. 'Come to think of it, apart from a sandwich earlier, I believe I completely missed out on dinner.'

'Didn't you feed her?' Oh, damn.

An alert light came to his eyes. 'You're not—jealous, Colly?' he asked, which did not surprise her in the slightest. She had heard that jealous note in her voice too. It would have been a miracle if he hadn't picked it up.

'Pfff!' she scorned, to bluff being the only way. 'I may be your wife, Livingstone, but I draw the line at having to be jealous as well.' Who was she—the blonde? And what, since eleven o'clock at night was probably early for Silas, was he doing here with her and not the blonde? 'Er—she looked very nice?' Colly found she was fishing anyway.

'She is,' he replied, and Colly wished she had not bothered. She was not sure she wanted to know any more when Silas went on, 'I was hoping to see you tonight when Naomi rang and asked if I would meet her. She was upset—'

'I don't really need to know about this,' Colly cut in coolly—now the name Naomi would haunt her for evermore.

'What did you want to talk about, Silas?' she managed to hold on to her cool note to enquire.

Silas looked at her levelly, either not liking her tone or wondering where to start. Since he never seemed at a loss for words, she doubted it was the latter.

Then his chin suddenly jutted, and his tone was totally un-compromising. 'I don't want to talk about divorce, that's for sure,' he said harshly.

And she immediately felt mean. Instantly she realised that he had every right to be angry that she had said she was thinking of divorcing him. 'I'm sorry, Silas. It was unfair of me to say, even in temper, that I was thinking of divorce.' For heaven's sake, she had known in advance that he would date other women. They were both free to date other people. 'It was particularly unfair when I knew you needed our mar-riage for the sake of the company. Will you—'

'This has nothing to do with the company!' he cut in grimly.

Colly stared at him. She was missing something here. 'We're… You… You're not here to talk about divorce?' she queried, trying to catch up. 'And this has nothing to do with the business?'

'Neither,' he agreed. But as she continued to stare at him, so she saw that his eyes seemed watchful on her.

'I—see,' she said slowly. But then had to confess, 'No, I don't.'

There was silence for several seconds before slowly, delib-erately, he said, 'Marriage, Colly. I want to talk to you about our marriage.'

Marriage? Their marriage? They had not got a marriage. Not really, they hadn't. What they had was just a piece of paper, a certificate that united them. 'Our marriage?' she be-gan to question. 'In relation to your family, you mean, and future meet—' Her voice tailed off. Silas was shaking his head.

'Our marriage in relation to—us,' he corrected.

'Oh,' she mumbled, while her heart pounded, as it did most

times when he was near. 'You're referring to what you said—about things sort of getting out of hand between us?' she dared bravely.

There was a hint of a smile about his mouth. 'It hasn't gone at all as I planned it,' he admitted.

'So much for forward planning.' She added her hint of a smile to his—he seemed encouraged.

'It seemed such a good idea at the start,' he confessed. 'You get your career and I got to keep long-term charge of the business. Only...' He hesitated.

'Only?' Colly prompted. It was odd. Silas was always so sure of what he was about, but if she did not know better she would say he was—nervous. Don't be ridiculous!

'Only at the outset the idea seemed flawless. I looked at it from every possible angle—or so I thought. And the more I thought about it, the more to marry you seemed the perfect solution—for you and for me. On my part, as suitable as you were, it wasn't as if I'd got to live with you.'

Thanks! 'A perfect solution, as you've said,' Colly murmured, striving not to sound sour.

'So I thought,' he agreed. 'But then events began to go off-plan.' Too true they had! Leave alone their personal involvement, he had been obliged, because of her 'letting the cat out', to introduce her to his family. 'They were never intended to go the way they did. Nor,' he added, his eyes on hers, 'did I ever expect I could feel the way I started to feel.'

'Oh,' Colly mumbled again. 'You—um—started to feel—um—differently—about something?' Now she was the one who was feeling nervous. What the Dickens did 'feel the way I started to feel' mean?

For answer, Silas stretched out a hand and took a hold of one of hers. Oh, help. Her heart did not merely pound, it thundered.

'You have to understand, Colly, that I'm a hard-headed businessman. Very little gets in the way of that.' She was not sure she believed that; not when it came to his family, she didn't. She had seen his respect for his father and his grandfather, his fond indulgence and also respect for his mother. 'But there we are, not even married yet, when here in this very room, on your first visit, you're getting all sparky when you think I'm doubting your honesty.' He paused. 'And there am I,' he resumed, 'experiencing a feeling of interest that shouldn't be there.'

Her eyes widened. 'Interest—in me?' she queried faintly.

He nodded. 'I scoffed at the very idea, of course.'

'Of course,' she agreed firmly.

'I scoffed again when I discovered I was not too keen on you dating other men.'

Her throat went dry. 'Well, you would, wouldn't you?' she murmured, which meant absolutely nothing, but gave her a chance to get her breath back.

He gave her hand a small shake. 'Colly,' he said, his dark blue eyes fixed on her wide green ones, 'I'm doing my best here to be restrained, but you've got me so that I don't know where the blazes I am.' Her eyes went saucer-wide. She'd got him so…! 'What I'm trying to tell you—hell, give me a tough board meeting any day—is that I have grown to l—care for you.'

'You haven't!' she denied instinctively. Then, because she wanted to believe it, 'Have you?' she asked huskily.

He did not answer for a moment or two. But, every bit as smart as she knew him to be, he had soon sifted through her brief reply. And, after another moment to check he had worked it out correctly, 'From what I've learned and know about you, I'd say you wouldn't ask "Have you?" if you weren't interested in knowing more.'

Oh, heavens! 'I—er—um—feel a bit on shaky ground here,' she confessed, and was rewarded with a smile.

'I know all about that shaky ground!' he said softly. 'And I'm trying with all I have not to rush you.'

'I remember once thinking that you were a man who liked things done yesterday,' she brought out of nowhere as nerves well and truly started to bite.

'But not now. Not here and now,' Silas took up. 'I don't

want to upset or worry you. Which is why I'm doing my best to take this slowly.'

She did not know what he meant. Why he thought she might feel rushed, or worried, or upset, so she stayed with what he had—astonishingly—so far said.

'You said you had grown to c-care for me?'

'I have, and I do,' he answered without hesitation. 'I wasn't supposed to. I did not want to. To care for you had no part in my plan. Yet there am I, on the day we marry, no less, kissing you—albeit briefly—and not because of the occasion but because I had to.'

Colly gaped at him. This couldn't be happening! 'I thought you kissed me because of people watching,' she whispered, with what breath she could find.

He shook his head in denial. 'It just came over me. I can see now that it was the first stirrings of starting to care for you.' Colly was still getting used to that when he went on, 'Naturally I, in my superior wisdom, denied any such nonsense.'

'Naturally,' she agreed, still feeling a touch breathless.

'So why are you in my head so much?'

'I am?'

'Even when I'm in tough board meetings,' he confirmed.

She stared at him incredulously. 'Heavens!' she said faintly.

'Several times I've had to control the urge to come and see you,' he surprised her by admitting. 'Just to check you were settled in all right—not for any other reason, obviously.'

'Why else?' she managed chokily.

'So I had mixed feelings when you wrote about your inheritance. At least it gave me a bona fide reason to call and see you.'

'Oh!' escaped her, but she was still too stunned to do more than sit tight—and hope.

'I decided I wouldn't come and see you again,' Silas revealed. Hope took on a dull sheen. 'But you were in my head so much,' he went on, to shoot her up to the high end of the see-saw she was on. 'Even when I landed up in hospital you were in my head,' he owned. 'Then I opened my eyes one day and there you were.' He paused, and suddenly the question she had once avoided was there again. 'Why did you come?' he asked.

'I—er...' She felt a great need to be honest with him. Silas appeared to be sharing the same piece of shaky ground, so whatever it might cost her, she felt an overwhelming urge to meet him halfway. 'The paper—the report in the paper said you were gravely ill.' She took a deep breath, held it for a moment, then, while her nerve held out, she plunged. 'And I'd begun to care for you too.'

'Sweetheart!' Silas breathed, and, his head coming closer, he gently kissed her. For ageless seconds they just stared at each other. Then Silas was saying, 'I have to confess that when I decided to leave hospital I did try to fight against the compulsion to ask you to come and stay at my place over-night.'

'Because...'

'Because I knew I was falling for you,' he admitted openly.

Did caring for her and falling for her mean that he loved her a little? She had no way, no experience, of knowing. The look in his eyes was warm, even tender, but... She started to feel a little scared. She decided to stick with that which she did know. 'But you did ask me to come. You phoned and—'

'And blamed my illness for my weakness. Had I been phys-ically stronger I would not have been so otherwise weak.'

'You—um—gave in...?'

'I gave in,' he took up. 'And found I enjoyed having you tinkering about my apartment. That,' he added with a self-deprecating look, 'bothered me.'

'You were a bit of a snarly brute at times,' she said with a smile.

'Why wouldn't I be? I found I didn't want you to leave. Yet I wasn't ready to face what was happening to me.'

Colly looked solemnly at him. His caring for her, did he

mean? 'You sent me flowers,' she recalled, trying hard to keep her head together.

'I should have phoned to thank you,' he apologised. 'But I was a bit narked that you'd left without saying goodbye. I suppose to send you some ''bread-and-butter'' thank-you flowers was my bright idea of stamping ''The End'' on it.' He smiled then, a smile that made her heart turn over. 'Only it wasn't the end,' he said softly. 'The next time I saw you, you were having dinner with Andrews and appeared to be thoroughly enjoying his company.'

Colly stared at Silas in amazement. As he had picked up that note of jealousy in her voice, so she thought she detected something similar in his. 'You—were—jealous?' she asked in wonderment.

'There wasn't any shade of green that didn't bombard me,' he admitted. 'Oh, I fought against you, Colly Livingstone,' he went on, to thrill her some more. 'Even the next evening, when I was phoning you and asking you to have dinner with me, I fought against you.'

'Against your—caring for me?'

'Absolutely. Time and again I reminded myself that ours was a purely business arrangement, and that was the way it must be. And that while I might feel I should like to get to know you better, what would be the point? I did not want to be *married*-married.' He squeezed her hand and disclosed, 'I again made up my mind not to contact you again. I would resist all temptation to phone or see you again.' His eyes caressed her. 'Then you, my dear, dear, Colly, rang me,' he said, with such a tender look in his eyes for her that she had to swallow hard before she could find her voice.

'I rang to confess I'd done something terrible.'

'Poor love,' he breathed. 'And I knew that night, when I experienced feelings of such murderous rage when I imagined that Andrews had assaulted you, that I was in love with you.'

Her mouth fell open. His caring—was love! 'Oh, Silas!' she cried tremulously.

'It—doesn't—upset you that I feel so deeply for you?' he asked.

'Oh, no, not a bit,' she whispered. 'You're sure?' She could not believe it.

'I'm very sure,' he replied tenderly. 'I knew that night that I could fight it no longer. While I wasn't sure then what it was I did want—it was all new, too shattering—what I *was* sure about, without having to think about it, was that I would not mind the world knowing that you and I were married.'

'You wouldn't…?'

'I wouldn't.' He took a moment out to gently kiss her, but pulled back to ask, 'How do you feel about me, Colly?'

Looking at him, she felt nervous, and too shy to say those words she had never spoken before.

'You said that you care for me,' he said, when she did not answer, 'and I'm trying hard to go at a pace you're comfortable with. But I really would like to know something of the extent of you caring, little love.'

'I—er…' Colly gave a small cough to clear her choked throat. 'Oh, Silas Livingstone,' she managed, and, her voice strengthening, 'I've cried tonight because I thought my…the way I felt about you was hopeless. I…'

'Some of your tears were over me?'

'More than some, I think,' she acknowledged.

'My darling,' he breathed, and just had to tenderly kiss her, a loving hand stroking tenderly down the side of her face. 'Go on,' he urged gently, after some moments of just looking at her.

'I promise you I'm not someone who gives way to tears easily.' She obeyed, with what voice she could find. 'But as I drove away on our wedding day I could have burst into tears. I knew then that for all, as you'd remarked, we were not emotionally involved you were having a most peculiar effect on me.'

'Do you think it was the start of you—caring—for me?' Silas wanted to know.

'I tried to deny any such nonsense,' she replied with a

tender smile. 'But when I read in the paper about you being gravely ill, and I saw you in hospital, when, as exhausted as you were, you laughed at my "widow" comment—I knew then that I was very much in love with you.'

'Oh, Colly,' he groaned, and reached for her. And for seconds, wonderful long-short seconds, he held her in his arms. 'You're sure?' He leaned back to question her, as if he, like her, could not believe his hearing.

'I love you,' she answered huskily, a little self-consciously, and was drawn close up to him again.

For long blissful minutes they held each other, pulling back occasionally to tenderly kiss, then to break apart and, rejoicing, hold each other once more. 'I love you so very much, my beautiful wife,' Silas breathed against her ear.

'I love you so,' she replied. 'I never knew I could feel like this.'

'Sweetheart,' he said softly, and kissed her long and lingeringly before, breaking his kiss, he leaned away, his expression never more serious. 'Every hour since I parted from you yesterday has been pure torment.'

'Has it?' she asked softly, sympathetically. She had been there, and knew all about that torment.

'I never want to spend another torturous night like last night,' he said, smiling now at her, then going seriously on, 'I knew I would know no rest until I had seen you. That I would have to make contact with you this evening—then Naomi phoned and delayed me. When I saw you with Rupert—' Colly stiffened in his arms and he broke off. 'What?' he asked. 'Was it—?'

'Naomi?' Having revealed so much of her feelings, Colly saw no point in holding back now.

'What about her?' he asked, seeming mystified.

'Your date tonight…?'

'*Date!* She wasn't my…! Oh, Lord, didn't I say?' He did a fast backtrack over his remarks with regard to Naomi. Then, with a groan, 'I didn't!' he exclaimed. 'Oh, my love, I've been so stewed up over you. So scared of frightening you away should I get to talk of love with you, that I completely forgot. I'm so sorry,' he apologised, but went quickly on to enlighten her, 'Naomi is Kit's wife.'

'Kit? Your cousin Kit?'

'One and the same. But let me explain. I had a meeting in Lisbon today—I was scheduled to stay over and return in the morning, but I was anxious to see you.' Already Colly was feeling dreadful about her jealousy. Poor darling, he must be tired out. He had declined to stay in Portugal because he had wanted to see her!

'You don't have to explain,' she told him hurriedly.

But he was not having that. 'I think I do,' he contradicted softly. 'I don't want any misunderstandings between us,' he said, going on, 'I'd barely got home, and was wondering whether to phone first or just call on you, when Naomi rang sounding extremely upset and asking if I would meet her to discuss a problem. It seemed churlish to say no. Kit being family makes Naomi family. I said I'd meet her for a coffee somewhere—anything more would take too long. She suggested an establishment that was close to her. "Our" hotel. I would have preferred somewhere else, but she seemed under enough pressure without me giving her further problems.'

'Were you able to help her?'

Silas shook his head. 'I doubt it. She may feel better for having sounded off about Kit's misdemeanours—she's fairly certain he's having an affair—but, while I'll have a word with him, I doubt anything I can say will make the smallest difference. But that's enough about a marriage that's going wrong. I'd prefer to talk about a marriage that I dearly hope will from now on start to go right.'

Oh, heavens! Colly wished she knew more of what he meant. She gave herself a mental shake. For goodness' sake, this was a man who, after what she knew would have been a full day of business, had dashed back to London because he was anxious to see *her*!

'*Our*—marriage?' she asked tentatively.

'Don't be scared, love,' Silas said gently. 'I mean our marriage. If you need more time, I'll wait. If you still want a career, that's fine. But I have to tell you that I love you so much it is my dearest wish that we make our marriage a permanent and a proper marriage.'

She looked at him, her heart thundering away. 'By p-permanent and proper, you mean…' Her voice faded.

Silas looked back at her steadily. 'By permanent and proper I mean I want you to come and live with me and be my wife,' he answered quietly. And when, with roaring in her ears, Colly stared at him speechlessly, 'I want you to be my wife—' He broke off, then, his eyes holding hers, added, 'In every sense of the word, Colly.'

She had an idea she had gone a touch pink, but his eyes were still quietly holding hers. 'But—but you don't want to do anything that in the long term will bind us together. You said so. On Saturday.' She clearly remembered. 'When we first went to our room, you said—'

'I lied,' he cut in.

'You—lied?' she queried, and just had to burst out laughing.

But Silas did not laugh. 'You're all right about that side of marriage?' he asked carefully. 'I won't rush you. If you…'

A light all at once started to dawn. 'Without wishing to sound too forward, I believe I'm very all right with—um—that side,' she murmured, wondering, after her response to him yesterday, how he could doubt it. 'I love you,' she told him solemnly. And, when he held her that little bit closer, yet still seemed a tiny bit unsure, 'I love you so much, Silas. I want you with my heart, with my mind, and with my body.'

He stared at her for ageless moments, then drew her yet closer up to him. He kissed her then, and it was a wonderful kiss, a kiss that was vastly different from the gentle tender kisses they had shared that evening.

Her heart was racing furiously when with gently seeking fingers his hand found its way inside the light wrap she wore, and as gently he cupped her breast in his hand.

'Oh, Silas!' she whispered, on a small gulp of breath.

He stilled. 'Oh, Silas, yes? Or, Oh, Silas, no?' he asked gently.

She looked at him, puzzled. But as he wanted no misunderstandings between them, neither did she. 'Yes,' she murmured shyly.

'Darling,' he said softly, and a little raggedly. 'I feel as if I'm treading on eggshells here—you said no yesterday…'

'No, I didn't,' she denied. Silas pulled back from her, taking his hand away from her breast and drawing the edges of her wrap together. 'When did I?' she asked. Her memory of it was…

'When I—'

'Oh!' she exclaimed, as all at once she recalled his fingers on the material of her nightdress.

'Oh?'

She went a little pink again. 'You'll have to forgive me,' she said quietly. 'I'm new to all of this.' But, determined as he, her dear love, to have no misunderstandings, she overcame her feeling of shyness to own, 'I wasn't saying no, I didn't want to—er—make love with you.' His words 'I don't want to worry or upset you' and 'I'm doing my best to be restrained, here' took on a new meaning, 'Oh, Silas. You said something about me not needing my nightie. I've never been naked in front of a man before. I couldn't hack it.' She coughed self-consciously. 'I seem to have a bit of a hangup… I just couldn't… B-but otherwise… That's what I meant! Not…' She felt very warm all at once.

'Oh, my sweet love,' Silas burst in. 'What an insensitive clod I am!' he grieved. 'Forgive me. I should have realised…'

'It doesn't matter. Not now,' she assured him. How could anything matter any more? Silas loved her and she loved him. Silas loved her, loved *her*.

'We won't make it matter,' he decreed. 'It's a minor obstacle that will pass as we get to know each other.' He smiled then, a wonderful smile. And then asked, 'Are you going to marry me, Mrs Livingstone? Are you going to live with me, and love with me, and stay—permanently—married to me?'

She smiled a beautiful smile; she had never been so happy. 'I'm so glad you came back from Lisbon,' she replied, love shining from her eyes. 'The answer, Mr Livingstone, is yes.'

Their smiles became grins, tender loving grins. 'Wife,' he said softly, as if savouring the sound. 'My wife,' he said lovingly. 'My extra-special—wife.'

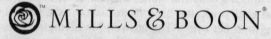